Information Systems for Healthcare Management

* * *

6th Edition

Information
Systems
for
Healthcare
Management

* * *

6th Edition

Charles J. Austin
Stuart B. Boxerman

AUPHA
HAP

Your board, staff, or clients may also benefit from this book's insight. For more information on quantity discounts, contact the Health Administration Press Marketing Manager at (312) 424-9470.

Library of Congress Cataloging-in-Publication Data

Austin, Charles J.
   Information systems for healthcare management / Charles J. Austin, Stuart B. Boxerman.—6th ed.
       p. cm.
   Includes bibliographical references and index.
   ISBN 1-56793-202-9 (alk. paper)
       1. Health services administration—Computer networks.   2. Health services administration—Data processing.   3. Information storage and retrieval. I. Boxerman, Stuart B.   II. Title.

   RA971.23 .A976 2002
   362.1'1'068—dc21

                                                    2002027614

The paper used in this publication meets the minimum requirements of American National Standard for Information Sciences—Permanence of Paper for Printed Library Materials, ANSI Z39.48-1984. ⊚™

Project manager: Jane C. Williams; Cover designer: Matt Avery; Acquisition manager: Audrey Kaufman

Health Administration Press
A division of the Foundation
   of the American College of
   Healthcare Executives
1 North Franklin Street, Suite 1700
Chicago, IL 60606-3491
(312) 424-2800

Association of University Programs
   in Health Administration
730 11th St., NW
4th Floor
Washington, DC 2001
(202) 638-1448

To our wives,
Carroll and Susan,
for their love and support
throughout our careers.

CONTENTS

PREFACE AND ACKNOWLEDGMENTS

This book is intended to assist healthcare managers in understanding principles of analysis, design, evaluation, selection, acquisition, and utilization of information systems in their organizations. The book reviews the state of the art of information technology and describes how information systems can support high-quality patient care and improve management decisions in healthcare organizations.

Sufficient technical detail on computer hardware, software, networks, and data management is included to enable the healthcare manager to become conversant with modern information technology and its use in healthcare organizations. However, the material is written from a management perspective with emphasis on the intelligent use of information for strategic planning, decision support, program management, continuous quality improvement, and the provision of high-quality patient care.

The book is suitable as a textbook for a one-semester graduate or advanced undergraduate course in health information systems. It can also serve as a reference for healthcare managers and others involved in the selection and utilization of health information systems. Extensive citations are included for those readers desiring additional information on the major topics covered.

Changes made in the sixth edition include new chapters on e-health and information security. Chapter 12 consolidates material on information systems project management from initial systems analysis through implementation, operation, and maintenance. All chapters have been updated to cover current technology and practice in information technology management.

We acknowledge the work of Andrea White and Gloria Wakefield who contributed the case study that follows Chapter 12.

It hardly seems possible that some 25 years have passed since the idea for this book was first conceived at a dinner meeting on a snowy evening in Ann Arbor, Michigan. Daphne Grew, the first director of Health Administration Press, provided the encouragement and support to make the book happen. We salute Daphne and all the staff members at Health Administration Press who helped to make six successive editions of this book come to pass. The responsibility for any errors or oversights in this edition lies entirely with the authors.

INTRODUCTION

HEALTHCARE INFORMATION TECHNOLOGY IN THE TWENTY-FIRST CENTURY

Healthcare is an information-intensive process. High-quality patient care relies on careful documentation of each patient's medical history, health status, current medical conditions, and treatment plans. Management and financial information is essential for strategic planning and efficient operational support of the patient care process. A strong argument can be made that the healthcare industry is one of the most information-intensive sectors of our economy.

This book is about management and how the management of health-care organizations can be improved by the *intelligent* use of information. Some management theorists discount the value of information in the management process, stating that management is still more an art than a science. They argue that experience, judgment, intuition, and a good sense of the political environment are the critical skills involved in administrative decisions. On the other end of the spectrum are the technocrats, who argue that management and information are inseparable and that all management decisions need to be completely rational and based entirely on an analysis of comprehensive information. The focus of this book lies between these two extreme views of the managerial world. The use of information is associated with both costs and benefits. These costs and benefits need to be assessed, and healthcare managers need to develop their skills in using information intelligently.

Pressures for improved management information are growing as healthcare organizations face ever-increasing demands to lower costs, improve quality, and expand access to care. Market-driven healthcare reform has led to the development of integrated delivery systems through mergers and acquisitions and changes in systems of payment for services. Healthcare organizations have grown larger and more complex, and information systems must keep pace with the dual effects of organizational complexity and continued advances in medical technology.

The intelligent use of information in healthcare management does not just happen. The manager must ensure that it occurs in a systematic, formally planned way. This book, then, deals with two important matters: (1) the management of information resources in healthcare organizations and (2) the effective use of information for patient care and organizational management.

Careful distinction should be drawn between data and information. As used in this book, *data* are raw facts and figures collected by the organization. *Information*, on the other hand, is defined as data that have been processed and analyzed in a formal, intelligent way so that the results are directly useful to clinicians and managers. All too often, computerized data banks are available, but they are little used because of inadequate planning of information content and structure needed to support management planning and control.

An essential element in a successful information systems implementation is carefully planned teamwork by clinicians, managers, and technical systems specialists. Information systems developed in isolation by technicians may be "technically pure and elegant in design," but rarely will they pass the test of reality in meeting organizational requirements. On the other hand, very few managers and clinicians possess the equally important technical knowledge and skills of systems analysis and design, and the amateur analyst cannot hope to avoid the havoc that can result from a poorly designed system. A balanced effort is required: operational personnel contribute ideas on system requirements and organizational realities, and technical personnel employ their skills in analysis and design.

Information technology has advanced to a high level of sophistication in recent years. However, technology can only provide tools to aid in the accomplishment of a wider set of goals. Analysis of information requirements in the broader organizational context always should take precedence over a rush to computerize. Information technology by itself is not the answer to management problems; technology must be part of a broader restructuring of the organization, including reengineering of business processes. Alignment of information technology strategy with management goals of the healthcare organization is essential.

Historical Overview

The first computer systems in healthcare date back to the early 1960s when a small number of hospitals began to automate selected administrative operations, usually beginning with payroll and patient accounting functions. These systems were developed by analysts and computer programmers hired by the hospital and were run on large and expensive centralized computers referred to as "mainframes" (see Figure 1.1). Little attention was given to the development of clinical information systems to support patient care. A few systems were developed for the electronic storage and retrieval of abstracts of inpatient medical records, but these systems contained limited information and were operated on a post-discharge, retrospective basis.

Advances in technology during the 1970s expanded the use of information systems in hospitals and marked the beginning of limited applications in other organizational settings, including clinics, physician practices, and long-term care facilities. Computers became smaller and less expensive, and some vendors began to develop "applications software packages"—generalized computer programs that could be used by any hospital, clinic, or physician's office that purchased the system. Most of these early software pack-

FIGURE 1.1

Mainframe
Computer

Source: Courtesy of International Business Machines Corporation. Unauthorized use not permitted.

ages supported administrative operations such as patient accounting, general accounting, materials management, scheduling, and practice management. Some clinical systems were developed as well, particularly for hospital clinical laboratories, radiology departments, and pharmacies.

The first revolution in computing occurred in the 1980s with the development of powerful and inexpensive personal computers (PCs)—desktop devices with computing power and storage capacity that equaled or exceeded the large mainframe systems of the 1960s and 1970s (see Figure 1.2). A second major advance in this period was the development of electronic data networks in which PCs and larger systems could be linked together for sharing of information on a decentralized basis. An increasing number of vendors entered the healthcare software business, and a much larger array of products became available for both administrative and clinical support functions. The use of PCs in physicians' offices, particularly for practice management, became commonplace.

The 1990s were marked by dramatic changes in the healthcare environment with the advent of market-driven healthcare reform and expansion of managed care. Much greater attention was given to the development of clinical information systems and strategic decision-support systems to assist providers in achieving a critical balance between costs and quality in the

FIGURE 1.2
Personal
Computer

Source: Courtesy of International Business Machines Corporation. Unauthorized use not permitted.

delivery of care. Electronic data interchange and networking were used to link components of integrated healthcare delivery organizations and support enterprisewide information systems. Healthcare organizations began to employ Internet technology to support internal communications and external connections with patients and business partners. Telemedicine applications began to be used to link primary care providers at remote locations with clinical specialists at larger medical centers.

The Current Healthcare Environment

Market-driven healthcare reform, initiated in the 1990s, has met with limited success. Managed care has helped contain costs by squeezing out inefficiencies in the delivery system, but its record on quality, access, and disease prevention is not as good. Health maintenance organizations (HMOs) have come under heavy criticism by consumers and physicians, and the political battles over the "patient's bill of rights" is a reflection of these concerns. Little progress has been made in reducing the population of uninsured and underinsured citizens, and prevention remains an elusive goal in most health plans today. According to Davis (2001), "lack of health insurance is a major barrier to care for 44 million Americans, and lack of high-quality, comprehensive insurance is a barrier to millions more."

Listed below are current trends in healthcare that will drive information technology priorities in the immediate future:

• Continued pressure for cost containment and quality improvement
• Consumer empowerment
• Concern about medical errors
• Growth in the use of evidence-based medicine
• Demand for protection of privacy and confidentiality of information

Cost Containment and Quality of Care

Cost and price pressures continue to plague healthcare providers. The Healthcare Financial Management Association reports that costs per adjusted hospital discharge increased steadily in 1998, 1999, and 2000 (*Healthcare Financial Management* 2000). According to the sixth annual survey report on purchasing value in healthcare, health plan premium costs for the year 2001 increased by 10.3 percent (*Healthcare Financial Management* 2001). Providers and consumers express concern that cost pressures are affecting quality of care. The survey report concludes: "Persistent and significant increases in the cost of medical benefits ensures that employers, healthcare providers, and health plans will be searching for solutions to the cost problem" (*Healthcare Financial Management* 2001). A national survey of 1,907 employers reports health insurance premium increases of 11 percent from spring 2000 to spring 2001 with HMO participation declining six percentage points to its lowest level since 1993 (Gabel et al. 2001).

Consumer Empowerment

Consumers have become increasingly sophisticated in their selection and use of healthcare. Empowered by the Internet, consumers are seeking medical information and joining together in self-help groups as they interact with physicians and other healthcare providers. Goldsmith (2000) states that "the patient is in charge of the process. . . . The Internet has enabled patients to aggregate their collective experiences across disease entities." Although providers express legitimate concerns about misuse and misunderstanding of information obtained from the Internet, the trend is clear and irreversible. Oravec (2001) suggests that the healthcare system should help develop approaches that will empower consumers to use the Internet effectively as one part of a total healthcare strategy, rather than simply warn about the potential hazards of using inaccurate or misunderstood information.

Medical Errors

According to the Institute of Medicine's (2000) landmark report, "To Err Is Human: Building a Safer Health System," medical errors cause unfortunate health consequences to many individuals and also result in direct and indirect costs that are borne by society as a whole. The report states that "the total national cost associated with adverse effects [of medical errors] was approximately 4 percent of national health expenditures in 1996" (Institute of Medicine 2000, 41).

Evidence-Based Medicine

Landry and Sibbald (2001) define evidence-based medicine (EBM) as "an information management and learning strategy that seeks to integrate clinical expertise with the best evidence available to make effective clinical decisions that will ultimately improve patient care." It is a systematic approach to diagnosis and treatment that encourages the physician to formulate questions and seek answers from the best available published evidence. EBM is gaining momentum as an important mechanism for improving healthcare delivery. Some are suggesting that EBM will become the new paradigm for organizations to follow in providing care. To be successful, participants in healthcare organizations (i.e., physicians, patients, managers) must agree to follow the evidence wherever it applies (Elwood 2001).

Information Privacy and Confidentiality

Protection of the privacy of health information is a major issue faced by all healthcare organizations. The Health Insurance Portability and Accountability Act of 1996 (HIPAA) allows individuals who change or lose jobs to maintain health insurance coverage for a period of time. The administrative simplification and privacy provisions of this law encourage electronic information exchange and establish standards and requirements for the electronic transmission of certain healthcare information. HIPAA also requires new safeguards to protect the security and confidentiality of that information, and it applies to any healthcare organization that provides or pays the cost of medical care under a variety of federal programs, including Medicare and Medicaid. HIPAA compliance is a major issue facing healthcare organizations today. The final rules for compliance took effect on April 14, 2001, and most organizations covered by the law have until April 14, 2003 to comply (United States Department of Health and Human Services 2001).

In addressing the question "Does managed care need to be replaced?" managed care pioneer Paul Elwood (2001) called for healthcare reform using the acronym HEROIC:

> H—health systems that emphasize the *health component* rather than the financial incentives
>
> E—medical care organized around principles of *evidence-based medicine*
>
> R—patients who assume greater *responsibility* for their own health and the cost of care they require
>
> O—*outcomes* accountability and adoption of mistake prevention measures

I—use of *information technology* to hold the system together

C—*continuous commitment* to long-term relationships, including continuous health insurance coverage for everyone

Healthcare Information Priorities Today

Healthcare organizations operating in this environment of change are developing sophisticated information systems to support clinical operations and strategic management. Some of the major priorities for system development include:

- Protection of information security
- Development of clinical systems to support disease-management programs and reduce medical errors
- Expanded use of the Internet and development of e-health applications
- Use of wireless devices to improve data entry and access
- Support for consumers through development of home applications

Information Security

HIPAA compliance was the top information technology priority listed by respondents to the 2002 Annual Leadership Survey conducted by the Healthcare Information and Management Systems Society (HIMSS). Survey respondents included a cross section of senior managers, information technology managers, and other healthcare industry professionals (HIMSS 2002). According to Tabar (2001, 46), "the data security requirements under the Health Insurance Portability and Accountability Act are straightforward: Physical, administrative and technical security access controls and alarms must be in place. Penalties will be issued for breaches."

Information technology managers are organizing efforts to assess risks and identify gaps in existing information-security processes and systems. Enterprisewide plans are needed that include privacy-protection policies, control of access to information systems, contingency planning, and disaster-backup and recovery procedures. Technical safeguards must be combined with management control and educational programs to have a complete security system. Information security is discussed in more detail in Chapter 13.

Clinical Information Systems

Upgrading and improvement of clinical information systems was another high-priority item identified by respondents to the 2002 HIMSS Annual Leadership Survey. Implementation of a computerized patient record (CPR) system was the stated priority of 32 percent of the respondents, and replacing or upgrading inpatient clinical systems was mentioned by 42 percent of the respondents. According to the survey, 78 percent of healthcare provider organizations have installed a CPR system, have begun installation, or have developed a plan for implementation (HIMSS 2002).

Clinical information systems are essential for programs of disease management and evidence-based medicine. Disease-management programs focus on prevention of crisis events among high-risk, high-cost patients (Baldwin 2001). The programs are rule-based and automated. Systems supporting these programs must be able to measure outcomes and conformity with best medical practices.

Clinical information systems are equally important in reducing medical errors. The Institute of Medicine (2001) followed up its landmark report on medical errors with "Crossing the Quality Chasm: A New Health System for the 21st Century." This second report calls for a complete upgrade of the information technology capabilities of healthcare delivery organizations throughout the United States. In addition, it also calls for government funding of a Hill-Burton type program for healthcare information technology (Lovern 2001).

Clinical information systems are discussed in more detail in Chapter 7.

Internet and E-Health Applications

Deployment of Internet technology was the second highest-ranked priority of respondents to the 2002 HIMSS Annual Leadership Survey. Development of Internet-based applications was listed as an immediate priority by 37 percent of the survey respondents. Ninety-four percent of the respondents' organizations have web sites, and they claimed that use of these sites for a variety of information-processing functions is growing. Promotion and marketing of services is the most widely used application, followed by employee recruitment and provision of consumer health information (HIMSS 2002). The number and variety of e-health applications is expected to increase dramatically in the next few years. These applications are discussed in more detail in Chapter 9.

Wireless Technology

According to the 2002 HIMSS Annual Leadership Survey, wireless technology led the list of technologies being considered by information technology professionals for use in the immediate future. Fifty-four percent of the respondents indicated that their organizations planned to begin using wireless information appliances for data entry and access (HIMSS 2002). Stammer (2001, 50) states that "with wireless local area networks, clinicians can access patient data from their offices or patients' bedsides and file the data in the hospital information system or an electronic patient record." Patient monitoring via wireless telemetry is becoming commonplace. Handheld devices are being used for order entry, wireless dictation, and medical reporting.

Wireless technology is described in more detail in Chapter 5.

Consumer Support Systems

As discussed previously, consumers have become increasingly sophisticated in their selection and use of healthcare. Healthcare organizations are developing support systems to attract and retain these empowered consumers to their health plans. Enhanced web sites are being used in support of this goal. The 2002 HIMSS Annual Leadership Survey reveals that the organizations represented in the survey are using web sites for such purposes as provision of consumer health information (71 percent) and provision of patient health-assessment tools (20 percent) (HIMSS 2002).

Development of customer relationship management (CRM) systems will take on high priority for healthcare providers operating in highly competitive markets. A comprehensive CRM system includes sales, marketing, and customer service programs tailored to individual patients or health plan members. According to Joch (2001), " . . . a well-run CRM system can deliver a complete profile of the customer to anyone in an organization who needs it, whether it's a nurse checking medical records or a webmaster gathering statistics. The goal is to make the individual patient and the Web surfer both feel that they're getting information customized for their needs. Personal attention, in turn, brings customer loyalty and strength to the healthcare organization in a cutthroat market."

Customer-oriented computer applications are discussed in more detail in Chapter 9.

Categories of Information Systems

Computerized information systems in healthcare fall into four categories: (1) clinical, (2) management, (3) strategic decision support, and (4) electronic networking and e-health applications.

Clinical information systems support patient care and provide information for use in strategic planning and management. Applications include computerized patient records systems; clinical department systems such as pharmacy, laboratory, and radiology; automated medical instrumentation; clinical decision-support systems (computer-aided diagnosis and treatment planning); and information systems that support clinical research and education.

Operational management systems support non-patient-care activities in the healthcare organization. Examples include financial information systems, payroll, purchasing and inventory control, outpatient clinic scheduling, office automation, and many others.

Strategic decision-support systems assist the senior management team in strategic planning, managerial control, performance monitoring, and outcomes assessment. Strategic information systems must draw data both from internal clinical and management systems in the organization as well as external data on community health, market-area demography, and activities of competitors. Consequently, information system integration—the ability of organizational information systems to communicate electronically with one another—becomes very important.

Healthcare organizations also engage in electronic data interchange with external organizations and business partners for such activities as insurance billing and claims processing, accessing clinical information from regional and national databases, communicating among providers in an integrated delivery system, and communicating with patients and health plan members. Many of these applications are web-based, e-health applications.

Computer applications in healthcare organizations are described in detail in Part III of this book.

The Healthcare Information Professional

A number of trade and professional organizations support the work of information professionals in the healthcare field, including:

1. *American College of Healthcare Information Administrators (ACHIA)*. A subunit of the American Academy of Medical Administrators, ACHIA is a personal membership organization for information managers with special focus on continuing education and research in healthcare information administration. For more information, contact www.aameda.org.
2. *American Health Information Management Association (AHIMA)*. Formerly the American Medical Record Association, AHIMA is a personal membership organization of information professionals who specialize in the utilization and management of clinical information. For more information, contact www.ahima.org.
3. *American Medical Informatics Association (AMIA)*. "Medical informatics" is a term used to describe the science of storage, retrieval, and optimal use of biomedical information for problem solving and medical decision making. AMIA is a personal membership organization of professionals interested in computer applications in biomedicine. For more information, contact www.amia.org.
4. *Center for Healthcare Information Management (CHIM)*. CHIM is a trade association of corporate members representing the leading firms (hardware, software, and consulting) in the healthcare information technology industry. For more information, contact www.chim.com.
5. *College of Healthcare Information Management Executives (CHIME)*. CHIME is a personal membership organization of chief information officers (CIOs) in the healthcare field. CHIME provides professional development and networking opportunities for its members. For more information, contact www.cio-chime.org.
6. *Healthcare Information Management Systems Society (HIMSS)*. HIMSS is a personal membership organization representing professionals in clinical systems, information systems, management engineering, and telecommunications. HIMSS provides professional development opportunities to its members through publications and educational programs. For more information, contact www.himss.org.
7. *Joint Healthcare Information Technology Alliance (JHITA)*. JHITA is an alliance of AHIMA, AMIA, CHIME, and HIMSS. This alliance provides

advocacy for legislation and regulation promoting the effective use of technology and its management. The alliance also offers educational and research services to its member organizations. For more information, contact www.jhita.org.

Summary

The management of healthcare organizations can be improved through intelligent use of information. This requires systematic planning and management of information resources to develop information systems that support patient care, administrative operations, and strategic management.

Change is occurring rapidly in healthcare. Major forces of change that have a direct impact on the application of information technology include (1) continued pressure for cost containment and quality improvement, (2) consumer empowerment, (3) concerns about medical errors, (4) growth in the use of evidence-based medicine, and (5) demand for protection of privacy and confidentiality of information.

These environmental trends have resulted in reordering of the information system priorities of healthcare organizations. These new priorities include (1) protection of information security, (2) development of clinical systems to support disease-management programs and reduce medical errors, (3) expanded use of the Internet and development of e-health applications, (4) use of wireless devices to improve data entry and access, and (5) support for consumers through development of home applications.

Health information systems fall into four categories: clinical, management, strategic decision support, and e-health applications. Clinical information systems support patient care and provide information for strategic planning and management. Operational management systems support non-patient-care activities such as financial management, human resource management, materials management, scheduling, and office automation. Strategic decision-support systems assist managers in planning, marketing, management control of operations, performance evaluation, and outcomes assessment. E-health network applications support electronic data interchange with external organizations and business partners, communication among providers in an integrated delivery system, and communication with patients and health plan members.

Discussion Questions

1.1 Why is healthcare one of the most information-intensive sectors of the United States' economy?

1.2 Describe the following categories of information systems in healthcare organizations: clinical, operational management, strategic decision support, and e-health applications. How important is the integration of information among these categories?

1.3 In what ways has growth in the use of evidence-based medicine affected the use of information technology in healthcare organizations?

1.4 What is HIPAA? How is this legislation affecting information priorities in healthcare?

1.5 In what ways have consumers become empowered in their selection and use of healthcare? How are healthcare organizations responding?

1.6 Why is use of wireless technology a high-priority item for health information professionals?

1.7 Develop a profile (mission, membership, programs, etc.) of one of the major professional organizations in the healthcare information management field.

References

Baldwin, F. D. 2001. "Disease Management." *Healthcare Informatics* 18 (2): 62, 64.

Davis, K. 2001. "Universal Coverage in the United States: Lessons from Experience of the 20th Century." *Journal of Urban Health* 78 (1): 46–58.

Elwood, P. M. 2001. "Does Managed Care Need to Be Replaced?" *Medscape General Medicine* 3 (5): 5.

Gabel, J., L. Levitt, J. Pickreign, H. Whitmore, E. Holve, D. Rowland, K. Dhont, and S. Hawkins. 2001. "Job-based Health Insurance in 2001: Inflation Hits Double Digits, Managed Care Retreats." *Health Affairs* 20 (5): 180–86.

Goldsmith, J. C. 2000. "A New Industrial Order for Physicians." *Physician Executive* 26 (1): 16–19.

Healthcare Financial Management Association. 2000. "Hospital A/R Days, Cost per Adjusted Discharge Increase in Quarter 2000." *Healthcare Financial Management* 54 (12): 75.

———. 2001. "Quality and Service Are Paramount: A Survey of Healthcare Purchasing Trends." *Healthcare Financial Management* 55 (6): 72–76.

Healthcare Information and Management Systems Society. 2002. *Thirteenth Annual Leadership Survey*. Chicago: HIMSS.

Institute of Medicine. 2000. "To Err Is Human: Building a Safer Health System." Washington, DC: National Academy Press.

———. 2001. "Crossing the Quality Chasm: A New Health System for the 21st Century." Washington, DC: National Academy Press.

Joch, A. 2001. "Customer Relationship Management." *Healthcare Informatics* 18 (2): 70, 72.

Landry, M. D., and W. J. Sibbald. 2001. "From Data to Evidence: Evaluative Methods in Evidence-based Medicine." *Respiratory Care* 46 (11): 1226–35.

Lovern, E. 2001. "IOM Strikes Again." *Modern Healthcare* (March 5): 4–6.

Oravec, J. A. 2001. "On the Proper Use of the Internet: Self-help Medical Information and On-line Health Care." *Journal of Health and Social Policy* 14 (1): 37–60.

Stammer, L. 2001. "Wireless." *Healthcare Informatics* 18 (2): 50, 52.

Tabar, P. 2001. "Data Security." *Healthcare Informatics* 18 (2): 46, 48.

United States Department of Health and Human Services. 2001. "Protecting the Privacy of Patients' Health Information." HHS Fact Sheet (May 9).

Additional Readings

Coile, R. C. 2001. "Competing in a Consumer Choice Market." *Journal of Healthcare Management* 46 (5): 297–300.

Colwell, V. J. 2001. "Healthcare's Fast Future." *Health Management Technology* 22 (10): 67, 68.

Healthcare Financial Management Association. 2001. "Data Trends, Cost and Price Pressures Continue to Plague Healthcare Providers." *Healthcare Financial Management* 55 (10): 103.

Lundberg, G. D. 2001. "American Health System Reform: Circa 2001–2002." *Medscape General Medicine* 3 (5): 10.

Montori, V. M., and G. H. Guyatt. 2001. "What Is Evidence-Based Medicine and Why Should It Be Practiced?" *Respiratory Care* 46 (11): 1201–14.

Paperny, D. M. 2000. "Computers and Information Technology: Implications For the 21st Century." *Adolescent Medicine* 11 (1): 183–202.

Shortell, S. M., R. R. Gillies, and D. A. Anderson. 1994. "The New World of Managed Care: Creating Organized Delivery Systems." *Health Affairs* (Winter): 46–64.

Sim, I. 2001. "Clinical Decision Support Systems for the Practice of Evidence-Based Medicine." *Journal of the American Medical Informatics Association* 8 (6): 527–34.

INFORMATION TECHNOLOGY AND MANAGERIAL CONTROL

Certain background concepts are important to an understanding of the effective application of information technology in healthcare organizations. These concepts, the subject of this chapter, include a review of general systems theory, key principles of management related to the development and operation of information systems, and the need for change management in adapting systems to the organizational culture.

Systems Theory

Systems theory provides the conceptual foundation on which the development of information systems is based. Healthcare managers should have a general understanding of this theory to understand how information systems function in their organizations, particularly in using information for management control. The systems approach is important because it concentrates on examining a process in its entirety, rather than focusing on the parts, and relates the parts to each other to achieve total system goals. Management control requires that performance be compared against expectations and that feedback be used to adjust the system when performance goals are not being met.

As discussed in detail in Chapter 12, systems analysis is a fundamental tool for the design and development of information systems. It is the process of studying organizational operations and determining information system requirement for a given application. Systems analysis employs concepts from general systems theory in analyzing inputs, processes, outputs, and feedback in defining requirements for an information system. The remainder of this section presents a general overview of systems theory and its application in healthcare organizations.

A variety of systems comprise the functioning of healthcare organizations. These systems can be categorized into three groups: mechanical systems, human systems, and man-machine systems. *Mechanical systems* are an integral part of the physical plant, serving such purposes as heating and cooling; monitoring temperature, pressure, and humidity; and supplying chilled and heated water.

Most of the essential functions of a healthcare organization are carried out through *human systems*—organized relationships among patients, physicians, employees, family members of patients, and others. Many of these systems are formally defined. For example, nursing care is provided in accordance

17

with a scheduled set of predetermined protocols and procedures, and nursing service personnel are trained and supervised in the proper execution of this "system of care." Many things also happen through informal relationships, which often become well defined and known to those in the organization. Thus, certain activities get accomplished by "knowing the right person" or sending informal signals to key individuals about actions that need to be taken.

With the development of modern information technology, many systems fall into the third category, *man-machine systems.* These are formally defined systems in which human effort is assisted by various kinds of automated equipment. For example, computer systems have been developed to continuously monitor the vital signs of critically ill patients in intensive care units of medical centers.

Information systems in healthcare organizations fall into the second and third categories of this simple taxonomy; that is, information systems will be either human systems or man-machine systems designed to support operations. Information systems that operate without any type of machine processing of data are referred to as *manual* systems. Although much of this book deals with computer-aided information processing, most of the principles set forth here, particularly those dealing with systems analysis and design, apply equally to the development of manual systems for processing of information.

Healthcare organizations also can be described in a broader context. Figure 2.1 is a systems diagram for a healthcare organization that shows the relationships among various inputs and environmental factors as these factors influence the provision of services to the community. In this context, mechanical, human, and man-machine systems would constitute elements, or subsystems, of the conversion process. The theoretical concepts on which this diagram is based are described below.

General Systems Theory

Scientists have done considerable research on systems and how they function in all phases of our society. Interest *in general systems theory* developed in the post–World War II period. Initial research efforts were focused primarily on the physical sciences, with the study of strategic military weapons systems, systems for space exploration, and automated systems of all kinds to reduce manual labor and improve the overall quality of life.

In the 1960s, attention shifted to the application of systems theory to the social sciences, including organizational theory and management. Although much of this work is highly theoretical and of primary interest to those involved in basic research, some general discussion of systems theory is useful background for understanding management control systems in healthcare delivery and for setting forth principles of information systems analysis and design.

FIGURE 2.1   The Healthcare Organization as a System

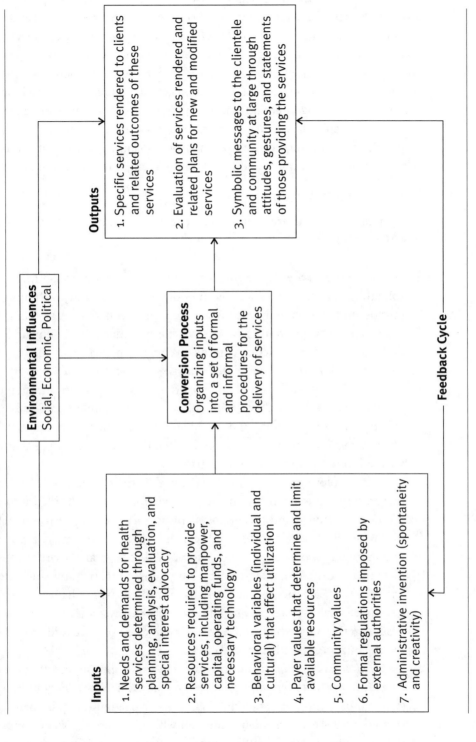

Environmental Influences
Social, Economic, Political

Inputs

1. Needs and demands for health services determined through planning, analysis, evaluation, and special interest advocacy

2. Resources required to provide services, including manpower, capital, operating funds, and necessary technology

3. Behavioral variables (individual and cultural) that affect utilization

4. Payer values that determine and limit available resources

5. Community values

6. Formal regulations imposed by external authorities

7. Administrative invention (spontaneity and creativity)

Conversion Process
Organizing inputs into a set of formal and informal procedures for the delivery of services

Outputs

1. Specific services rendered to clients and related outcomes of these services

2. Evaluation of services rendered and related plans for new and modified services

3. Symbolic messages to the clientele and community at large through attitudes, gestures, and statements of those providing the services

Feedback Cycle

Social scientists have defined systems in various ways. Simply defined, a system is a set of objects and the relationships between the objects and their attributes (Hall and Fagen 1968). *Objects* in this definition constitute the component parts of the system. *Attributes* are the properties of these objects, abstract descriptors that characterize and define the component parts of the system. Essential to the concept of a system are defined relations, which tie the component parts together and thus enabling the parts to equal some greater unity rather than simply constituting an uncoordinated assemblage of objects or people. Relationships can be planned or unplanned, formal or informal, but they must exist if the collection of components is to constitute a system.

Systems Characteristics

Certain basic concepts are central to a general understanding of systems and how they function:

1. *A system must have unity or integrity.* This means that a system must be something that can be viewed as an entity in its own right, with unity of purpose in the accomplishment of some goal or function. A system must have an identity and must have describable boundaries that allow it to be defined without reference to external events or objects.
2. *Systems at work in healthcare organizations are for the most part very complex.* The intricate web of complex relationships that constitute most social systems often makes it difficult to describe simple cause-and-effect relationships among individual components of the system. The phenomenon of system complexity is often described by stating that a system is more than the sum of its parts.

   Complex systems are further defined by their *hierarchical structure;* that is, large systems in healthcare organizations can be divided into several subsystems, and these subsystems in turn are subject to further subdivision in a nested format. For example, the patient care component of an integrated delivery system is composed of several subsystems—a diagnostic subsystem, a therapeutic subsystem, a rehabilitative subsystem, and so forth. Each of these subsystems in turn can be further described by a series of smaller systems. The entire network of systems and subsystems nests together in a structured way to describe the patient care system of the organization (see Figure 2.2).
3. *Although most organizational systems are dynamic and subject to frequent change, they nonetheless must possess some stability and equilibrium.* The system must continue to function in the face of changing requirements and changes in the external environment in which it operates. To accomplish this, procedures must be sufficiently generalized to accommodate a variety of situations that can be expected to develop. Complex systems must be self-adapting and must include control functions that are continuous and automatic. When the system can no longer adapt to changing

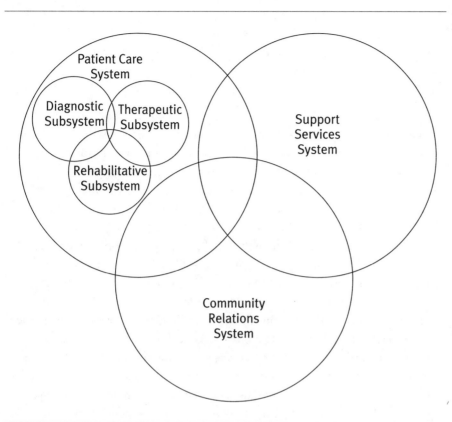

FIGURE 2.2
Healthcare
Organization
Systems
Network

requirements or major changes in the external environment, it no longer
functions as a system and breakdown has occurred.

4. *Systems can be either deterministic or probabilistic.* In a deterministic
   system, the component parts function according to completely predictable
   or definable relationships. Most mechanical systems are deterministic.
   On the other hand, human systems or man-machine systems (including
   information systems) are probabilistic because all relationships cannot
   be perfectly predicted. In healthcare organizations, for example, most
   clinical systems are subject to fairly extreme fluctuations in the quantity
   and nature of the demand for patient services.

      Systems theory, then, provides a perspective—a way of viewing not
   just the parts, not just the whole, but the spectrum of relationships of
   the parts viewed in the context of the unitary purposes of the system as a
   whole.

5. *The simplest of all systems consists of three essential components: one or
   more inputs, a conversion process, and one or more outputs* (see Figure
   2.3). Consider for example the appointment-scheduling process of
   an ambulatory care center as a simple system. *Inputs* to the system
   consist of appointment requests from patients; physician schedules; and
   clinic resources, including personnel, treatment rooms, and supporting

FIGURE 2.3
Diagram of a
Simple System

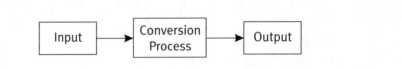

materials. The *conversion process* includes a set of actions: the scheduling clerks collect information from patients, match patient requirements to available time slots, and make appointments. *Output* of this simple system consists of patients scheduled for service in the clinic. Note that the output of this system becomes the inputing for several other functional systems of the clinic—medical records, patient accounting, and others.

6. *Most systems also involve feedback. Feedback* is a process by which one or more items of output information "feeds back" and influences future inputs (see Figure 2.4). In the example just cited, feedback will occur in the form of adjusted information on the number of time slots available as patients are scheduled for the clinic. Each time an appointment is made, input data on times available are revised and updated.

7. *Systems are either open or closed.* A *closed system* is completely self-contained and is not influenced by external events. In an *open system*, the components of the system exchange materials, energies, or information with their environment (see Figure 2.5); that is, they are influenced by, and themselves influence, the environment in which they operate. All closed systems eventually die (cease to function as a system). Only open systems that adjust to the environment can survive as systems over time.

FIGURE 2.4
Simple System
with Feedback

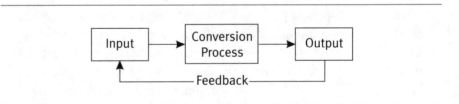

FIGURE 2.5
Open System
Diagram

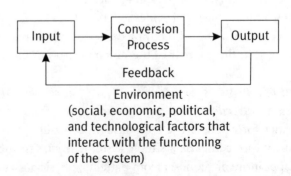

Healthcare systems, with the exception of certain purely mechanical systems ***Environmental*** in the physical plant, fall into the category of open systems. Human or man- ***Factors in*** machine systems in healthcare organizations are influenced by a variety of ***Open Systems*** environmental factors (sometimes referred to as *exogenous factors* or variables) that are important to consider in understanding how a system functions. These environmental factors fall into four broad categories.

Healthcare systems are influenced by *social factors*—characteristics of individuals and groups of people involved in the transactions that organizations undertake. Social factors affect patient behavior and patterns of utilization of services. Informal patterns of behavior develop among employees, and these have definite effects on the way operating systems function. Role playing by physicians and other health professionals interacts with the formal functioning of systems. Social factors are important determinants of system functioning, and systems analysts need to be well versed in the art of human-factors engineering when designing systems.

A second major category of environmental factors is *economic* in nature. Systems are directly dependent on the availability of resources, and fluctuations in the local and national economy will influence both demand and resources. It is well known, for example, that elective procedures are often deferred by patients during times of economic recession.

Healthcare systems are also affected by *political factors*. A variety of special interest groups place competing demands on healthcare organizations, and systems are influenced both by community politics and by organizational politics. These political realities must be considered in the analysis and design of systems for the institution.

The *physical environment* constitutes the final category of environmental factors affecting organizational systems. The amount of space available and the way in which system components relate physically to each other will influence the effectiveness of a system.

To summarize briefly, healthcare systems are open systems influenced by a variety of social, economic, and political factors and by the physical environment within which they function.

The final concept to be introduced in this brief review of general systems ***Cybernetic*** theory is the concept of a cybernetic, or self-regulating, system (Weiner 1954). ***System*** Figure 2.6 is a generalized diagram of a cybernetic system. Feedback in a cybernetic system is controlled to adjust the future functioning of the system within a predetermined set of standards. The following components are added to the general system components to provide this automatic control:

1. A *sensor* element continuously gathers data on system outputs
2. Data from the sensor are fed into a *monitor* for continuous matching of the quantity or quality, or both, of performance against *standards*— predetermined expectations of system performance

FIGURE 2.6
Cybernetic
System

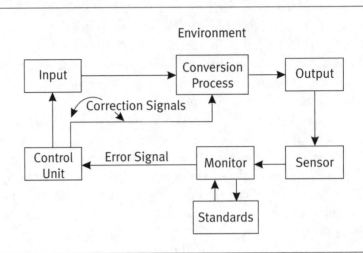

3. Error signals from the monitor are sent to a *control unit,* whose purpose is to generate correctional signals that automatically modify inputs and conversion processes to bring the functioning of the system back into control

The most often-cited example of a cybernetic system is a thermostatic control system for the automatic heating and cooling of a building. The sensor unit continuously measures ambient temperature and sends signals to the monitor that compares the current temperature to preset standards. Through the control process, automatic correction signals are sent back to the heating/cooling units of the system to keep the temperature within control limits.

Management Control and Decision-Support Systems

Organized systems in healthcare organizations should be designed as cybernetic systems with formal management controls built in as an integral part of the design. Figure 2.7 is a conceptual diagram of a generalized cybernetic system for a healthcare organization.

The inputs to this generalized system include the demand for services by patients and those who represent them and the resources required to provide services such as labor, materials, capital, and technology. The conversion process consists of actions taken by employees of the healthcare organization aided by formalized procedures, informal patterns of functioning, and supporting equipment. System outputs include the services rendered to patients and the specific patient and community outcomes related to these services.

Management control is introduced in cybernetic components of the system. The sensor component continuously gathers data on the quantity of

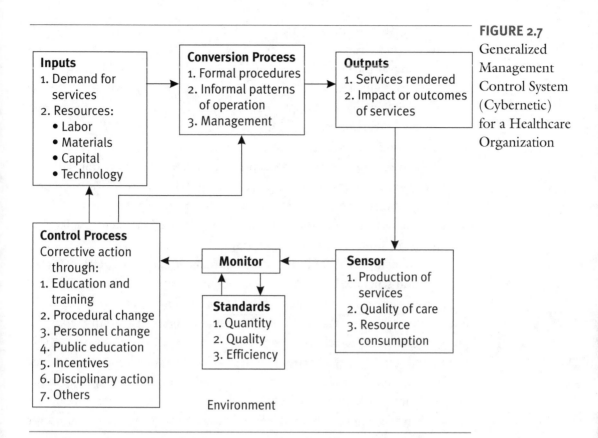

FIGURE 2.7
Generalized
Management
Control System
(Cybernetic)
for a Healthcare
Organization

services rendered, the quality and other characteristics of these services, and the resources consumed in their provision. Data from the sensor (management reports) are monitored against preestablished standards of quantity (production and service goals), quality of care, efficiency of the service process, and patient outcomes. When standards are not met, a control process is activated to initiate necessary changes and improvements. The control process contains several components, including education and training of personnel, community education programs, reengineering of the process of care, personnel changes to improve service, utilization of employee incentives, initiation of disciplinary action, and many others.

A key component in the establishment of management control systems is the establishment of standards for performance and quality control. The task of developing standards is not an easy one and requires considerable effort and thoughtful planning among managers and professional personnel practicing in or employed by the healthcare organization. Standards can be developed in a number of ways. They can be established by administrative or medical authority in the institution. In some cases they may be developed through negotiation and subsequent agreement between employees and supervisors. Empirical studies of previous performance, using industrial engineering techniques, offer another approach to standards setting. In certain areas of operation, standards are mandated by external regulations, legal requirements, or accrediting agencies.

Whatever the approach to their development, standards are essential if management control is to operate on other than an ad hoc basis. Standards require careful management planning, continual review and revision, and frequent reinforcement through incorporation into the formal reward system. They are essential to effective management control.

As an example of these concepts, the operation of a centralized clinical laboratory in an integrated delivery system (IDS) can be described as a cybernetic system with planned controls built into the system for quality assurance and performance-control purposes. Figure 2.8 is a schematic diagram describing the functioning of the laboratory in system terms.

System inputs include scheduled demand (laboratory tests planned, ordered, and scheduled in advance) and unscheduled demand (tests required to be processed on an emergency, or stat, basis). Resource inputs include technical personnel in the laboratory, materials and equipment used in the testing process, and related technology. The conversion process consists of those formal and informal organizational actions related to collecting of specimens; conducting laboratory tests; and reporting results to appropriate points in the hospitals, outpatient clinics, and other service units of the IDS. System outputs include the test reports sent back to clinicians ordering the tests, charges for services transmitted to the patient accounting department for billing purposes, and various statistical reports.

Cybernetic components for management control are also included in Figure 2.8. The sensor component is the management reporting system of the laboratory by which data on the number of tests conducted by various categories, quality control data, and records of resources consumed (including personnel time of laboratory technicians) are collected and recorded. These data are used by laboratory managers who monitor actual performance against predetermined standards, including those established by the Joint Commission on Accreditation of Healthcare Organizations (JCAHO), professional standards of quality established by the chief pathologist and medical staff, and cost and efficiency (productivity) goals established jointly by the administrative and medical personnel in the organization. When standards are not met, corrective actions are initiated, including activation of continuing education and retraining; revision of operating policies and procedures, including recalibration of test equipment if necessary; change in staffing patterns and scheduling; and the like. The laboratory operates overall as an open system influenced by several contextual or environmental factors, including the physical environment of the laboratory facility, current economic conditions of the IDS, social and political factors related to interaction of personnel in the laboratory, and the advancement of technology.

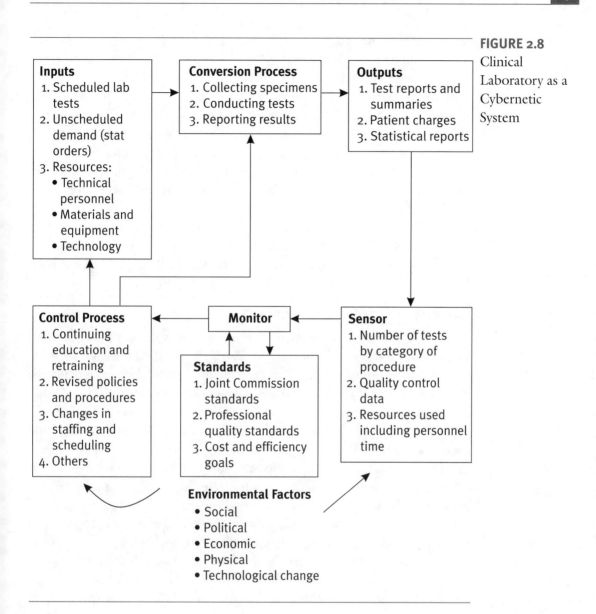

FIGURE 2.8
Clinical Laboratory as a Cybernetic System

Information For Management Control

Any management control system is information dependent. Information requirements permeate the system diagrams presented in the preceding parts of this chapter. For health programs to be properly managed, information is needed about each of the major system components previously described.

Input information must be collected to monitor demand continuously, both scheduled and unscheduled, as well as the resources consumed in the provision of services. Operational procedures must be constantly observed through information on exceptions, error rates, system malfunctions, and similar performance measures on a management-by-exception basis. Output information on the quantity and quality of services rendered must be matched with information on related outcomes of the provision of specific services. In addition, the effective manager must keep in close contact with the environment in which his or her department or institution functions. Environmental information—such as demographic characteristics of the service population, previous utilization patterns, services offered by other organizations, and recent changes in community values—is essential to this task. An effective information system will be designed with these kinds of management information needs in mind.

What, then, are the attributes of information useful for management control in the delivery of healthcare? Some of the more important characteristics of effective management information are listed in Figure 2.9 and discussed below.

Characteristics of Useful Information

The first, and perhaps most essential, characteristic is that for information to be useful it must contain *information, not just raw data*. Data must be intelligently processed in accordance with predesigned plans before they become information useful to management or operating personnel.

Health information must be *relevant* to the purposes for which it is to be used. It must be sufficiently *sensitive* to provide discrimination and meaningful comparisons for operating managers. Many information systems provide data that are so aggregated that they provide no meaningful indicators for management planning or control purposes. Overall hospital cost per patient day is a good example. By contrast, separating costs into fixed and variable components and allocating variable costs by diagnostic groupings and level of care provide more useful information to management.

Useful information must be *unbiased* and not collected or analyzed in such a way that it meets self-fulfilling prophecies. Information should be *comprehensive* so that all elements or components of a system are visible to those responsible for administering that system.

FIGURE 2.9
Characteristics
of Useful
Management
Information

- Information—not data
- Relevant
- Sensitive
- Unbiased
- Comprehensive
- Timely
- Action oriented
- Uniform (for comparative purposes)
- Performance targeted
- Cost effective

Information must be *timely*, presented to users in advance of the time when decisions or actions are required. Many information systems produce beautiful reports that are completely useless because of failure to meet operational time requirements. Information should be *action oriented*, designed to aid the manager directly in the decision process rather than just to present passive facts about current operations. For example, information from an inventory control and materials management system should include direct indicators of when specific items need to be reordered rather than just give data on current numbers in stock.

Information systems should have as their goal the production of *uniform* reports so that performance indicators can be compared over time both internally against previous performance and externally against the experience of other comparable organizations. Good information will also be *performance targeted*, designed and collected in reference to predetermined goals and objectives of the institution. Finally, information should be *cost effective*. The anticipated benefits to be obtained from having the information available should be worth the costs of collecting and processing that same information.

Principles of Information Resource Management

Listed below are three key management principles that are very important for successful application of information technology in healthcare organizations. Many other principles could have been included, some of which are discussed in later chapters of this book. However, the items presented here are overarching principles that are critical to successful information resource management (Austin and Howe 1994, 230).

1. *Treat information as an essential organizational resource.* Managers in healthcare organizations should treat information as a fourth major type of resource required to do business, on a par with human resources, financial resources, and capital facilities and equipment. As such, information resource management should receive the same care and attention given to human resources management, financial management, and materials management in the organization.
2. *Obtain top-executive support for information systems planning and management.* Given the importance of information resources and the costs and complexities involved in information systems development, top-level support is essential to success. The chief executive officer and key members of the executive management team should be knowledgeable and involved in information systems planning and establishment of priorities for system development. Information resource management should be the responsibility of a corporate-level executive—the chief information officer (CIO) in larger organizations and health systems. (See Chapter 14 for more details on the role and responsibility of the CIO.)

3. *Develop a strategic vision and plan.* Healthcare organizations need an enterprisewide vision of how information technology will be used to support
   patient care and strategic management. An information systems plan must
   be strategically aligned with the vision, mission, goals, and objectives of
   the organization. Alignment with organizational strategy " . . . involves
   the review of the organization's 'formal' strategic plan (if it has one),
   as well as interviews with key executives and stakeholders . . . Regional
   alliances, new care-delivery locations, product-line changes, marketing
   plans and other projects must be thoroughly, creatively and cost effectively
   addressed as part of the I/S planning process" (Spitzer 1993, 30).

Strategic information systems planning must be driven by the business
plans of the healthcare organization. Gabler (2001, 76) states that "executive
management and boards of directors are increasingly concerned about the
business value returned by IT investments. . . . The only reason to invest
in IT is to improve the business. As the IT/business relationship matures,
technology's promise is replaced by technology's value."

Strategic information systems planning is discussed in more detail in
Chapter 11.

Management of Change

The application of information technology in healthcare organizations inevitably involves change, often major change, in the way business is done.
Change is threatening to organizational stakeholders, particularly employees.
Careful attention must be paid to human factors and the organizational culture within which information systems must function.

Fear of change is a common problem encountered in many system-
development efforts, with resultant anxiety and tension. Employees may have
concerns about possible effects of the new system on their own jobs and possible changes in the work environment that may be required. Managers may
have concerns about changes that could result in the redistribution of power,
greater centralization of authority, or increased demand for accountability as
byproducts of the new system. Some may have concerns that the information
system will result in more-rigid and less-flexible patterns of operation, with
resultant lack of discretion in carrying out the task. Often these concerns are
unfounded and based on misunderstanding of the technology. But they are
very real to the individuals involved.

Effective change management requires an understanding of behavioral
and cultural factors in information system development. Open communications are essential. Avoid being secretive and provide a comprehensive program of staff orientation and training prior to initiation of a major project.
Structure the project in such as way that users will be active participants
and will "buy in" from the beginning. Make top-level support visible, and
reinforce that support regularly.

Horak (2001) describes human factors that affect the implementation of information management initiatives. To deal with these factors, a change management approach should be followed. The process includes assessment, planning, organizational development (including training and orientation), team building, and continuous evaluation and improvement.

Active management of change should be planned and implemented in advance of the implementation of an information system. According to Lorenzi et al. (1995, 152), "a lot of money is spent on consultants brought in to put out the fires caused by technical implementations that did not consider the people and organizational issues. . . . The use of change management strategies at an early stage might have saved a great deal of money and organizational pain—i.e., the pain experienced by everyone connected with the information system regardless of his or her organizational position or attitude about the technology, the process, or the circumstances."

Barcia (2001) describes techniques employed in preparing for change during implementation of a new pharmacy information system. He stresses the importance of "accentuating the positive." Diligence, patience, and a positive attitude are keys to success, and leadership is essential.

The best technology in the world will be ineffective if system planning is not accompanied by careful attention to change management.

Concluding Comments

In concluding this brief review of essential concepts, two final points are offered. First, as noted above, information has both costs and benefits associated with its use. Before initiating major system development projects, managers should consider whether the benefits to be obtained from information (tangible and intangible) will be worth the investment required to install the system.

Second, it is important to recognize the difference between the ability to use a personal computer (PC) and the ability to understand the management of information in complex organizations. Sophistication in PC use does little to enhance knowledge of information systems development and the application of computer systems to problems of patient care, administration, and strategic management in healthcare organizations. For this reason, the emphasis throughout this book is on the management of information resources, with PCs being only one component of a complex information architecture found in most organizations.

Summary

An understanding of general systems theory is useful for healthcare managers in designing and developing management control systems and in obtaining the kinds of information that are required to enable such systems to function effectively.

A system is a set of objects and the relationships between the objects and their attributes. Systems are characterized by unity of purpose, complexity, hierarchical relationships with other systems, and a need for stability in the face of a dynamic environment. Most healthcare systems are probabilistic, in that relationships cannot be perfectly predicted or described in the design of the systems.

A simple system consists of one or more components of input, a conversion process, and one or more outputs that flow from that process. Most systems also include feedback, by which system outputs influence future inputs and processes.

Open systems are influenced by the environment in which they function, and they exchange information and energy with that environment. Environmental factors include political, social, and economic variables that influence system performance as well as the physical environment in which the system functions.

Cybernetic systems include formally planned components that introduce automatic control into the systems. Cybernetic components include sensors to gather data on current system functioning; monitors to compare these data against predetermined standards; and control elements to change inputs or process, or both, when system functioning is out of control. Management control systems in healthcare organizations can be designed according to principles of cybernetic system theory.

Healthcare delivery viewed in a systems context is information dependent. Effective information for management control purposes has several important characteristics, including relevance, sensitivity, objectivity, comprehensiveness, timeliness, action orientation, uniformity, performance targeting, and cost effectiveness. Good information systems are developed with these characteristics constantly in the minds of those charged with design and implementation.

The following key management principles are essential in successful application of information technology in healthcare.

1. Information should be treated as an essential organizational resource.
2. Obtaining top-executive support for information systems planning and management is important.
3. Healthcare organizations need an enterprisewide strategic vision and plan for the application of information systems to patient care and strategic management.

Information systems operate within an organizational culture. Key stakeholders are affected by the changes associated with installation of information systems in the organization. Effective change management is an important component of an information systems development project.

Discussion Questions

2.1 Define the term *system*. What are the three general kinds of systems found in healthcare organizations?

2.2 What is the difference between an open and a closed system?

2.3 What are some of the environmental factors that influence open systems in integrated delivery systems? How important are these factors in systems design?

2.4 What is a cybernetic system? Explain how cybernetic theory can be utilized in the development of management systems in healthcare organizations.

2.5 Why is stability an important characteristic of a system? How can system stability be achieved in the dynamic environment of a modern healthcare organization?

2.6 Why are most systems in healthcare organizations described as probabilistic rather than deterministic?

2.7 What are some of the attributes of information that make it useful for management control purposes?

2.8 What is change management? Why is it important in information system development projects?

Problems

2.1 For the functions listed below, use cybernetic theory to describe the operation and management control of each in systems terms:
   a. the emergency room of an acute care general hospital
   b. the medical records department of an ambulatory care center
   c. the enrollment management section of an HMO
   d. the patient billing function in a long-term care institution
   e. the nurse scheduling function of a home health care agency
   f. an outpatient rehabilitation and physical therapy program
   g. the patient registration process of a medical group practice

2.2 For each of the systems listed in Problem 2.1, develop a list of information components needed for each system to operate effectively.

2.3 Prepare a brief report to the board of directors of an integrated delivery system commenting on the general characteristics of useful information for assisting in strategic planning and management of the system.

References

Austin, C. J., and R. C. Howe. 1994. "Information Systems Management." In *The AUPHA Manual of Health Services Management*, edited by R. J. Taylor and S. B. Taylor. Gaithersburg, MD: Aspen Publishers.

Barcia, S. M. 2001. "Managing Change." *Health Management Technology* 22 (6): 22.

Gabler, J. M. 2001. "Linking Business Values to IT Investments." *Health Management Technology* 22 (2): 76–77.

Hall, A. D., and R. E. Fagen. 1968. "Definition of System." In *Modern Systems Research for the Behavioral Scientist*, edited by W. Buckley. Chicago: Aldine Publishing Co.

Horak, B. J. 2001. "Dealing with Human Factors and Managing Change in Knowledge Management: A Phased Approach." *Topics in Health Information Management* 21 (3): 8–17.

Lorenzi, N. M., M. J. Ball, R. T. Riley, and J. V. Douglas. 1995. *Transforming Health Care Through Information*. New York: Springer-Verlag.

Spitzer, P. G. 1993. "A Comprehensive Framework for I/S Planning." *Computers In Healthcare* (May): 28–33.

Weiner, N. 1954. *The Human Use of Human Beings: Cybernetics and Society*. Garden City, NY: Doubleday Anchor.

Additional Readings

Baker, F. (ed.). 1973. *Organizational Systems: General Systems Approaches to Complex Organization*. Homewood, IL: Richard D. Irwin.

Baldwin, F. D. 2001. "Putting Your Assets to Work." *Healthcare Informatics* 18 (4): 47–50, 52.

Bertalanffy, L. V. 1968. *General Systems Theory*. New York: Braziller.

Cerchiara, K. M. 2000. "Show Me the Money: The Tough ROI Assessment." *Health Management Technology* 21 (7): 14.

Cummings, T. G. (ed.). 1980. *Systems Theory for Organization Development*. New York: John Wiley and Sons.

Kilroy, J. E. 2001. "Managing for Results." *Health Management Technology* 22 (7): 16–18.

O'Neil, J. 2001. "Project Management." *Health Management Technology* 22 (6): 32.

Reynolds, G. W. 1995. *Information Systems for Managers*, 3rd Edition. St. Paul, MN: West Publishing Company.

Starkweather, D. B., and D. G. Shropshire. 1994. "Management Effectiveness." In *The AUPHA Manual of Health Services Management*, edited by R. J. Taylor and S. B. Taylor. Gaithersburg, MD: Aspen Publishers.

Technology

COMPUTER HARDWARE

The management of information resources and the effective use of information typically do not require the healthcare manager to have an in-depth knowledge of computer technology. However, as the leader of an information-intensive organization, the healthcare manager must have at least a basic understanding of computers and their components. Such an understanding is of particular importance when the manager is part of a multidisciplinary team—along with physicians, other clinicians, financial experts, and computer system specialists—charged with the responsibility of defining system needs, acquiring new systems, or implementing new applications. To be effective, the manager must not be intimidated by technical computer concepts or "buzzwords."

This chapter discusses the physical components that comprise a computer and the physical devices that combine to form a computer system. These components and devices are known collectively as hardware. The personal computer, or PC, used by a large segment of the population is an example of computer hardware. No attempt is made here to present an exhaustive treatment comparable to what is found in computer science texts. Readers interested in such coverage of the topic are referred to the Additional Readings section listed at the end of the chapter. Rather, an overview is offered that provides the healthcare manager with an appropriate background to understand the important role that hardware plays in making possible the implementation of the information system applications discussed in later chapters of this book.

An Overview of Computer Components

A computer is an electronic, digital device characterized by its ability to store a set of instructions, known as a program, as well as the data on which the instructions will operate. The Electronic Numerical Integrator and Calculator (ENIAC) was the first such device built in the United States (Rosen 1969). Completed in 1946 at the University of Pennsylvania, this computer launched what has since become known as the first generation of computer hardware. Today, more than half a century later, the computer world has evolved to the fourth generation of hardware (some observers designate it the fifth generation). A user can now hold in one hand a device that has the computing power that once required a large room with special air-conditioning equipment.

Although this hardware evolution has been quite impressive, the basic schematic of a computer remains the same. Figure 3.1 depicts the major components of a computer system. Six categories of components comprise this system: the central processing unit, primary storage, secondary storage, input units, output units, and communications devices. The communications devices are the hardware that allows the computer to communicate with other computers, either within the organization or external to the organization. Such communication gives rise to the concepts of networking and telecommunications. Discussion of the hardware necessary to support this communication can be found in Chapter 5. The remaining five categories of computer components are discussed and illustrated in this chapter.

Central Processing Unit

The central processing unit (CPU) might be called the "brains" of the computer. Here is where the actual "computing" takes place. The CPU consists of three major subcomponents: the arithmetic/logic unit, the control unit, and registers.

Arithmetic/ Logic Unit (ALU) The basic computational and comparison capability of the computer lies in the ALU. The ALU has the ability to perform addition and subtraction and thus, by extension, multiplication and division. Of course, it is capable of performing these operations quite rapidly. In addition, the ALU can perform the logical operation of comparison—that is, determining if two quantities are equal or if one is greater than the second. This logical comparison can be performed on both numeric as well as character (non-numeric) data. The speed of the ALU is an important performance characteristic of a computer, and faster processing speeds can improve the performance of applications that

FIGURE 3.1
Major
Components of
a Computer
System

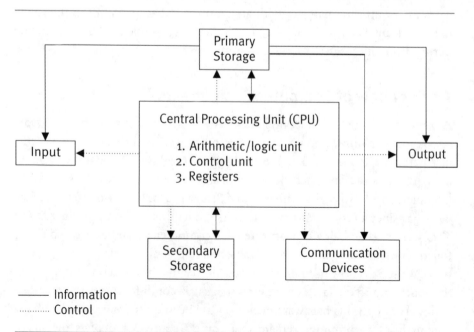

involve a large number of arithmetic operations. Examples of such applications, sometimes known as computation-bound applications, include image processing, interpretation of EKG data, and statistical analysis of very large sets of data.

No matter what "language" is used to communicate a problem to the computer, the problem description is ultimately converted to a series of machine instructions that the computer is able to "understand." The instructions are stored in primary storage. (How this conversion takes place is described in the chapter on software; the notion of primary storage is described below.) The control unit orchestrates the sequential processing of these machine instructions. *Control Unit*

To process one machine instruction, the control unit must coordinate two distinct operations. First, the instruction must be retrieved from primary storage and interpreted. This operation is known as an instruction cycle. Second, the control unit must locate any required data (also stored in primary storage), instruct the ALU to perform the necessary operation, and ensure that the result gets put into the proper primary storage location. These operations constitute the execution cycle. The instruction cycle and execution cycle together are known as a machine cycle.

When program instructions or data are transferred from primary storage to the CPU for processing, they are held in a high-speed memory area within the CPU known as registers. The instruction to be processed is held in the *instruction register* and the address of the data to be operated on is held in the *address register*. When the data value is retrieved from primary memory, it is put into a *storage register*. When the desired operation is performed on this data value, the result is placed into the *accumulator* from which it is transferred back to primary memory. Once this cycle is completed, the process begins all over again. Enhancing the computer's performance is possible by increasing the number of operations performed within the CPU (using the CPU's registers) and minimizing the number of accesses to data stored in memory. Figure 3.2 illustrates a popular microprocessor CPU. *Registers*

Comparing two or more computer processors can be a complex task for the healthcare manager. In making such comparisons, the manager will encounter several terms, which are briefly reviewed below.

The *clock rate* provides a measure of the rate with which the CPU executes a simple instruction. This rate is typically expressed in units of hertz (abbreviated Hz and equivalent to cycles per second). Rapid changes in CPU technology have led to clock rates in excess of 2.0 Ghz (1 Ghz = 10^9 hz).

Alternatively, the clock rate can be expressed in terms of the elapsed time for completing a simple instruction, which equals the reciprocal of the clock rate. Thus, on a 2.0 Ghz computer, the instruction would require $(2 \times 10^9)^{-1}$ seconds or one-half nanosecond (a nanosecond is 10^{-9} seconds).

FIGURE 3.2
Microprocessor
CPU

Source: Reprinted by permission of Intel Corporation, Copyright Intel Corporation 2002.

Sometimes it is preferred to characterize this performance in terms of the number of simple instructions that can be executed in a second, typically expressed in units of millions of instructions per second (MIPS).

The CPU *word length* is the number of bits that the CPU can process at one time. Larger word lengths will increase the speed of the computer. The speed of the computer is also affected by the *data bus width*. The *data bus* refers to the pipeline through which data flow into and out of the CPU. Larger bus widths allow for the simultaneous transfer of larger amounts of information, thus increasing the processing speed of the computer.

Finally, processing speed can be increased if the processor design is based on *reduced instruction-set computing (RISC)* rather than the conventional complex instruction-set computing (CISC) technology. Computers employing RISC technology execute most of their instructions in one machine cycle, as opposed to CISC machines that might require multiple cycles to execute an instruction.

Combining these processor characteristics into an appropriate comparison can be problematic. Henning (2000) describes a CPU benchmark suite, CPU2000, developed by a nonprofit consortium of vendors, universities, customers, and consultants. The group's mission is "to develop technically credible and objective component- and system-level benchmarks . . . that are derived from real-world applications so that . . . purchasers can make decisions on the basis of realistic workloads" (Henning 2000, 28). Although these benchmarks are certainly helpful, in the final analysis the best benchmark is one that the users create and run from their own applications.

Primary Storage

The primary storage in early computers consisted of a large number of small toroid-shaped pieces of magnetic material called *magnetic cores* with a wire looped several times around the core. Electric current passing through the wire could affect the direction of the magnetism in the core, and depending on this direction the core could be said to be storing a "0" or a "1." Because of the use of these core elements, early computer users often referred to primary storage as "core memory." Today, small silicon chips, known as semiconductors, have replaced the magnetic cores as the basis for primary storage. Each chip contains a large number of transistors printed on it, which allow millions of pieces of information to be stored.

Information is stored within the computer using the binary number system because it is straightforward to equate a 0 or 1 with the absence or presence of an electrical signal. Numeric data are stored simply as their binary equivalent. Non-numeric, or character, data are represented by unique binary values that are distinguishable from numerical data. Each "digit" in the binary system is known as a *bit*. Depending on the particular computer design, 8, 16, 32, 64, or more bits are clustered together to form a "word." For convenience, the bits of a word are separated into groups of eight and each group of eight bits is called a *byte*.

A group of 1,000 bytes is called a *kilobyte* (kb). Because computers operate in the binary system, a kilobyte actually equals the power of two that is closest to 1,000, or 1,024 bytes (1,024 is equal to 2^{10}). Similarly, a group of 1 million bytes is known as a *megabyte* (mb). Again, consistent with the binary system, a megabyte actually is equal to 1,048,576 bytes (1,048,576 is equal to 2^{20}). The size of a computer's primary storage is typically stated in units of megabytes.

Whereas the "core" memory in early computers was quite expensive, memory "chips" found in today's computers are relatively inexpensive. As a result, the amount of primary storage contained in today's computer systems continues to increase, thus enabling these systems to run increasingly complex and sophisticated applications.

Several types of primary storage can be found in the computer. Specifications for a computer system will typically indicate the amount of each type that the computer contains. Therefore, a brief definition of each type will help the manager to understand better the meaning of these specifications.

Read-Only Memory

The first type of primary storage is known as read-only memory or ROM. The contents of this type of memory can be read, but nothing can be written into these storage locations. ROM is typically used to store small sets of instructions used by a computer to perform special tasks, such as the sequence to be followed when the computer is first turned on. These instructions remain in ROM even when the computer is turned off. Memory that retains its contents in this way is said to be *nonvolatile*.

Random-
Access
Memory
Random-access memory (RAM), the second type of storage, constitutes the majority of primary storage. Data and program instructions are held in RAM until needed for processing. Remember that the control unit is responsible for retrieving the data and instructions as they are needed for program execution. Each location in memory has an *address* associated with it. The control unit is able to locate the needed data or instructions by knowing the address at which they are stored.

The notion of "random access" refers to the fact that the control unit is able to proceed directly to a given address. By contrast, a "sequential access" device would require that the control unit proceed through the memory contents sequentially from the beginning, until the desired address is reached. Tape devices (described below) are examples of sequential devices. Even though the control unit can go directly to the desired address, a finite time is required to read the contents of a memory location or to write a value into such a location. This time (typically of the order of magnitude of nanoseconds or 10^{-9} seconds) is important because it affects the overall speed of operation of a given computer.

In general, RAM is *volatile* memory so that its contents are lost when the computer's power is turned off. On some computers, a portion of RAM can be designated to be nonvolatile memory. Its contents are preserved by means of a battery. This is of particular value in a portable computer (described later in the chapter).

Cache Memory
The third type of primary storage is known as cache memory. The speed of this type of memory is generally higher than that of conventional RAM, but its cost is typically higher as well. Cache memory is often used in conjunction with other components in the computer, including the CPU itself as well as disk drives. In all cases, the goal is to achieve higher processing speed by keeping important data or instructions available where they can be read more quickly. Although the amount of RAM in today's computers might be in the hundreds of *megabytes*, the amount of cache memory is more typically in the hundreds of *kilobytes*.

Secondary Storage

Despite the decreasing cost of primary storage, it is not practical for a computer system to have sufficient primary storage to accommodate all of the information that must be maintained to support the many healthcare information system applications in use today. Of course, it would be quite inconvenient if this information were to "disappear" when the computer was turned off. What is needed is large capacity, nonvolatile storage media from which desired information can be obtained as necessary. Secondary storage media are designed to meet this need. Several such storage media are available today, and each is described below.

Magnetic tape is one of the older secondary storage media. Like the tape used **Magnetic Tape** in the "reel-to-reel" audio tape recorders, magnetic tape travels from one reel to another on a *tape drive,* passing over a transducer capable of detecting the sequence of magnetized and nonmagnetized spots on the tape. These spots, typically arranged in nine "tracks" running the length of the tape, correspond to 0s and 1s and can thus store a series of nine-bit binary values representing either data or program instructions. Large amounts of data or programs can be stored on a single reel of tape.

     Advantages of magnetic tape include its low cost, relative stability, and large storage capacity. Disadvantages are its relatively slow speed and the fact that tape drives are sequential devices. To find a particular piece of information on a tape, one must start reading the tape at the beginning and proceed until the desired information is found. As a result, users typically limit their use of tape to the archiving of inactive data in "tape libraries." In addition, on small computer systems, tape cassettes provide a medium for "backing up" (making copies of) other secondary media to protect against the loss of data from these media. These tape backup units have capacities of 8 gigabytes (gb) or more. (A gigabyte (gb) is equal to 2^{30} or 1,073,741,820 bytes.)

The secondary storage medium most widely used today is the magnetic disk. **Magnetic** This disk can either be rigid, in which case it is called a *hard disk*, or flexible, **Disks** in which case it is called a *floppy disk*. In either case, the disk stores data or program information as magnetized spots. The storage capacity of a popular 3.5" floppy disk is 1.44 mb, while hard disk capacities are in the order of magnitude of tens of gigabytes (see Figure 3.3).

     Hard disks are rigid platters, 3.5 or 5.25 inches in diameter, that are coated with a magnetic medium so that data can be stored on both sides. Typically a *hard-disk drive* consists of two, three or more platters stacked on top of each other with a common spindle that turns the whole assembly at several thousand revolutions per minute (see Figure 3.4). This stacking of multiple disk platters facilitates the increasing disk drive capacities being offered on today's microcomputers. The hard drive case is hermetically sealed, and its interior is maintained in a partial vacuum so that the platter will be as dust-free as possible.

     By sliding along the diameter of the disks, transducers can position themselves over one of a number of concentric rings called *tracks*. The platter has tracks on both of its sides. Tracks physically above one another on the platters are grouped together into *cylinders* that are then further subdivided into *sectors* of 512 bytes apiece. The sector is a disk's smallest accessible unit (see Figure 3.4). To increase storage capacity, drives can use a technique called *zoned-bit recording* in which tracks further from the center of disk contain more sectors than those nearer the center.

FIGURE 3.3
A Micro-
computer
Hard Drive
and Floppy
Disk

Source: Courtesy of International Business Machines Corporation. Unauthorized use not permitted.

The concept of cylinders is important because cross-platter information in the same cylinder can be accessed without having to move the transducers or *read/write heads.* These transducers can be directed to read data from, or write data to, any desired sector. For this reason, disk drives are known as *direct-access storage devices* (DASDs) (PCTechGuide 2002b).

Typically, hard-disk drives are an integral part of the computer and cannot be removed. Floppy-disk drives, on the other hand, are built so that the floppy disk can be removed. Some hard-disk drives are designed to allow removal of part of the drive from the computer. In this way, the data on these disks can be stored away from the computer and carried from one machine to another. These removable disks are mounted in a cartridge into which the arm holding the read/write head can slide or, in more expensive removable disk configurations, that contains its own arm and read/write head assembly.

Even though disk drives are direct-access devices, a finite time is required to read or write data. This required time is known as *disk access time* and typically measures in the millisecond range. Many healthcare information system applications involve frequent interactions with the disk drive so that disk access time becomes an important specification of any hardware system under consideration.

FIGURE 3.4
Typical Layout
of a Disk

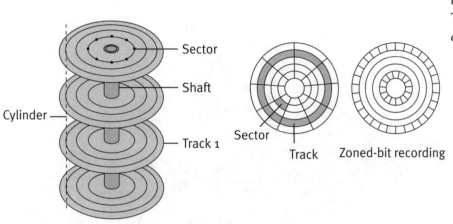

Source: Reprinted with permission from PCTechGuide. http://www.forums.pctechguide.com/

Optical Disks

Optical storage offers the advantage of being able to store a large amount of information on a relatively small disk. An optical disk is a rigid disk of plastic on which crevices have been burned by a special laser. Just as the presence or absence of magnetism can be used to represent 1s or 0s on magnetic disks, so can the presence or absence of a crevice represent a 0 or 1 on an optical disk. Several forms of optical storage are in general use, including compact-disk read-only memory (CD–ROM), compact disk–recordable (CD–R), compact disk–rewritable (CD–RW), and digital versatile disks (DVD) (PCTechGuide 2002a).

A *CD–ROM* drive is capable of reading a CD–ROM disk (see Figure 3.5). These disks, 4.75 inches in diameter, have a capacity of about 650 megabytes, which is equivalent to more than 400 floppy disks. Because a CD–ROM disk can store up to 300,000 pages of text, it is ideal for storing bibliographic material, journal articles, meeting abstracts, and government reports. In addition to text, color photographs, video clips, animations, stereo sound, and software are being released in this medium. Stromberg et al. (2002) describe the role of a CD–ROM in an interactive computer-based educational program for heart-failure patients. A CD–ROM nutrient database plays a key role in helping Air Force personnel monitor their behavior while receiving nutrition counseling for weight loss (Heetderks-Cox et al. 2001).

Data are stored on CDs differently from magnetic disks. Rather than being arranged in concentric circles, the data form a single track that winds in spiral fashion from the inside of the disk to its outside. This design results from the fact that CD–ROMs originally were used in audio applications where the "data" on the disk were typically accessed sequentially. In fact, the CD–ROM drives used in computers are capable of "reading" audio compact disks

FIGURE 3.5
CD–ROM
Drive

Source: Courtesy of International Business Machines Corporation. Unauthorized use not permitted.

as well. Because, as their name indicates, CD–ROMs are read-only devices, data cannot be written to them. Therefore, they are not appropriate for use as a medium for files that are continuously updated to reflect transactions being processed.

One variation of the CD–ROM to which data can be written is the *CD–R* (compact disk–recordable). Like the CD–ROM, this disk has a spiral track preformed during its manufacture. During the recording process, data are written to this track and erasure of data is not possible. However, unlike a *WORM* (write-once, read many) disk, to which data can only be written once, writing to the CD–R in multiple sessions is possible as long as subsequent "writes" are made to different areas of the disk. CD–R disks have served as a storage medium for the digital photographic images captured in an orthopedic surgery department (Elbeshbeshy and Trepman 2001).

A third form of optical storage is a *CD–RW* (compact disk–rewritable). Once known as a CD–Erasable, this storage medium makes it possible to record over old redundant data or to remove selected files from the disk. Because the user is able to replace data on the CD–RW as well as add to the disk's contents, many people prefer this medium to a CD–R. Of course, this storage medium is more expensive than the CD–R. Three numbers (separated by a "/") associated with a CD–RW drive indicate the relative speed with which the device can write to a CD–RW, write to a CD–R, and read a CD–ROM, respectively.

Some people believe that the fourth form of optical storage, *DVD* (digital versatile disk), ultimately will replace the compact disc. Like the CD, it is available in a number of different formats: read only, recordable, and rewritable. However, it can store data on both of its sides and is available in capacities ranging from 4.7GB to 17GB. The DVD can be the appropriate storage solution in a variety of situations. Tabar (2001, 2002) suggests that DVDs can be a key factor in the decision to implement an in-house picture archiving and communications system (PACS), which is discussed more fully in Chapter 7), and can provide the medium for maintaining current backups of data and applications.

Magneto-Optical Disks

Sometimes known as erasable optical disks, magneto-optical (MO) disks enjoy the cost and capacity advantages of an optical device while being able to have data written on them like magnetic disks. Their capacity can range up to the gigabyte range, and data are arranged on them in concentric rings divided into sectors.

The name magneto-optical reflects the fact that a laser is used to heat the alloy coating of the disk to a sufficiently high temperature at which the material responds to magnetism. The data are written by magnetically altering the alloy in one direction or the other. A laser beam can then "read" this direction and determine the presence of a "0" or "1."

Large numbers of MO disks can be aggregated in what is known as an optical jukebox storage system or simply a jukebox (see Figure 3.6). These systems can make large amounts of data available for immediate online access. One system, for example, described by Kondoh et al. (1998) has three workstations, each with an MO disk jukebox, serving as PACS servers to collect images from eight computed radiography systems and three CT scanners.

Optical or Laser Cards

Resembling a small plastic credit card, an optical or laser card uses a laser to permanently store data. The data are nonerasable, but new data can be added as appropriate. Optical cards can hold from 4 to 6.6 megabytes of data, and thus they are able to store a variety of inputs, including signatures, photographs, fingerprints, x-rays, and voice. The literature suggests that optical cards have gained acceptance in Japan. Tofukuji (2000) touts the benefits of an optical card (that is, large memory capacity, permanent data, and protection from disruption by magnetic force or static electricity) and suggests that the card will play an important role in facilitating recording or exchanging individual health data. Hara (2000) describes a perinatal management system that

FIGURE 3.6
Optical
Jukebox
Storage System

Source: Courtesy of Hewlett-Packard Company.

makes use of an optical medical card and an information network linking four hospitals. Shiina (2000) refers to the optical card as a second medical chart that has a large capacity for electronic storage, a low price, and high security.

Smart Cards Like a laser card, a smart card also resembles a plastic credit card. However, in addition to memory, the smart card "has an embedded computer chip that can store information, process information or serve as a key to an online database or network" (Leonhirth 2001). These cards can potentially store an individual's medical record, determine eligibility for specific procedures, and even maintain a cash balance to cover insurance copayments as needed. Of course, if the patient has lost or forgotten either type of card when care is sought, previous healthcare records will be unavailable, and it will not be possible to update the records with new data.

Adoption of smart card technology has been more widespread in some European countries than it has been in the United States (Hagland 2000). Nevertheless, increasing numbers of applications of this technology are being reported in the literature. Dakins (2001) indicates that a Florida medical center is using smart cards to help in the development of preventive-care programs tailored for seniors. The medical center has provided 12,000 seniors with chip cards, installed readers in its hospital and ambulances, and added staff to track and authenticate the card-based patient data. The medical center's director of senior services hopes that "the senior group's ranks will swell once word spreads of the improved services available as a result of the card" (Dakins 2001, 45).

In addition to their use in marketing, smart cards can be applied in a number of other key areas. A San Diego-based start-up company has teamed with the MedicAlert Foundation to create a smart card that can store emergency patient record information that can be read in hospital emergency departments nationwide (Hagland 2000). The Health Insurance Portability and Accountability Act (HIPAA) has spurred the development of smart cards in healthcare (Dakins 2001). A number of smart card vendors are working on applications that ensure secure access to online records for patient and physicians.

Input Units

The power of an information system can only be realized when data (and programs) have been entered into its storage. The process of entering data into the computer can often be a very time-consuming and costly operation. Fortunately, the field has progressed from the era in which keypunched cards served as the exclusive input medium. The variety of techniques used to input data today are reviewed below.

Keyboards

A common device for entering data into a computer is a keyboard. It resembles a typewriter but has a number of extra keys with special characters or commands. In addition to keys containing the 26 letters of the alphabet, the keyboard has ten keys arranged like a calculator for entering the digits zero through nine; several keys for controlling the position of a pointer, or *cursor*, on the display screen (described below); and a set of keys called *function keys* that perform specific operations depending on the particular software being implemented. Some keyboards have additional special keys that facilitate easy, direct interaction with e-mail (see Chapter 8) and with the Internet (see Chapter 9).

Interestingly, many people who spend extended periods of time using a keyboard experience symptoms of physical stress, like carpal tunnel syndrome. As a result, a variety of ergonomically designed keyboards are available that help the user's hands to be placed in a more comfortable and natural position.

Comfort aside, the need to use a keyboard (and in some cases a mouse) is often viewed as a deterrent to potential computer users, especially physicians. In many cases younger users, who "grew up" with computers, have a higher comfort level with this technology. In any event, healthcare managers wanting clinician support for information systems must be sensitive to the type of input media that the system utilizes.

Pointing Devices

The use of pointing devices provides an alternative to typing text into a keyboard. However, these devices can be used for data entry only if the software makes available on the screen a list of data choices known as a *menu*. By pointing to a given choice, the user is able to select that data value for entry into the computer. Two ways of implementing this process are described briefly below.

A common way of pointing to a menu item is to use a handheld device known as a *mouse*. The original configuration of this device has a "ball" on its bottom that rolls along the desk surface as the user moves it. This rolling motion causes the cursor on the screen to move. A newer version replaces the moving parts of the mouse with an infrared optical sensor and on-board digital signal processor that electronically creates a smooth, precise pointer movement. On laptop computers, the mouse is integrated into the keyboard, either in the form of a *rollerball* (see Figure 3.7) or a touchpad, a smooth surface over which the user moves a finger to control the position of the cursor on the screen. When the cursor is pointing to the desired menu item (or in some applications when the selection is "highlighted"), the user can depress a button on the mouse to complete the selection process. The combination of moving the cursor so it points to a menu item and pressing a button to enter the selection is known as "point-and-click" data entry.

A simple application is the selection of a patient whose vital signs are to be entered. By pointing to the correct patient's name and "clicking" on that choice, the nurse can ensure that vital signs will be associated with the correct patient. Of course it might be necessary to use the keyboard to enter the actual value of the vital sign. To avoid the need for typing, some software designers create a menu consisting of the digits from 0 to 9 along with a decimal point. Thus, a temperature of 99.3 would be entered by "clicking" on the 9, followed by the 9 again, followed by a decimal point, followed by a 3. It remains for a prospective purchaser to decide the comparative advantage of this approach relative to simply typing the value "99.3" directly into a keyboard.

A second pointing device is a *touch screen*—a video display monitor that is sensitive to the presence of a finger or other pointer on the surface of its screen. Rather than moving the cursor to a desired menu item with a mouse, the user of a touch screen can select an item by simply pointing to it. Detection of the location being chosen can be accomplished with one of several available technologies: resistive (change in electrical current), infrared (interruption of light beam), surface acoustic wave (change in sound waves), or capacitive (change in frequency). PCTechGuide (2001a) summarizes the advantages and disadvantages of each.

Touch screens are found in a wide range of applications, from locating the aisle where a given item can be found in a supermarket to choosing descriptions of items of interest to a visitor in a museum. Webster and Copenhaver (2001) describe the use of touch-screen technology with a structured data entry system for electronic patient records. The system includes a program that

FIGURE 3.7
Keyboard and
Rollerball on a
Portable
Computer

Source: Courtesy of International Business Machines Corporation. Unauthorized use not permitted.

coordinates preset screens for detailed history, physical examination, treatment, and prescription modules. The program presents "pick lists" that allow further customization and individualization of data inputs.

Scanning Devices

Healthcare information systems utilize a variety of scanning devices to input data. These devices are designed to scan the assortment of source documents generated within healthcare organizations: documents containing specially designed characters or codes, special forms such as questionnaires or evaluation sheets, and documents containing text and/or graphics. Each is discussed below.

Printed labels containing sets of vertical black/white bars can be "read" by a *barcode scanner.* Each barcode pattern denotes a different character (see Figure 3.8). Many types of barcode printers may be used to print barcodes for pharmacy prescription dispensing and inventory, laboratory tests, equipment inventory, medical records, and other areas. The scanning itself may be performed using a barcode wand connected to a computer with an interface cable or a wireless handheld unit, containing a wand or built-in gun-type scanner, which transmits data to a central computer.

FIGURE 3.8
Specimens with
Barcode Labels
in an
Automated
Laboratory
System

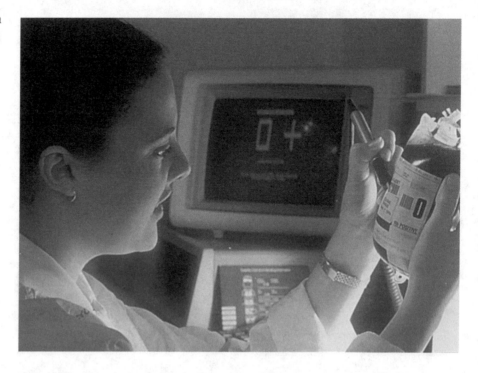

Source: Courtesy of International Business Machines Corporation. Unauthorized use not permitted.

Johnson et al. (2002) report that the Veterans Health Administration has developed Bar Code Medication Administration software that uses wireless, point-of-care technology with an integrated barcode scanner. The authors indicate that the system is able to greatly reduce medication-administration errors by enabling clinicians to verify a patient's identity and validate the medications against active orders.

In a desire to assess customer satisfaction and the quality of the care being provided, healthcare organizations are utilizing increasing numbers of questionnaires and evaluation instruments. Inputting the data from these documents can be time consuming. *Optical mark readers* can be used if the documents have been designed as "multiple-choice" questions on which the respondent shades a box adjacent to his or her response.

Finally, *optical scanners* can be used to enter a variety of source documents containing both text and graphics. These scanners lie at the heart of a document-management system that uses "digital scanning devices to convert paper documents into digital image files that can be electronically stored, transmitted and displayed" (Gillespie 2002, 50). The document-management systems also "manage" the images and data by overseeing their routing to the correct database.

Several types of scanners are available, including high-end drum scanners, compact document scanners, dedicated photo scanners, and handheld scanners for the budget end of the market. Most popular is the flatbed scanner that looks and functions like a desktop personal photocopier. Prospective purchasers of scanners should be familiar with the scanner's resolution, gray scale levels, and bit-depth characteristics. "Optical" resolution, measured in dots per inch, indicates how detailed an image the scanner can produce. "Gray scale levels" denotes the number of levels of gray that a black-and-white scanner can distinguish. Similarly, "bit depth" is related to the number of colors distinguishable by a color scanner. The bit-depth value is the exponent to which two must be raised to obtain the actual number of colors that the scanner can handle. Thus, a 36-bit scanner can distinguish 2^{36} or more than 68 billion (1 billion = 10^9) colors.

Remember that scanners are hardware devices that convert source documents into "tiny dots" (called pixels). Even text characters are converted into pixels, so the computer cannot recognize individual letters or words. This picture of the original page can be viewed and stored, but, because it lacks structure, it cannot be manipulated. "Some document management systems, however, can convert scans of paper documents into electronic data instead of just electronic images of the paper documents. Such systems use computer output to laser disk technology . . . (that) converts a scanned image into data . . . and stores it alongside scanned document images" (Gillespie 2002, 50).

Areas where optical scanners may be useful in healthcare settings are varied. Text material like a radiology report or consultant's evaluation can be added to the patient record without the time-consuming process of key-punching. Graphical material like EKG traces can also be incorporated into the computerized record and thus can be conveniently accessible to a clinician. In the administrative areas, scanning documents that are only available as "hard copy" can potentially prevent the need to do large amounts of word processing. The need to scan "hard copy" might possibly decrease as digital devices, which produce data in digital form, become more prevalent in the clinical setting.

Handwriting Recognition

Small devices, like the personal digital assistant (PDA) discussed later in the chapter, have space limitations that make typing on their keyboard rather slow and difficult. A more convenient form of input with these devices is frequently *writing* data directly on a special screen. The device must, of course, have the ability to understand the written text.

PCTechGuide (2001b) describes two approaches to a computer's understanding written material. The Graffiti recognition system understands each letter shape as a unique pattern for that letter with no attempt to understand words or context. Apple Computer took a more ambitious approach with its Newton™ machine, which attempted to read the user's writing and convert it into words. The computer tried to "learn" the way the user wrote, but the approach turned out to be a costly mistake for Apple. On the other hand, other developers have emulated the success of the Graffiti approach, and their systems are often found in PDAs.

Voice Input   Many people would define voice input as the ultimate computer input medium. What could be easier than simply "telling" the computer what operations you wish it to perform and then "dictating" the input data you want the instructions to operate on? Certainly practitioners who have been reluctant to use "conventional" input media would have difficulty finding a basis for criticism of voice-input techniques.

Like handwriting recognition, voice input has several levels of implementation. Devices capable of voice input are designed to change sound waves into digitized data that can simply be stored and later replayed. Although the data can be modified to change its sound, no interpretation or translation of the data is possible. By contrast, "speech recognition systems should have the ability to interpret human speech and parse the audible words into text, sounds, and commands that represent exactly or symbolically what the person said. More sophisticated systems and algorithms can actually interpret what the user meant and then act on that belief" (Erdel and Crooks 2000, 14).

Kelly (2001) provides an excellent overview of speech-recognition technology and identifies several challenges, including lower than desirable accuracy levels, the need to train the system to recognize user voices, and the fact that many applications are not designed to be networked. By contrast, Simmons (2002, 38) describes the installation of a voice recognition system in their physical therapy practice as "a smooth process. . . . Training was painless. . . . Within two weeks (they) were completely reliant on the new system—and growing more fluent every day."

In summary then, experts report "at least 75% of today's health care speech recognition market is in radiology. . . . Getting physicians outside of radiology to use speech recognition technology to dictate, edit and create their reports will be challenging . . ." (Goedert 2002). On the other hand, Bergeron (2001) suggests that the same economic pressures that drove many clinicians to learn the keyboard instead of relying on a secretary may push clinicians from the keyboard to the microphone.

Output Units

An important objective of information systems is to produce output of value to the user. Types of output that are of particular value to healthcare managers include visual displays, printed output, and voice output.

Visual Displays   The oldest and still most widely used form of displaying output from an information system is a *video display terminal* (VDT). Typically called a "monitor," the VDT has evolved from the small monochrome screens commonly used just a few short years ago. Although it resembles a television screen, a VDT is generally designed to display a much sharper, detailed image. Its text display is typically 80 columns by 24 rows.

Two important characteristics associated with a VDT are screen size and resolution. The screen size is usually measured in inches diagonally across the screen. Resolution indicates the quality or clarity of the display. It is measured in units of *pixels*—individual dots that can be illuminated to help form a particular character or graphical pattern. A 21" monitor, for example, can support 1600- by 1200-pixel resolutions. Large-screen, higher-resolution monitors present images that have greater detail and accuracy and are important in applications such as radiology systems. They also make displays of multiple windows or very large spreadsheets easy to read.

A second visual display is the *liquid crystal display* (LCD). Using what is known as flat-panel technology, this display consists of a "sandwich" of fluorescent light, filters, liquid crystal cells, and a glass plate. Monochrome displays have a single liquid crystal cell for each pixel, while color displays have three cells for each pixel. Signals from the computer are applied to cells, which in turn affect the polarization of the fluorescent light. One of the filters then affects the brightness of the light reaching the glass plate.

Performance improvements in flat-panel color screens have been achieved by utilizing Thin Film Transistor (TFT) technology. The TFT screen, which is also known as active matrix, utilizes many more transistors to apply a charge to the cells, thus charging each cell repetitively to produce a brighter picture. Higher production costs make this technology more expensive than passive matrix displays.

Usage of flat-panel displays is particularly popular in applications where desk space is limited because their "footprint" is so much smaller than conventional CRT (cathode-ray tube) monitors. In addition, projectors that combine the features of an overhead projector and LCD panel are gaining increasing use. These projectors, connected to laptop computers (discussed below), are now "standard equipment" at meetings, allowing speakers to display computer-generated slides as part of their presentations. The presentation software that is used to create the slides is discussed in Chapter 4.

Printed Output

Printers, too, have developed extensively from the early devices used to create "hard" output. These devices were quite similar to typewriters, using raised characters that impacted the paper through an inked ribbon. Because they were capable of only printing those raised characters that comprised their "character set," they were unable to print graphics. Today, healthcare managers will generally encounter one of three printing technologies: dot matrix, inkjet, or laser printers. In addition, when shopping for a printer to be used with a portable computer, the manager may encounter thermal printers.

Dot matrix printers are also known as impact printers because they contain a print head that impacts the paper to produce the printed output. Early print heads contained 9 pins, but today's dot matrix printers generally contain 24 pins. The print head is capable of sliding horizontally across the page. As it slides, electromagnets control whether a given pin strikes the paper through an inked ribbon. Electronics within the computer control the movement of the print head and the individual pins.

After a row has been printed, the paper is advanced vertically and printing continues onto the next row. This way, the contents of an entire page can be printed. The paper used with dot matrix printers consists of a continuous roll of pages joined together with "perforations." After a given document has been printed, these pages can be separated into a completed stack of output. The sophistication of the computer's electronics greatly influences the quality of the output, including the high-quality graphics that can now be achieved with dot matrix printers. Although several inked ribbons can theoretically be combined to print color output, dot matrix printers are generally not used for color applications.

In the past, dot matrix printers were a popular choice because they had a lower purchase price and generally lower maintenance costs. Today, however, the cost of competing technology is comparable, maintenance is less of a problem, and the noise associated with dot matrix printers can be a problem in many healthcare settings. As a result, other types of printers are being increasingly used.

Inkjet printers are similar mechanically to dot matrix printers. Instead of a print head, however, an inkjet printer contains a print cartridge. As the cartridge slides across the page, ink is sprayed from a reservoir through very small nozzles, which produces dots on the page. Once a row has been printed, the paper moves vertically so the next row can be printed. Single-sheet plain paper is used in these printers. When a page has been completed, it is mechanically moved out of the way and allowed to dry, and a new blank page is positioned for printing. Black-and-white printers have a single reservoir of black ink, whereas color printers have three or more ink reservoirs. The quality of color printing that can be achieved with an inkjet printer is quite good, particularly in view of their very reasonable cost.

Laser printers are becoming the most popular type of printers in use today. The quality of laser-printer output is quite high, and color laser printers are available that can produce copies of sufficient quality to be used in reproducing artwork. Purchasers of laser printers should be aware of several of their characteristics. First is the size of the printer's memory, where pixel information is stored in preparation for pages to be printed. Graphical images can quickly exhaust the memory capacity and result in a "Memory Overflow" error message. Memory capacities can range from a standard of 1 megabyte to 80 megabytes or more. Second is resolution, which is a measure of the print quality. Higher resolution requires more memory and slows down the printing. Standard resolution can range from 600 dots per inch to 1,200 dots per inch or more. Finally, print speed is also of importance. This can range from 10 to 19 or more pages per minute for printers typically used with microcomputers. In large volume, mainframe settings, one can find laser printers capable of printing more than 100 pages per minute.

The technology of laser printers is quite similar to that of photocopying, except that the image source is information in the computer controlling a laser rather than an original hard copy, bright light, and mirrors. In both systems, however, a photosensitive drum becomes electrically charged wherever a dot is to be printed, and a black powder, known as toner, sticks to those electrically charged locations. A sheet of paper, given the opposite charge, is fed over the drum and picks up the toner from the drum. A heating process, known as fusing, causes the toner to stick permanently to the paper and produces a finished copy.

Portable printers, used in conjunction with portable computers allow the traveling manager to produce printed copies of computer work performed "on the road." These printers can employ either ink-jet technology, which works like the desk-model version, or thermal technology, which involves a heat transfer from a thermal print head to chemically treated thermal paper.

Voice Output

A potentially useful form of computer output for healthcare applications is voice output. Here, the digital text of the computer's memory is converted to understandable speech by means of a process known as voice synthesis. The sounds that comprise the words and phrases of speech are assembled electronically using basic sound components. A major objective is to create an output that sounds natural and pleasant rather than synthetic and robot-like. Available hardware works moderately well at very reasonable prices.

A potential application for voice output in a healthcare setting would involve situations where clinicians want to use an ordinary telephone to obtain information stored within the information system. For example, laboratory systems typically create output records within the computer containing the results of a particular test. A physician needing those results could use a telephone to "call" the laboratory system and hear the results "read" by a voice synthesizer. The financial community uses similar technology to supply account balances to its customers at any time that they might call into the system.

Classes of Computers

Until recently it was not very difficult to construct a classification of computers based on their capabilities. Large, expensive, mainframe systems were clearly more powerful than small, less expensive PCs. The categories of computers were relatively easy to define. Today, however, the picture is somewhat blurred. Most healthcare managers have laptop computers that have more capabilities than the computers that ran their organization's financial systems just a few years ago. Nevertheless, the classification paradigm persists, and the industry continues to use the terms supercomputers, mainframes, minicomputers, workstations, and personal computers. The meaning of these terms is reviewed next.

Supercomputers

By definition, the class of computers known as supercomputers has more processing power than other computers available. Typically, these machines are used in military and scientific applications. Their strength lies in their ability to perform a large number of complex calculations with considerable speed. This performance is achieved in two ways. First, the processors themselves are quite fast. Second, many processors are linked together into a *parallel-processing* configuration. Parallel-processor devices break a problem into a number of smaller parts, and then they solve each part using a different processor. Special consideration must be given to the software design to take full advantage of the power of these parallel processors.

A newspaper article announcing IBM's plans to build a computer designed to work 300 times faster than any existing machine contained an analogy that illustrates the speed of a supercomputer (*St. Louis Post Dispatch* 1996). If one equates home computers to the current world record of nine seconds for the 100-meter dash, then the newly announced computer could run from New York to Philadelphia in the same nine seconds.

Mainframe Computers

Healthcare information processing has historically been performed on large mainframe computer processors, centrally located and under the tight control of the data processing department. These machines are characterized by their large size, fast processing speed, primary storage of several hundred megabytes, online secondary storage in the order of magnitude of billions of bytes, and large magnetic tapes used for off-line secondary storage.

Originally, mainframe computers typically were stand-alone processors, usually connected to only dumb terminals. (A dumb terminal has a keyboard and screen but no processing capability.) However, these stand-alone systems frequently had difficulty keeping up with the large volume of data processing needed by more and more data end-users and by more sophisticated software systems. Therefore, shared-processing configurations were added to the mainframe to increase computing power and data transfer.

Shared configurations include processor clusters, front-end processors, and networks with microcomputers and workstations. *Processor clusters* can greatly increase processing power without a great increase in cost. Clusters consist of several CPUs that share the processing load. The information services (IS) manager can use operating system software to perform load balancing so that no one processor is slowed down too much. *Front-end processors* typically are small minicomputer processors or powerful microcomputers that can perform selected processing tasks or share general computing with the mainframe processor, thus taking a large part of the processing load off the main CPU. Often, these specialized computers manage all of the routine communications with peripheral devices.

Mainframes are also being configured in *networks* with minicomputers and microcomputers. In addition, they can be used as the platform for Web servers. The configuration of these networks and the role that mainframe computers play in their operation is discussed in Chapter 5.

The long-term future of mainframe computers is an interesting topic of speculation and discussion. Many people have predicted the demise of this hardware and are frankly surprised at its persistence. Nevertheless, these same people do acknowledge that mainframe computers are able to handle large data processing and data storage jobs that cannot be accomplished with other computers.

Organizational decisions regarding mainframe computers have been varied. Some organizations have replaced them with other "in-house" systems (Anderson and Stafford 2002); others have utilized the services of an applications service provider (ASP, see Chapter 12) for the applications that formerly ran on the mainframe system (Blaschka 2000); while others have simply built on their existing mainframe system (Nakamoto 2000). In deciding the fate of an organization's mainframe computer, the manager should bear in mind that the value of a piece of hardware is ultimately its ability to allow some application to be processed. So long as a program is available and supported by its vendor for processing on a mainframe computer, one can frequently build a strong case for continuing its use.

Minicomputers

Minicomputers have a physical size and computing capability between the mainframe and the microcomputer, although the continuum of computing power is increasingly blurred. In addition to their role as front-end processors to mainframe computers or as part of a network with mainframes, minicomputers are often used as stand-alone systems. Several integrated software systems, discussed in more detail in Chapter 4, have been designed to run on a minicomputer and are targeted specifically for small- to medium-size healthcare organizations.

Even in large healthcare organizations, minicomputer systems are used for specific processing tasks that can be performed separately from the main processor, thus alleviating the main data-processing load. The minicomputer system may still be networked to the mainframe if needed.

Workstations

The term workstation is generally used to refer to a high-end microcomputer with a large amount of primary storage; a fast processor; a high-quality sound card; high-resolution graphics; a CD–RW drive; and, in many cases, a DVD drive. Initially, these machines were targeted at the engineering, design, and technical communities. Today, however, workstations are used in a variety of application settings, including the healthcare environment.

Radiology Imaging Units High-resolution workstations connected to imaging equipment support the recording, storage, and retrieval of patient x-rays by radiologists and technicians. These systems generally have very large amounts of disk storage so x-ray images can be kept for a certain period of time, and they may be connected to a mainframe computer to allow incorporation of the images into electronic patient files for permanent storage.

Hirschorn et al. (2001) demonstrated that the introduction of a single workstation in the on-call reading room reduced the time required to reach a final diagnosis by obviating the need to print and transport the images to the on-call radiology resident. Passadore et al. (2001) suggest that even when primary diagnosis is performed on film, the availability of an image review workstation can be helpful to enhance communication with referring physicians and to increase technologists' and radiologists' efficiency.

Simulation The computing power of workstations enables them to be an important component of a simulation tool. For example, Devarajan et al. (2001) developed a workstation for the simulation of laparoscopic procedures to support training and treatment planning. The workstation includes a custom built frame to which surgical tools can be attached. The instruments are interfaced to a high-speed PC with fast graphics capability. The system transduces the three-dimensional motion of the surgical instruments into slave maneuvers in virtual space, which in turn probes the simulated organ.

Similarly, Freudenstein et al. (2001) describe a system that provides support for planning and training in neurendoscopic interventions. A UNIX workstation performs the rendering of the images providing a three-dimensional view of the cerebral ventricles, with good visualization of anatomic details. Sequences for the entire ventricular system can be generated in real time. The system enables the neurendoscopic procedures to be simulated prior to surgery based on the patient's individual anatomy.

Personal Computers

Technological advances in PCs have caused the distinction between them and workstations to become quite blurred. As a result, many healthcare applications are currently being performed on PCs, either in a "stand-alone" mode or in a distributed processing configuration. (See Chapter 5 for details.) The processor in a PC typically consists of a single electronic chip known as a microchip. Therefore, PCs are also called microcomputers and are characterized by their relatively low-cost, small-size, and easy-to-maintain hardware components.

From its initial function of helping managers perform analyses of the raw data contained in printed reports, the microcomputer has evolved into a powerful platform for significant information processing in healthcare settings. Microcomputers support the analysis of clinical data in research studies, help managers make strategic decisions, support major clinical systems, provide the computing power for medical office financial systems, and provide word-processing capability for manager and secretary alike. The list of applications seems almost endless. In fact, in some cases microcomputers have provided the computing power for the entire healthcare organization (Glaser et al. 1991).

Smaller versions of microcomputers are gaining popularity in the healthcare setting. These include laptop computers (about the size of a small briefcase), notebook computers (about the size of a small three-ring binder), palmtop computers (able to be held and operated in a single hand), and personal digital assistants (PDAs, see Figure 3.9). "The PDA is effectively a handheld PC, capable of handling all the normal tasks of its leather-bound ancestor—address book, notepad, appointments diary and phone list" (PCTechGuide 2001b). In addition, however, the PDA offers additional computing applications such as spreadsheet, clock, calculator, or games. Although a keyboard can be attached to the PDA, the user typically employs a pen to write data into the device.

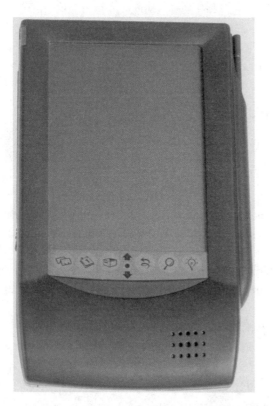

FIGURE 3.9
Personal Digital
Assistant

Like the desktop microcomputers, these smaller machines can be used in a "stand-alone" mode, where all of the information being processed resides within the computing device, or in a "wireless" mode, where the device is in contact with a computer *network*. Much of the enthusiasm in the literature regarding these devices, in particular the PDAs and palmtop computers, concerns their use in a wireless mode. This application will be discussed in Chapter 5.

Summary

Computer hardware spans a broad spectrum, from small palmtop computers that can be held in one hand to extremely large and powerful supercomputers. No matter where on the spectrum a given system lies, it is composed of six basic components: a CPU, primary storage, secondary storage, input units, output units, and communications devices. The CPU is the "brains" of the computer and its speed and power greatly influence the computer's capabilities. The capacity and speed of the primary storage also affect the computer system's performance, and fortunately the cost of this component is generally falling.

Secondary storage devices include a variety of disk and tape units and are designed to maintain the large quantities of data common to healthcare applications. Optical storage has become more prevalent and is increasingly important. The speed with which data are entered into and retrieved from secondary storage devices is also an important specification within the overall system.

A number of peripheral devices are available to facilitate the process of entering data into the computer in a variety of formats, including keyboard entry, scanning, and voice input. Similarly, data can be obtained from the computer on a display screen, in printed form, magnetically for future processing, or in spoken form. The goal of the industry is to make data entry and retrieval as simple as possible.

Computer hardware technology changes at such a rapid pace that keeping up is difficult even for the information systems specialist, let alone the healthcare manager. Like any other investment decision, consideration must be given to the size and power of the computer that is appropriate for a given application. Nevertheless, the hardware fundamentals discussed in this chapter are designed to make the manager feel comfortable participating in the planning, implementation, and evaluation of new hardware systems.

Discussion Questions

3.1 Name each of the six components of a computer system and indicate the function of each.

3.2 Give a brief description of three secondary storage media.

3.3 Discuss the relative advantage of using a pointing device to enter a patient's vital signs compared to simply typing in the values using a keyboard.

3.4 Suggest how the use of a patient ID bracelet containing a barcode representation of the patient's ID and a barcode scanner can lead to improved quality of care in a hospital.

3.5 Explain the difference between devices capable of voice input and voice recognition.

3.6 Explain what is meant by the resolution of a video display terminal, and indicate applications where high resolution is quite important.

3.7 Name three types of printers and briefly explain the major characteristics of each.

3.8 Give a brief description of three applications of workstations.

Problems

3.1 Interview the chief information officer in a medical center of your choice to obtain a list of its currently installed computer hardware and the applications running on each hardware platform. Determine the rationale for the organization's allocation of applications to each hardware platform.

3.2 Design and administer a survey to a group of physicians to identify their attitudes toward the various types of input devices. In particular, determine the extent to which the need to type data serves as an impediment to their use of information systems.

3.3 Assume that a large multispecialty physician group is considering scanning reports and letters from consultants into their patients' electronic medical record. Obtain vendor data on document scanners, including performance, price, and staffing information. Make a recommendation on whether the group should indeed scan these documents or maintain a separate paper chart.

3.4 Using the literature, the Internet, and vendors as sources of information, determine the feasibility of using optical-storage devices as a backup medium for an electronic medical record system.

3.5 Choose a sample of patients utilizing a clinic in an institution to which you have access. Conduct a survey of these patients to determine their attitude toward the use of a palmtop computer to enter data during a patient visit.

References

Anderson, L. K., and C. J. Stafford. 2002. "The Big Bang Implementation: Not for the Faint of Heart." *Computers in Nursing* 20 (1): 14–20; quiz 20–22.

Bergeron, B. P. 2001. "Voice Recognition in Clinical Medicine: Process Versus Technology." *The Journal of Practice Management* 16 (4): 213–15.

Blaschka, S. 2000. "Improving Efficiency Without Disrupting Patient Care." *Health Management Technology* 21 (10): 58.

Dakins, D. R. 2001. "Is the Future in the Cards?" *Health Data Management* 9 (7): 44–46, 48.

Devarajan, V., D. Scott, D. Jones, R. Rege, R. Eberhart, C. Lindahl, P. Tanguy, and R. Fernandez. *2001.* "Bimanual Haptic Workstation for Laparoscopic Surgery Simulation." *Studies in Health Technology and Informatics* 81: 126–28.

Elbeshbeshy, B., and E. Trepman. 2001. "Digital Photography in Orthopaedic Surgery." *Foot and Ankle International* 22 (1): 67–74.

Erdel, T., and S. Crooks. 2000. "Speech Recognition Technology: An Outlook for Human-to-Machine Interaction." *Journal of Health Information Management* 14 (2): 13–21.

Freudenstein, D., D. Bartz, M. Skalej, and F. Duffner. 2001. "New Virtual System for Planning of Neurendoscopic Interventions." *Computer Aided Surgery* 6 (2): 77–84.

Gillespie, G. 2002. "Paper Documents Get Sharper Image." *Health Data Management* 10 (2): 50–52, 54.

Glaser, J. P., R. F. Beckley, P. Roberts, J. K. Marra, F. L. Hiltz, and J. Hurley. 1991. "A Very Large PC LAN as the Basis for a Hospital Information System." *Journal of Medical Systems* 15 (2): 133–37.

Goedert, J. 2002. "Newsline: Is the Speech Recognition Market Finally Ready for Growth?" *Health Data Management* 10 (2): 12, 14.

Hagland, M. 2000. "Smart Cards Knock at Healthcare's Door." *Healthcare Informatics* 17 (10): 77, 78, 80, 82.

Hara, K. 2000. "Development of Perinatal Management System Using Optical Card and Regional Health Information Network" [in Japanese]. *Rinsho Byori— Japanese Journal of Clinical Pathology* 48 (10): 910–14.

Heetderks-Cox, M. J., B. B. Alford, C. M. Bednar, C. J. Heiss, L. A. Tauai, and K. K. Edgren. 2001. "CD–ROM Nutrient Analysis Database Assists Self-Monitoring Behavior of Active Duty Air Force Personnel Receiving Nutrition Counseling for Weight Loss." *Journal of the American Dietetic Association* 101 (9): 1041–46.

Henning, J. L. 2000. "SPEC CPU2000: Measuring CPU Performance in the New Millenium." *Computer* 33 (7): 28–35.

Hirschorn, D. S., C. R. Hinrichs, D. M. Gor, K. Shah, and G. Visvikis. 2001. "Impact of a Diagnostic Workstation on Workflow in the Emergency Department at a Level I Trauma Center." *Journal of Digital Imaging* 14 (2, Supplement 1): 199–201.

Johnson, C. L., R. A. Carlson, C. L. Tucker, and C. Willette. 2002. "Using BCMA Software to Improve Patient Safety in Veterans Administration Medical Centers." *Journal of Healthcare Information Management* 16 (1): 46–51.

Kelly, B. 2001. "Caregivers Talk About Speech Technology." *Health Data Management* 9 (3): 56–58, 60, 62, 64, 66.

Kondoh, H., T. Washiashi, M. Sasagaki, J. Arisawa, H. Nakamura, and K. Inamura. 1998. "Development and Evaluation of PC-based HIS-RIS-Modality-PACS

Coupling: The Results of Evaluation of Initial Stage with Personal Computer Applications." *Computer Methods & Programs in Biomedicine* 57 (1–2): 63–68.

Leonhirth, J. 2001. "Ahead of Its Time: The Promise of Chip-Embedded Smart Cards May Be Too Late." *Modern Physician* 5 (1): 32–33.

Nakamoto, G. 2000. "Building on a Legacy System." *Health Management Technology* 21 (10): 56.

Passadore, D. J. 2001. "Use of a Low-Cost, PC-based Image Review Workstation at a Radiology Department." *Journal of Digital Imaging* 14 (2, Supplement 1): 222–23.

PCTechGuide. 2001a. "Input-Output/Input Devices." [Online article; retrieved 6/30/02]. http://www.pctechguide.com/14input.htm.

———. 2001b. "Components/Mobile Computing." [Online article; retrieved 6/30/02]. http://www.pctechguide.com/25mob3.htm.

———. 2002a. "Glossary by Category: Optical Storage (109 Terms)." [Online article; retrieved 6/30/02]. http://www.forums.pctechguide.com/glossary/bycat.php?catSelected=9&catSearchSubmit=View+Category.

———. 2002b. "Storage/Hard Disks." [Online article; retrieved 6/30/02]. http://www.pctechguide.com/04disks.htm.

Rosen, S. 1969. "Electronic Computers: A Historical Survey." *Computing Surveys* 1 (1): 7–36.

Shiina, S. 2000. "Past, Present, and Future of Optical Cards for Medical Use," [in Japanese]. *Rinsho Byori—Japanese Journal of Clinical Pathology* 48 (10): 906–9.

Simmons, J. 2002. "Speech Recognition: Talking It Through." *Health Management Technology* 23 (2): 38.

St. Louis Post Dispatch. 1996. "New Computer to Be Fastest in World." *St. Louis Post Dispatch* 118 (209): 1a, 5a.

Stromberg, A., H. Ahlen, B. Fridlund, and U. Dahlstrom. 2002. "Interactive Education on CD–ROM—A New Tool in the Education of Heart Failure Patients." *Patient Education and Counseling* 46 (1): 75–81.

Tabar, P. 2001. "Brave New Imaging World." *Healthcare Informatics* 18 (11): 29, 30, 32, 34.

———. 2002. "Planning Ahead for Business as Usual." *Healthcare Informatics* 19 (2): 36, 38.

Tofukuji, I. 2000. "On Standardization of Optical Memory Cards" [in Japanese]. *Rinsho Byori—Japanese Journal of Clinical Pathology* 48 (10): 915–18.

Webster C., and J. Copenhaver. 2001. "Structured Data Entry in a Workflow-Enabled Electronic Patient Record." *Journal of Medical Practice Management* 17 (3): 157–61.

Additional Readings

DeVille, K. A. 2001. "The Ethical and Legal Implications of Handheld Medical Computers." *The Journal of Legal Medicine* 22: 447–66.

Dzingle, D., G. A. May, and H. T. Garland. 2001. "Digital Radiography and Film Scanners: Automating the Transition to Filmless Radiology." *Journal of Digital Imaging* 14 (2, Supplement 1): 128–30.

Englander, I. 2000. *The Architecture of Computer Hardware and Systems Software: An Information Technology Approach*, 2nd Edition. New York: Wiley.

Ernst, R., W. Carpenter, W. Torres, and S. Wheeler. 2001. "Combining Speech Recognition Software with Digital Imaging and Communications in Medicine (DICOM) Workstation Software on a Microsoft Windows Platform." *Journal of Digital Imaging* 14 (2, Supplement 1): 182–83.

Johnson, R. L. 2000. "Is Your Legacy System Compatible with Today's IDNs?" *Healthcare Informatics* 17 (2): 85, 86, 88.

Kurihara, Y., S. Yoshida, H. Geshi, Y. Kubo, and Y. Kitazoe. 2001. "Economic Analysis of a Filmless System Based on the Hospital Information System." *Medinfo 2001* 10 (Part 2): 1166–70.

Lal, S. O., F. W. Smith, J. P. Davis, H. Y. Castro, D. W. Smith, D. L. Chinkes, and R. E. Barrow. 2000. "Palm Computer Demonstrates a Fast and Accurate Means of Burn Data Collection." *The Journal of Burn Care and Rehabilitation* 21 (6): 559–61.

Laudon, K. C., and J. P. Laudon. 2000. *Management Information Systems: Organization and Technology in the Networked Enterprise*, 6th Edition. Upper Saddle River, NJ: Prentice-Hall, Inc.

Stair, R., and G. W. Reynolds. 2001. *Principles of Information Systems: A Managerial Approach*, 5th Edition. Boston: Course Technology/Thomson Learning.

Sutherland, J. 2001. "Power to the PDA." *Healthcare Informatics* 18 (7): 44.

Ulm, A. J., F. J. Bova, and W. A. Friedman. 2001. "Stereotactic Biopsy Aided by a Computer Graphics Workstation: Experience with 200 Consecutive Cases." *Surgical Neurology* 56 (6): 366–71; discussion 371–72.

Vorbeck, F., A. Ba-Salamah, J. Kettenbach, and P. Huebsch. 2000. "Report Generation Using Digital Speech Recognition in Radiology." *European Radiology* 10 (12): 1976–82.

COMPUTER SOFTWARE

The hardware components of even the most powerful supercomputer cannot by themselves produce output of value to the healthcare manager. These components need a detailed set of instructions that describe, step by step, the tasks they should perform to achieve a desired objective. This detailed set of instructions is known collectively as a *program*.

A program can be permanently stored within the computer's read-only memory (ROM). An example, noted in Chapter 3, is the small, special-purpose set of instructions that describes the sequence to be followed by the computer when it is first turned on. However, it is much more practical for a program to be stored on secondary storage devices—a disk, for example—and read into the computer's primary storage when the user wishes to run it. In the early days of computing, programs were stored on tape or even on punched cards. Perhaps these "soft" storage media gave rise to the use of the term *software* as a synonym for computer programs.

The tasks of selecting, implementing, and testing software are at least as complex as the corresponding hardware tasks and are often more important for the success of the overall computer implementation. These tasks are discussed in detail in Chapter 12. To be knowledgeable participants in this process, healthcare managers can benefit from an understanding of basic software concepts, including a description of application software, the distinction between integrated and interfaced systems, the role of system management software, an introduction to programming languages, and the functions of language translators. This chapter presents these basic concepts.

Application Software

From the user perspective, the most important category of software is application software. After all, this software is that which accomplishes the useful tasks that justify the purchase of the information system. In fact, application software can be further classified as general purpose or application specific.

General Purpose Software

Many computer programs provide an environment in which a user can solve a particular *class* of problems rather than a single, narrowly defined problem. Examples include word processors, desktop-publishing software, spreadsheet software, statistical packages, database-management software, presentation graphics software, and web browsers. These programs, known as general purpose application software, are most often run today on a microcomputer, although in some cases where large data sets are involved a minicomputer might be employed.

Word Processors

The preparation of manuscripts, letters, forms, manuals, or just about any material once completed on a typewriter is now made much easier with the availability of *word-processing* software. Older word-processing packages usually resided on bulky, dedicated hardware systems and had a limited set of rudimentary features. Modern word-processing programs have a variety of sophisticated capabilities and are available for most hardware platforms.

The power of word processing lies in its editing capabilities. The need to retype a page to make a simple correction is a thing of the past. This, of course, can have a negative side as people find it perhaps too easy to make "just one more refinement" to a letter or report. Other capabilities that contribute to the power of word processing include

- the ability to merge form letters with a list of addresses,
- the ability to insert graphical images or figures into a document,
- the ability to easily convert a document from one word-processing format to another,
- the ability to check spelling and grammar,
- the ability to use a thesaurus for determining synonyms, and
- the ability to create tables and perform basic arithmetic operations on the values in a table.

Many newcomers choose word processing as a good starting point for learning and gaining experience in the field of computing. Word processing is actually one of many office automation systems in use. See Chapter 8 for a discussion of these applications. Popular word-processing programs include Microsoft® Word and Corel® WordPerfect.

Desktop-Publishing Software

Slightly more powerful than traditional word-processing software is *desktop-publishing software* (although as word processors become more sophisticated the two types of software have a number of similarities). Desktop-publishing software is designed to create camera-ready copy of newspapers, invitations, programs, bulletins, and other similar documents typically produced by typesetting just a few years ago. Professional results can be achieved quite easily with desktop-publishing software running on a microcomputer and a laser printer.

An important feature of desktop-publishing software is the ability to support a wide array of fonts so that the desired printed effect can be achieved. Also important is the ability to import photographs, diagrams, and other figures as well as the facility to easily combine these with text to produce exactly the page layout that is desired. Although these features continue to be refined in word-processing systems, they receive particular emphasis from developers of desktop-publishing software.

Tietz and Tabor (1995) report that the availability of relatively inexpensive desktop-publishing software has facilitated their developing a monthly newsletter. Through this medium, information about continuous quality improvement activities is being disseminated. Popular desktop packages include Adobe® PageMaker®, QuarkXPress®, and Corel Ventura™ 8.

Users can prepare, edit, and print a wide range of financial, administrative, and other types of tables with the use of *spreadsheet software*. Developed in the late 1970s, the electronic spreadsheet, like the word processor, provided the impetus for many purchases of microcomputers. VisiCalc, as the first spreadsheet program was called, clearly demonstrated that a computer could be used to perform functions useful to the organization without a need for in-depth programming skill.   **Spreadsheet Software**

On initiating (or "booting-up") a spreadsheet program, the user is presented with a rectangular array of cells (see Figure 4.1). Numbers, formulas, functions, or clusters of instructions (called macros) can be entered into the cells. All of the standard mathematical operations can be performed on the cell values, and the results of these operations change if the cell values involved in the computations change. Thus, skeleton spreadsheets, called templates, can be designed and then run after cell values have been filled in. For example, a department overtime report can be designed as a template, and a report can

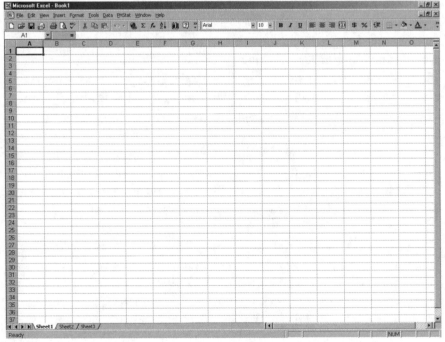

FIGURE 4.1
A Microsoft®
EXCEL
Spreadsheet

be generated when the labor hours for a given month are entered into the spreadsheet.

The spreadsheet formulas are written in terms of constant values and/or values located in other cells. If a cell value changes, all of the cells containing formulas involving that modified cell will also change. This property gives the spreadsheet much of its power. A user can systematically change the value of a given cell and observe the impact of this change on other cells in the spreadsheet. Such systematic investigation is known as "what-if" analysis. As an example, consider a spreadsheet that evaluates the income and expenses of three potential configurations of a hospital department. If one of the variables on the spreadsheet is patient volume, one can systematically change this value and observe the impact on each configuration. Changing the value of patient volume until expenses just equal income is also possible. This gives rise to the "break-even volume." (See, for example, Austin and Boxerman 1995, Chapter 2.)

Today's spreadsheet software has a number of additional features that greatly enhance its power. These features include creation, insertion, and printing of sophisticated graphs into the spreadsheet; text enhancement, such as cell shading, outlining, underlining, and multiple fonts; data import and export to and from other file formats; and user-friendly data-editing capability. In addition, the software can perform sophisticated statistical and economic analyses, database functions, and optimization. Boxerman (1996) describes the use of a spreadsheet to perform a simulation study.

A number of healthcare-related applications of spreadsheet software have been reported. Dunscombe, Roberts, and Valiquette (2000) have used a spreadsheet-based model to perform a quantitative financial analysis of scheduled and unscheduled downtime in a radiation treatment program. Giovachino and Carey (2001) describe the development of a spreadsheet tool that allows planners to compare the consequences of different speeds of response to a covert bioterrorist attack using the metric of preventable deaths. The breadth of computing power offered by spreadsheet software is illustrated by Bowen and Jerman (1995), who use spreadsheets to perform nonlinear regression analysis, and by Bagust et al. (2001), who have developed a spreadsheet model that allows the assessment of costs and long-term complications experienced by people suffering from Type II diabetes. Popular spreadsheet programs include Lotus® 1-2-3, Quattro® Pro 10, and Microsoft® Excel.

Statistical Packages   The analysis of data has been greatly simplified by the availability of a wide range of *statistical packages*. With this software, users can easily enter raw data, make changes as necessary, sort the values, create subsets of the data using a specified criterion, merge data sets, and perform a variety of analyses from obtaining the simplest descriptive statistics to developing the most complex multivariate models. Many of these packages also construct high-quality graphical presentations that allow the user to visualize the data in a specified format.

Although modern spreadsheets have excellent statistical capabilities, the term *statistical package* is usually applied to software specifically written to perform statistical computations. In all cases, the user begins the analytical process by building a "data set," which contains the raw data values and data names associated with each data field. These names make it easier for the user to refer to those data fields that are to be used in a given analysis. Full-screen editing of this data set allows the user to add or delete records or change the contents of a given record.

The user of the statistical software does not need to specify formulas for a given analysis. All of the mathematics for a given statistical procedure are built into the software. All that the user must do is to specify, by name, the particular statistical method to be applied along with the options to be used in the analysis. Herein lies the power, as well as the danger, of statistical software. Certainly the drudgery of statistical problem solving has been eliminated. But at the same time it is perhaps too easy for a naive individual to subject a set of data to extremely sophisticated methodology. The software cannot judge the appropriateness of the method being used. Therefore, the use of this software requires a healthcare manager with a reasonable background in statistics and/or collaboration with a functional expert in this area.

Finally, statistical packages report the results of the analyses in an easily read form without the user incurring the drudgery of specifying the output format. Descriptive statistics, which are labeled well; cross-tabulations of data; detailed output from complex regression analyses; and graphs are all produced with minimal effort. Popular statistical software packages include SPSS (SPSS Inc. 2002); SAS (SAS Institute, Inc. 2002); Statgraphics *Plus* (Manngistics, Inc. 2002); and StatView (SAS Institute, Inc. 2002). With the availability of this software, healthcare managers have the potential for employing statistical analysis as part of their decision-making process.

Dickson, Hodgkinson, and Kohler (1994), for example, report the use of statistical software to examine the profile of patients admitted to an inpatient rehabilitation unit. Their analyses allowed them to identify factors that produce a prolonged stay or failure of patients to progress in their recovery. Using statistical software, Desselle (2001) applied multivariate procedures to data collected from 504 patrons of selected community pharmacies in the Pittsburgh area. His goal was to study variations in the patrons' level of satisfaction with their pharmacy benefit plans. Carey (2002) describes the value of control charts in analyzing data variation and documenting process improvement and provides suggestions regarding appropriate software for constructing the control charts.

Database-management software allows users to easily interact with databases— **Database-** organized collections of files that are designed to provide easy access to **Management** needed information. The software makes it relatively straightforward to enter **Software** data, edit the data, and create reports based on those data to answer specific questions of interest. The increasing presence of managed care makes it imperative that users are able to access data from all entities within the organization. The implications of this imperative on the organization's data management are discussed in Chapter 6.

In addition, however, individual users often find the use of database-management software quite beneficial for small projects or studies. In this context, the software is often described as a personal or end-user database-management program, and it functions quite similarly as a spreadsheet or statistical software. Once the user has created a database, the software supports a variety of functions including data editing and printing, extraction of a subset of records based on one or more criteria, creation of reports, data import/export to and from other file formats, and an easy-to-use file record query language.

Bielefeld et al. (1995) describe their development of a research database for a five-year prospective investigation of the correlates of chronic lung disease during the first three years of life. The database software was used along with a statistical software package to handle a variety of data functions. Nyiendo et al. (2002) explore the data-management issues encountered in the design, conduct, and analysis of a research project involving 74 community-based sites and a central data-management system. They stress the importance of early recognition of the effort that will be needed for data management. Popular personal database-management software includes Alpha Five from Alpha Software, Inc. and Access from Microsoft. Chapple (2002) provides a web site with numerous links to helpful database resources.

Presentation Graphics Software

Remember from Chapter 3 that projectors connected to laptop computers have become "standard equipment" at meetings. The slides that are often the subject of the presentation can be created and displayed with *presentation graphics software* (see Figure 4.2). This software allows the user to create custom slides with any desired text, chart, graphics, or picture. Sophisticated graphic effects such as dissolves, fades, or animation as well as audio effects can be incorporated into the presentation. The result is a highly sophisticated slide show that, prior to the availability of this software, might require the efforts of a professional graphics designer. Some people feel that presenters are giving more attention to the graphic appearance of the talk rather than to the substantive content.

Evans (2000) provides some important pointers on how to develop professional-appearing presentations. Included are "tips" on fonts, colors, use of graphics, animation, and sound. Eakin, Brady, and Lusk (2001) describe the use of a multimedia program in promoting the use of hearing-protection devices by factory workers. By tailoring the presentation to the audience, the authors believe they can be more effective in motivating behavior change. Microsoft's PowerPoint is a commonly used presentation graphics software product.

FIGURE 4.2
Microsoft®
PowerPoint
Presentation
Graphics Slide
Building Screen

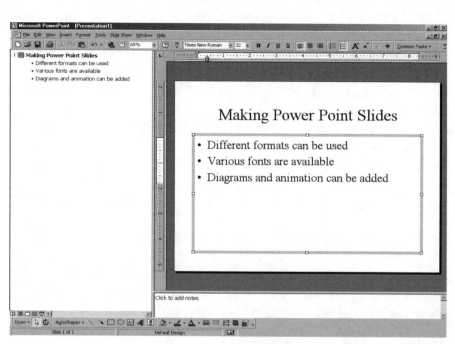

Simulation is a problem-solving approach in which the decision maker per- ***Simulation*** forms sampling experiments on the model of the system being studied rather ***Software*** than the system itself. It is typically applied to problems where the complexity of the system or system model precludes solution by analytical methods. This approach to problem solving has been used in many industries and is gaining increasing use in the healthcare field. A detailed review of simulation is presented in Austin and Boxerman (1995, Chapter 11).

Early simulation work was performed in general purpose programming languages such as FORTRAN, which is discussed below. Today, implementing relatively simple simulation models on a spreadsheet is also possible. However, more complex models require software specifically designed for simulation modeling. This software allows the user to focus on the details of the problem to be solved rather than to be concerned with solution or programming issues. Other features include animation, graphical interfaces, built-in probability distributions, standard reports, and the ability to export results to programs such as Microsoft® EXCEL. Examples of simulation software are MedModel® from ProModel® Corporation and Extend® from Imagine That Inc®. Mason (2002) presents a comprehensive buyer's guide to simulation software.

Groothuis and van Merode (2000) indicate that students in the health policy and management program at Maastricht University in The Netherlands receive mandatory training in simulation modeling using MedModel® as part of their lessons in learning to analyze and design workflow processes in healthcare. The authors indicate that the students consider the training an important part of their program. Kopp (2000) describes how the University of North Carolina Health System in Chapel Hill used MedModel® to assist in their process improvement and space planning in their centralized preanesthesia clinic. This approach has helped to enhance UNC's total quality management efforts in this clinic as well as other planning projects. A dynamic model developed using STELLA software provided the basis for predicting costs and patient outcomes of coronary artery bypass graft surgery (Anderson et al. 2002). The analysis indicated that the most important factors affecting costs and outcomes are gender, age, whether or not the surgery is a reoperation, and whether the patient experiences postoperative complications.

Integrated Software Programs Integrated software programs consist of a series of menu-driven module programs, all in the same software package. Module packages may include word processing, spreadsheet, database, graphics, communications, and Internet hooks among others. Frequently used integrated software packages include Lotus Smart Suite, Microsoft, and Corel WordPerfect Office Suite.

Application-Specific Software

The term *application-specific software* denotes a computer program that has been designed to solve a single, somewhat specifically defined problem. A good example is a payroll program, which is developed to accumulate labor hours, compute deductions, write payroll checks, post summaries to the general ledger, and complete the several forms that are required by federal and state governments. Although the files associated with this program contain a lot of information, the user has no access to the information unless the programmer specifically built in this capability.

Numerous vendors offer an array of application-specific software aimed at the healthcare field. *Healthcare Informatics* (2001) publishes an annual listing of information technology companies, products, services and associations. Table 4.1 displays the categories into which *Healthcare Informatics* classifies application-specific software. Details of these application areas comprise the material in Part IV of this book.

Healthcare organizations have the option of developing application-specific software in-house or purchasing (or leasing) a "package" and simply installing it on their computer system. (This process is not always as trivial as it might sound.) Each approach has its advantages and disadvantages. With in-house development the software can be tailored specifically to the organization's needs, and when changes are needed they generally are easier to make. Purchased (or leased) software, by comparison, is generally cheaper, requires less time to get running, and requires fewer in-house computer personnel. A third approach, modifying an existing package, attempts to integrate the advantages of both alternatives.

TABLE 4.1

Categories of
Application-
Specific
Software in
Healthcare*

- Claims Management
- Clinical Laboratory
- Coding and Classification
- Computer-Based Patient Record
- Data/Warehouse/Repository/ Mart/Base
- Decision Support
- Document Imaging
- E-Prescribing
- Electronic Data Interchange
- Financial Information
- Home Health Care
- Interface Engine/Interface Tool
- Long-Term Care
- Managed Care
- Medical Management
- Patient Monitoring
- Pharmacy/Medication Automation
- Physician Practice Management
- Radiology
- Scheduling
- Storage/Data Recovery
- Supply Chain Management
- Telehealth

*Categories defined by *Healthcare Informatics*. 2001. "2002 Resource Guide." *Healthcare Informatics* 18 (12): 33–72.

In-house development of application software used to be a favorite choice of many healthcare organizations. Today, most software is purchased (or leased). Most healthcare managers have decided that they are in the business of providing healthcare services, not developing software. These managers, however, must be knowledgeable participants in the process of purchasing (or leasing) software. In addition, involving key users in software purchase decisions is very important, especially when major systems are being acquired. Other factors that must be considered when choosing application software are the required staffing and equipment resources, the cost of maintenance, complexity of the operations being automated, the number of potential users, and data security issues. Complete details of evaluating and selecting systems are discussed in Chapter 12.

Integrated Versus Interfaced Systems

Two general approaches are available for acquiring and implementing application software in a healthcare organization. In the first approach, all of the modules required to satisfy the organization's computing needs are identified and purchased from a single vendor. Typically, these modules will have been designed to work with one another so that data transfer among modules proceeds smoothly. This type of system is known as an *integrated* information system.

By contrast, each of the required modules could be purchased from the vendor thought to be the leader in that particular application area. In some cases, the decision might reflect the personal bias of influential members of a particular organizational department. In any event, although a given module might work quite well for its particular application area, connecting the module to other modules could cause a problem. For example, the data contained in the module could be incompatible with the data format of other modules. The solution very often is the development of an *interface*, which acts as a bridge between the two modules and which, for example, translates the data format into one that the receiving module can handle.

The use of an *interfaced* approach is made somewhat simpler if the modules comprising the interfaced system have all been developed in accordance with a standard that makes their data formats compatible. An important standard followed by many system vendors is HL7. Hammond (1996, 58) provides a very concise historical overview of the development of this standard: "A group of interested users, vendors and consultants" met in March 1987 at the University of Pennsylvania to deal with the problems of interfacing departmental systems. In 1990, Version 2.1 was presented, and a large number of systems have been implemented adhering to that standard. Current work on Version 3.0 focuses on "an object-oriented model using standardized health care objects." A more detailed discussion of this and other important standards applicable to healthcare information systems is presented in Chapter 11.

Advantages of an integrated system include compatibility among the modules, no "finger pointing" by one vendor toward another, and the need to have only a single source for system support and maintenance. Interfaced systems, on the other hand, allow users to choose the leading system for a given module (the so-called "best-of-breed"), can sometimes result in lower costs by leveraging one vendor against another, and obviate the need to replace all existing modules.

System-Management Software

System-management software is the group of programs that manage the resources of a computer system and perform a variety of routine processing tasks. Unlike the role of application software, the function of system-management software is often not obvious to the user. Thus, many computer users are unaware of the important functions being performed by the *operating system* and by *utility programs*. These functions are described below.

Operating Systems

Operating systems serve as the interface between the human user and the computer. These systems allow the computer to run application programs by providing these programs with access to the resources that they require. The efficiency and functionality of an operating system determine how effectively a particular computer system is employed. Thing (2002, 502) describes the types of services provided by an operating system, including:

- managing the sharing of internal memory among multiple applications;
- handling input and output to and from attached hardware devices such as hard disks, printers, and dial-up ports; and
- displaying messages about the status of the operation and any errors that may have occurred.

The complexity of the operating system and the scope of services that it must provide depend on the complexity of the computing environment in which the operating system is installed. An environment that allows only one user to run one program at a time possesses the least complexity and places the fewest demands on the operating system. Examples include the early mainframe computers as well as the early PCs. Although these computers create few problems for the operating system, they do not make optimal use of their computing power.

The computing power of a given computer can be more effectively utilized when multiple tasks can be run by either a single user or by multiple users. In such an environment, known as *multitasking*, the operating system plays a more essential role. Because the computer's CPU is only capable of working on one instruction at a time, working on more than one program at the same time is not possible. Rather, a technique called *time-slicing* is employed, where the CPU executes a few instructions from one program, then works on a few instructions from the second program, and so forth. The operating system assumes responsibility for overseeing this process in the most efficient manner possible. The speed involved in this technique makes it appear to the users that the programs are running simultaneously.

Three operating systems serve to illustrate the range of such systems across the micro-, mini-, and mainframe-computer lines. Englander (2000, Chapter 19) provides a more detailed discussion of these operating systems. **Three Representative Operating Systems**

Windows XP Professional illustrates a popular microcomputer operating system for the business community. It is designed to manage system resources, such as memory, CPU time, and file operations, in a way that results in very efficient multitasking. It incorporates a graphical interface (see discussion below) with visual effects that are automatically matched to the capabilities of the computer on which the operating system is installed. Windows XP Professional also makes efficient use of available memory without affecting performance, is ready to work very shortly after the computer is turned on, and is able to launch execution of a program very quickly.

UNIX is an operating system originally developed for mid-sized minicomputers that now runs on many microcomputers and mainframe computers as well. It has a command set that is, in many ways, similar to DOS (the PC-based operating system that preceded Windows) but is more robust for multiuser applications. The operating system coordinates the use of the computer's resources, allowing multiple users to perform a variety of tasks with each user believing that he or she is the only person working on the computer. Although initially programmers developed UNIX for programmers, the operating system provides an environment so powerful and flexible that it is found in businesses, sciences, academia, and industry.

MVS "has been said to be the operating system that keeps the world going" (Thing 2002, 507). It supports large, complex computer systems and offers support for a wide range of input/output facilities, for CPU multiprocessing, and for system interconnection. Installations with large mainframe computers using the MVS operating system must be willing to commit to significant personnel to support the system operations.

Interfacing with the Operating System

Users can take advantage of the functional capabilities of an operating system by issuing a command that a particular function be performed. For example, if a given file is to be copied to another disk drive, the user must indicate which file is to be copied and where the copy is to be stored. Two general approaches for communicating with the operating system are typically used: a command-based user interface and a graphical user interface (GUI).

Command-based user interfaces consist of text commands that the user inputs into the computer. This type of interface is common in mainframe systems. The commands available to the user comprise a language of their own, known as *job control language* (JCL). In some cases, the complexity of the syntax of these commands rivals that of the application programs themselves. Early PC operating systems also used command-based user interfaces.

Graphical user interfaces use icons (graphical symbols on the screen) to represent available operating system commands. The user simply clicks on a given icon with the computer's mouse to invoke the desired command. Early GUIs were actually *shells* that resided between the operating system and the user. *Windows 3.0* and *Windows 3.1* are examples of such shells, which actually worked in conjunction with DOS—a command-based operating system. Windows XP, on the other hand, is a complete operating system, has a built-in graphical interface, and does not require DOS.

Utility Programs

Utility programs are software packages that perform generalized data processing or computational functions on computers. These functions are not specific to any particular computer application (e.g., patient billing, medical records), but they offer general utility and support to a variety of information-processing tasks. In some cases, this support can be viewed as supplementing the role of the operating system. In others, the utility might be performing a function that supports an application program.

Utility programs fall into three general categories:

1. *Programs that support computer operations.* Examples include programs that save and provide backup copies of computer programs written by users and programs that perform operational housekeeping tasks such as disk formatting.
2. *Programs that provide generalized file manipulation.* Examples include generalized database-management systems and programs that sort or merge records in files.

3. *Generalized computational programs.* Examples include packages of mathematical subroutines that perform complex operations that can be called by application software. In this way, the application software developer does not have to be concerned with writing the programming code to perform these complex operations.

Some mainframe utility programs are purchased from the computer manufacturer as part of the operating system and are fairly extensive. Most microcomputer utility programs are purchased separately, often from vendors different from those providing the hardware.

An Introduction to Programming Languages

All software—application, system, or utility—consists of a detailed set of instructions describing the specific steps that the computer is to perform. Just as two people communicate in a specific language, so too must this detailed set of instructions be communicated to the computer in a specific *programming language*. When a spreadsheet user enters a formula in a particular cell on the spreadsheet, that user is actually writing a program statement. Although the typical healthcare manager will make limited use of programming languages, the material presented in this section provides useful background material for a fuller understanding of software.

The format of a particular programming language is known as the *syntax* of that language. Interestingly, humans are much more forgiving with regard to language errors than are computers. If, for example, the programming language syntax calls for a comma at a particular point in the "conversation," omission of that comma can lead to unpredictable, if not disastrous, results.

A discussion of computer programming languages can be organized along a time continuum. Each decade between the 1940s and the 1980s roughly marked the beginning of a new "generation" of programming languages. These four generations of programming languages, summarized in Table 4.2, are described below.

Generation	General Characteristics
1	Machine language; strings of zeros and ones
2	Assembly language; uses mnemonics
3	Procedural languages; focuses on solution to problem
4	Variety of application and program-generating languages; focuses on description of problem itself

TABLE 4.2
Four Generations of Programming Languages

First-Generation Programming Languages

When computers were first developed, users needed to provide instructions in *machine language*, which consisted of strings of zeros and ones. The collection of strings understood by the computer is known as that computer's instruction set and allows the user to perform a variety of arithmetic operations, data comparisons, and data movement within the computer's central processor and memory. Each instruction provides a numeric code for the desired operation and, where applicable, the location in memory of the data on which the operation is to be performed. In general, the machine language is unique to a given computer make (and perhaps model). Machine languages represent the first generation of computer programming languages.

Although machine language is the only language that the computer is capable of "understanding," the average prospective computer user did not find learning the complex sequences of zeros and ones particularly appealing. It was obvious to computer developers that widespread use of these machines would occur only if communication with them were made easier. This recognition led to the development of assembly languages and ushered in the second generation of programming languages.

Second-Generation Programming Languages

An *assembly language* essentially replaces a string of zeros and ones with an alphabetic symbol known as a *mnemonic*. For example, the "code" for addition might be AD, for subtraction SUB, etc. In addition, memory address locations can also be replaced with mnemonics so that the user does not need to keep track of these locations. Although these mnemonics were somewhat easier for the user to learn, the computer can only deal with binary strings of zeros and ones. Thus, the set of instructions written by the user in an assembly language needs to be converted or translated to the binary codes recognized by the computer. This translation is accomplished by special software described later in this chapter.

Even the use of mnemonics, which bore some resemblance to the corresponding computer operation, was considered intimidating to the average computer user. These users were accustomed to thinking of their problems in a language associated with their particular problem area. Thus, engineers and scientists typically model their problems as equations, while business analysts frequently describe their business processes verbally. Problem solvers still considered the tedious process of constructing a sequence of mnemonics to describe their problem to be a burden.

Third-Generation Programming Languages

The desire to enable a user to focus more on the structure of a problem's solution and less on the computer's internal processes led to the development of *procedural, high-level languages*—the third generation of programming languages.

The term *procedural* signifies that these languages still require the user to describe to the computer, in a structured format, the detailed solution steps that are to be followed. However, the term *high level* indicates that the format of the user's description resembles the language of the problem more closely than do the zeros and ones of machine language or the mnemonics used in an assembly language. In fact, one high-level language statement might generate several machine language instructions. The details of how this occurs are covered later in the chapter.

Table 4.3 presents a summary of representative third-generation languages, and a brief description of each is presented below.

The first higher-level language, which appeared in 1957, is known as **FORTRAN** FORTRAN (an acronym for FORmula TRANslation). Scientists and mathematicians quickly embraced this language because of its use of mathematical notation. The language has undergone many revisions, and despite the introduction of other scientific and engineering languages, FORTRAN maintains its popularity for numerical analysis.

Shortly after the release of FORTRAN, a committee of representatives from **COBOL** business, manufacturing, government, and academia was formed to create a computer language. Programs written in that language were to be capable of running on a variety of computers and were to use a syntax closely resembling simple English sentences. The result of the committee's efforts was the COBOL programming language, which quickly gained popularity among

Language	Major Characteristic
FORTRAN	Early scientific language
COBOL	Early business-oriented language
ALGOL	Influenced the development of several contemporary languages
PL/1	Intended to combine best features of FORTRAN, COBOL, and ALGOL
BASIC	Important language in early days of personal computing
MUMPS (renamed M)	Specifically developed for use in healthcare environments
Pascal	Replacement for BASIC that is suitable for business and scientific applications
C (newer version is C++)	Suitable for business and scientific applications; allows operations close to machine language

TABLE 4.3
Representative Third-Generation Languages

the business community comparable to that afforded FORTRAN by scientific users.

COBOL has also been revised several times since its introduction. Nevertheless, because a large portion of computer applications have been in the business area, many computer systems have been developed in COBOL. For nearly three decades COBOL was used almost universally for the business and accounting functions in hospitals. In fact, many healthcare managers are now trying to decide whether to keep these COBOL-based systems, which typically run on mainframe hardware, or replace them with alternative technology.

ALGOL   Although never widely used, ALGOL (Algorithmic Language) was created in 1958 for scientific use. Its instructions were "English-like," and its statements employed conventional algebraic terms. ALGOL greatly influenced the development of other third-generation languages: PL/1, PASCAL, and C.

PL/1   Initially called NPL (New Programming Language), PL/1 was intended to combine the best features of FORTRAN, COBOL, and ALGOL into a single language attractive to both the scientific and business communities. The language finds less-frequent use today, although it has been used in healthcare settings.

BASIC   A relatively easy high-level language to learn, BASIC was developed in the mid-1960s at Dartmouth College in New Hampshire. BASIC (Beginner's All-Purpose Symbolic Instruction Code) was intended for use in introductory computer programming courses. Early PC manufacturers typically included the BASIC language with their hardware. Although the language has had widespread use among PC users, it has found little use among serious business users.

MUMPS   The MUMPS programming language was developed in the 1960s at Massachusetts General Hospital for healthcare environments. Subsequently renamed M, MUMPS (Massachusetts General Hospital Utility Multi-Programming System) is expressly set up for a multiuser environment, with data stored in a tree structure rather than the traditional file structure of most other languages.

MUMPS works well in many healthcare applications that need multiuser access to many central files and report generation capabilities, such as patient admitting and records, patient bed scheduling, and nurse personnel staffing and scheduling, among others. Successful applications include COSTAR, an outpatient record system; DXplain, a diagnostic decision-support system; and a variety of systems developed by the Department of Defense and the Veterans Administration.

Pascal   Developed in the late 1960s, Pascal was meant to be a good medium for teaching computer programming. In fact, Pascal replaced BASIC as the language taught in many introductory university computing courses. It is well suited for both business and scientific applications. For example, Grouven, Bergel, and Schultz (1996) have used the Pascal language to develop a PC program that, unlike widely available statistical software, incorporates unequal misclassification costs as part of a discriminant analysis with more than two groups.

The C programming language was developed at Bell Laboratories in 1972. *C* C is a high-level language that is appropriate for both business and scientific applications. It incorporates some features that allow its users to perform operations typically possible only with an assembly or machine language (Donovan 1993). For this reason, the C language was used to program the UNIX operating system (discussed earlier in this chapter).

This language is popular because programs written in C can be run on most computers, a property known as machine portability. In fact, a number of healthcare applications described in the literature have been developed in the C language or its enhanced successor, C++. Examples include an algorithm for constructing schedules of nursing personnel on a day-by-day basis (Liao and Kao 1997); an expert system for the diagnosis of sleep disorders (Fred et al. 2000); and a system for collecting, showing, and measuring data of dental casts (Lu et al. 2000).

Exhibit 4.1 illustrates a simple program written in each of four third-generation programming languages. Using an annual interest rate and time period provided by the user, each program computes the amount to which $1,000 will grow if compounded daily at the specified interest rate for the specified time period. Although the illustration is relatively straightforward, these sets of programming code allow the reader to compare the syntax of four commonly used languages: FORTRAN, BASIC, C++, and Pascal.

FORTRAN Programming Language

```
integer n
real*16 r,di,nd,a
write(*,*) "Enter the number of years the investment is held"
read(5,*) n
write(*,*) "Enter the annual interest rate (as a percent)"
read(5,*) r
di=r/36500
nd=n*365
a=1000*(1+di)**nd
write(*,*)
write(*,*)
write(*,*) "An investment of $1000 held for", n, "years"
write(*,10) a
```

EXHIBIT 4.1
The Structure and Syntax of Some Typical Programming Languages

continued

EXHIBIT 4.1
Continued

```
10 format("will grow to",f10.2, "at an interest rate")
    write(*,20) r
20 format("of",f6.1, "% compounded daily")
    end
```

Output

```
Enter the number of years the investment is held    8
Enter the annual interest rate (as a percent)       10.2

An investment of $1000 held for 8 years
will grow to 2261.18 at an interest rate
of 10.2% compounded daily
```

BASIC Programming Language

```
CLS
INPUT "Enter the Number of Years the Investment is Held", n
INPUT "Enter the Annual Interest Rate (as a Percent)", i#
di# = i# / 36500
nd# = n * 365
a# = 1000 * (1 + di#) ^ nd#
PRINT
PRINT
PRINT USING "An Investment of $1,000 held for ###.### years"; n
PRINT USING "will grow to $$###,###,###.##"; a#;
PRINT "at an interest rate"
PRINT USING "of ###.#% compounded daily"; i#
```

Output

```
Enter the Number of Years the Investment is Held    8
Enter the Annual Interest Rate (as a Percent)       10.2

An Investment of $1,000 held for 8.000 years
will grow to $2,261.18 at an interest rate
of 10.2% compounded daily
```

C++ Programming Language

```
// program to compute future value of $1,000

#include <iostream.h>
#include <iomanip.h>
#include <math.h>
main( )
{
    double di,n,nd,a,r;
    cout << "Enter the number of years the investment is held \n";
    cin >> n;
    cout << "Enter the annual interest rate (as a percent) \n";
    cin >> r;

// Calculations
    di=r/36500;
    nd=n*365;
    a=1000*pow(1+di,nd);

// Output
    cout << "\n";
    cout << "\n";
```

continued

EXHIBIT 4.1
Continued

```
cout << "An investment of $1,000 held for" << n << "years\n";
cout << "will grow to" << a << "at an interest rate\n";
cout << "of" << r << "% compounded daily\n";

return 0;
}
```

OUTPUT

```
Enter the number of years the investment is held    8
Enter the annual interest rate (as a percent)       10.2
```

An investment of $1,000 held for 8 years
will grow to 2261.18 at an interest rate
of 10.2% compounded daily

Pascal Programming Language

```
program INVTMENT (input, output);
var
   di,n,nd,a,r:real;

begin
   writeln ('Enter the number of years the investment is held');
   readln (n);
   writeln ('Enter the annual interest rate [as a percent]');
   readln (r);
   di := r/36500;
   nd := n*365;
   a := 1000*exp(nd*ln(1+di));
   writeln;
   writeln;
   writeln ('An investment of $1000 held for', n:4:1, 'years');
   writeln ('will grow to', a:10:2, 'at an interest rate');
   writeln ('of', r:6:1, '% compounded daily');
   end.
```

Output

```
Enter the number of years the investment is held    8
Enter the annual interest rate [as a percent]       10.2
```

An investment of $1000 held for 8.0 years
will grow to 2261.18 at an interest rate
of 10.2% compounded daily

Fourth-Generation Programming Languages

Whereas third-generation languages require specific step-by-step instructions on how the solution to a problem is to be obtained, fourth-generation languages allow the user to focus on a description of the problem itself. The computer, in turn, then determines the appropriate sequence of operations necessary to obtain the desired solution. As a result, some might suggest that writing a new program need no longer be an activity restricted to professional programmers or technically trained individuals.

A wide spectrum of categories can be used to classify fourth-generation languages; (see, for example, Laudon and Laudon 2000, 207). These categories range from the programming capabilities built into spreadsheets and database managers (discussed earlier in "General Purpose Application Software") to sophisticated application development software. Spreadsheet users may be unaware that they are generating a program when they create a macro using the "Record Macro" feature. Although it is reasonable to assume that healthcare managers might feel comfortable making use of this type of application software programming capability, it is quite doubtful that they will ever be personally involved in the use of development software.

The Next Generation of Programming Languages

Despite the improvements offered by fourth-generation languages, many people still find interacting with a computer difficult. These individuals cannot understand why an "equal sign" is so important for the correct evaluation of a formula in a spreadsheet cell. They would likely find a *natural language* to be much more appealing. A natural language has the property that the user is able to utilize it as easily as he or she communicates with other people. A translator program is employed to convert the natural language statements into the binary number commands intelligible to the computer.

One would assume that healthcare managers (or physicians) have a greater inclination to make "hands-on" use of a computer if the question to be answered or problem to be solved can be described orally to the computer with the same ease that words are currently spoken into a dictating machine. Of course, the technology necessary to recognize the spoken words, interpret their content, transform them into a set of procedures, and translate this sequence into machine commands is quite complex and currently not completely perfected. Perhaps, however, this is the model that the evolution of programming languages is moving toward and the model that will make computer utilization even more widespread than it currently is.

The preceding discussion has presented an overview of the evolution of programming languages from the earliest machine languages to the notion of natural languages. Across the entire spectrum of these languages, the objective of the user is quite simple: communicate with the computer in some prescribed format so that useful output can be generated. For the nonprogrammer user, the satisfaction of this communication process lies in the output created, not in the communication process itself. For many users, the communication process can only be described as a major source of frustration and inconvenience.

In fact, this communication process is often more than just a source of inconvenience. It is expensive, both in terms of time and money. The introduction of newer generations of programming languages represents one trend that helped to make the creation of software a more efficient process. The healthcare manager should be aware of two other approaches to software development. The first, computer-aided systems engineering (CASE) tools, are discussed in Chapter 12. The second, object-oriented approaches, offer the advantages of lower development costs and faster development times by integrating previously developed modules into the current project; see, for example, Van Vliet (2000).

Language Translators

Because computers are only capable of "understanding" instructions written in machine language, any program that is written in a language that is second generation or higher must first be converted to machine language before it can be executed. This conversion is performed by software known as language translators.

The set of instructions comprising the program to be translated is known as *source code*, and these instructions comprise the *input data* to the language translator. The machine-level equivalent to which the source code gets translated is known as *object code*, and this code constitutes the translator's *output data*. Three types of language translators are in common use: *assemblers*, *compilers*, and *interpreters*. In addition, *code-generation* software, which produces as output higher-level language code, might also be viewed as a language translator. Each is briefly described below.

Assemblers

A language translator capable of converting assembly-language program code into machine-language code is known as an *assembler*. The translation process involves substituting binary operation codes and memory addresses, respectively, for the mnemonics and label names that comprise the assembler language instructions. In many cases, this process requires two passes through the assembly language program. Each source statement gets translated into one object statement.

Compilers

A *compiler* is a language translator that generates the necessary machine-language code to carry out the instructions contained in a program written in a high-level language. Unlike assemblers, a single source statement can generate several machine code instructions. This process of generating object code is known as *compilation*. The compiler first performs a *syntax analysis*, which assesses whether source code statements have been written correctly so that object code can be created unambiguously and can generate error messages as required. Next, it performs *code generation*, which creates the actual object code. Some compilers might also perform *optimization*, which analyzes whether reducing the amount of object code is possible.

Two points about compilers bear mention. First, the optimization stage is quite important. The size and execution time of the object code created by the compiler depend on the quality of the optimization process. Second, whereas changes in the source code associated with a given application are easy to make, making changes in object code is relatively difficult. When application software is purchased, the product is typically delivered in object code format. Managers need to be sure that the source code for the application is being held in a secure location and will be available even if the vendor goes out of business.

Interpreters

The compiler described in the previous section translates all of the source statements of a higher-level language to object form before any execution of the statements occurs. In fact, after the compilation process has been completed, the object code can be run as many times as needed. As an alternative, the source statements can be translated to object code format one at a time, and, following translation, each statement can be executed. A language translator that performs this step-by-step conversion process is known as an *interpreter*. A classic illustration of an interpreted language is BASIC.

Interpreted languages work well for applications scheduled to be run only a few times or subject to frequent changes, because the compilation process can be avoided. However, compiled languages are preferred for production runs because the translation process needs to be performed only once.

Code-Generation Software

Some of the fourth-generation languages include code-generation features that produce third-generation language code as output. This software can be viewed as a language translator, where the fourth-generation language statements comprise the input and the third-generation language code represents the output. Typically the output represents a significant percentage of the total code necessary for a given programming project. A programmer then writes the rest of the code. The third-generation language code, of course, must then be compiled to obtain the object module necessary to allow the application to be run.

Concluding Comments

Software issues are of importance to healthcare managers at a number of levels. First, although most healthcare organizations do little in-house development of software, the manager must be a knowledgeable participant in software acquisition. This topic is covered in Chapter 12. In addition, the manager must understand the potential challenges created by the need for interfaces linking disparate software packages.

Second, all software must be appropriately licensed. Although this might appear rather obvious, it is quite easy for someone to make a copy of a piece of software or to load a single copy on multiple machines without any thought of impropriety. Frequent radio advertisements from the Business Software Alliance (http://www.bsa.org/usa) suggest a concerted effort to "crack down" on software piracy. Policies should be in place emphasizing the organization's strong stance on exclusive use of legally licensed software.

Third, managers should be aware of the rapid evolution of software versions. Operating systems and application software are constantly being revised. Sometimes, users will campaign to upgrade a software package solely to have the "latest version." In other cases, the vendor might actually cease to support a given version, thereby forcing the user to upgrade. Again, knowledgeable participation by the manager is valuable here.

Finally, one final question can be asked: What is the quality of the wide range of software described in this chapter? In fact, the quality is quite variable, and in some cases software purchasers wind up with systems that fall short of their expectations. Perhaps knowledgeable and informed managers participating in the evaluation, acquisition, and implementation of software will help to ensure that high-quality systems are installed in their organizations.

Summary

Computer software includes application software, operating systems, programming languages, software development tools, and language translators. Application software, in turn, can be divided into two categories: (1) general purpose programs, such as word processors, desktop publishing, spreadsheet, statistical, and database software, and (2) a variety of application-specific software packages that perform specific functions in administrative as well as clinical areas.

In addition to application software, computers also require software that manages the computer's resources. The complexity of this software, known as operating systems, is dependent on the complexity of the computing environment. Modern operating systems have graphical user interfaces and are more user-friendly than early operating systems.

Programming languages have evolved up to a fourth generation, and range from binary instructions native to the computer to program-generating languages that allow the user to focus on a description of the problem itself. The next generation of languages will very likely focus on natural languages that are essentially English-language statements.

Although little, if any, in-house program development is being done, a knowledge of the role of programming languages helps the manager to better appreciate some basic concepts associated with the software in use within the organization. The healthcare manager must consider many factors in choosing computer software. Among them are number of existing and potential users, hardware configurations available, security considerations, future computer applications growth, and functional requirements for individual applications.

Discussion Questions

4.1 List the four generations of programming languages and briefly describe the characteristics of each.

4.2 Briefly describe an important characteristic of the C programming language that led to its having been chosen as the language in which to develop the UNIX operating system.

4.3 Why are users doing so little in-house development of software today?

4.4 What are the major advantages of using a microcomputer graphical user interface program?

4.5 Explain the difference between interfaced and integrated systems, and state one advantage of each.

4.6 Explain the difference between word-processing and desktop-publishing software.

4.7 What is the difference between a compiler and an interpreter?

4.8 List three specific functions of an operating system.

4.9 Explain how computers can run multiple tasks at the same time when they only contain a single CPU?

Problems

4.1 Assume that an ambulatory care center is about to purchase word-processing software for its staff. Choose two different systems (e.g., WordPerfect and Word) and compare the price of each system as well as the functional features of each. Indicate your choice and explain the rationale for your decision.

4.2 Talk to the chief information officer of a local healthcare organization. Determine to what extent the support requirements for the accounts payable system depend on the language in which the program was developed. Questions to be answered include (1) Does the vendor provide support? (2) Are there in-house programmers capable of making changes to the system? (3) Are there plans to replace the system within the next year? (4) To what extent did the language in which the software was developed influence the organization's decision to purchase that software?

4.3 Perform an inventory of the information systems in use in a local healthcare system. In particular, determine the operating systems under which the software applications are running.

4.4 Refer to Problem 4.3. As part of the inventory, determine whether independent departmental modules have been implemented. Determine whether these modules have been interfaced, and, if so (1) Who wrote the interfaces? (2) What was the cost of obtaining these interfaces? (3) Are there problems associated with data being smoothly passed from one module to another through the interfaces?

4.5 Assess the use of personal computers among the managerial staff of a local healthcare institution: (1) Determine the level of proficiency that the managers have. (2) Ask what specific categories of software they routinely employ (e.g., word processing, statistical, database). (3) Ask if there are standards operative within the organization directing specific software packages for which the information systems department of the organization offers support.

4.6 Consult a reference on object-oriented programming languages. Name and explain the three attributes that characterize such a language.

References

Anderson, J. G., W. Harshbarger, H. C. Weng, S. J. Jay, and M. M. Anderson. 2002. "Modeling the Costs and Outcomes of Cardiovascular Surgery." *Health Care Management Science* 5 (2): 103–11.

Austin, C. J., and S. B. Boxerman. 1995. *Quantitative Analysis for Health Services Administration.* Chicago: AUPHA/Health Administration Press.

Bagust, A., P. K. Hopkinson, W. Maier, and C. J. Currie. 2001. "An Economic Model of the Long-Term Health Care Burden of Type II Diabetes." *Diabetelogia* 44 (12): 2140–55.

Bielefeld, R. A., T. S. Yamashita, E. F. Kerekes, E. Ercanli, and L. T. Singer. 1995. "A Research Database for Improved Data Management and Analysis in Longitudinal Studies." *M.D. Computing* 12 (3): 200–5.

Bowen, W. P., and J. C. Jerman. 1995. "Nonlinear Regression Using Spreadsheets." *Trends in Pharmacological Sciences* 16 (12): 413–17.

Boxerman, S. B. 1996. "Simulation Modeling: A Powerful Tool for Process Improvement." *Best Practices and Benchmarking in Health Care* 1 (3): 109–17.

Carey, R. G. 2002. "How Do You Know that Your Care Is Improving? Part II: Using Control Charts to Learn from Your Data." *Journal of Ambulatory Care Management* 25 (2): 78–88.

Chapple, M. 2002. "Databases." [Online article; retrieved 6/30/02]. http://www.databases.about.com.

Deselle, S. P. 2001. "Determinants of Satisfaction with Prescription Drug Plans." *American Journal of Health-System Pharmacy* 58 (12): 1110–19.

Dickson, H. G., A. Hodgkinson, and F. Kohler. 1994. "Inpatient Quality Assurance by Local Analysis of Uniform Data Set." *Journal of Quality in Clinical Practice* 14 (3): 145–48.

Donovan, J. 1993. "Careful Programming Lets C Replace Assembler in Fast Embedded Applications." *EDN* 38 (April 15): 81.

Dunscombe, P., G. Roberts, and L. Valiquette. 2000. "Preventative Maintenance and Unscheduled Downtime from an Economic Perspective." *Journal of Applied Clinical Medical Physics* 1 (2): 68–75.

Eakin, B. L., J. S. Brady, and S. L. Lusk. 2001. "Creating a Tailored, Multimedia, Computer-Based Intervention." *Computers in Nursing* 19 (4): 152–60; quiz 161–63.

Englander, I. 2000. *The Architecture of Computer Hardware and Systems Software: An Information Technology Approach*, 2nd Edition. New York: John Wiley and Sons, Inc.

Evans, M. L. 2000. "Polished, Professional Presentation: Unlocking the Design Elements." *Journal of Continuing Education in Nursing* 31 (5): 213–18.

Fred, A., J. Filipe, M. Partinen, and T. Paiva. 2000. "PSG-EXPERT. An Expert System for the Diagnosis of Sleep Disorders." *Studies in Health Technology & Informatics* 78: 127–47.

Giovachino, M., and N. Carey. 2001. "Modeling the Consequences of Bioterrorism Response." *Military Medicine* 166 (11): 925–30.

Groothuis, S., and G. G. van Merode. 2000. "Discrete Event Simulation in the Health Policy and Management Program." *Methods of Information in Medicine* 39 (4–5): 339–42.

Grouven, U., F. Bergel, and A. Schultz. 1996. "Implementation of Linear and Quadratic Discriminant Analysis Incorporating Costs of Misclassification." *Computer Methods and Programs in Biomedicine* 49 (1): 55–60.

Hammond, W. E. 1996. "How Long Does It Take to Write A Standard?" *Healthcare Informatics* 13 (1): 58.

Healthcare Informatics. 2001. "2002 Resource Guide." *Healthcare Informatics* 18 (12): 33–72.

Kopp, V. J. 2000. "Preoperative Preparation. Value, Perspective, and Practice in Patient Care." *Anesthesiology Clinics of North America* 18 (3): 551–74.

Laudon, K. C., and J. P. Laudon. 2000. *Management Information Systems: Organization and Technology in the Networked Enterprise*, 6th Edition. Upper Saddle River, NJ: Prentice-Hall.

Liao, C. J., and C. Y. Kao. 1997. "Scheduling Nursing Personnel on a Microcomputer." *Health Manpower Management* 23 (2–3): 100–6.

Lu, P., Z. Li, Y. Wang, J. Chen, and J. Zhao. 2000. "The Research and Development of Noncontact 3-D Laser Dental Model Measuring and Analyzing System." *Chinese Journal of Dental Research* 3 (3): 7–14.

Manngistics, Inc. 2002. "Overview of Statgraphics Plus Products." [Online article; retrieved 6/30/02]. http://www.statgraphics.com/.

Mason, S. 2002. "Simulation Software Buyer's Guide." *IIE Solutions* 34 (5): 45–51.

Nyiendo, J., M. Attwood, C. Lloyd, B. Ganger, and M. Haas. 2002. "Data Management in Practice-Based Research." *Journal of Manipulative and Physiological Therapeutics* 25 (1): 49–57.

SAS Institute, Inc. 2002. "Products." [Online information; retrieved 6/30/02]. http://www.SAS.com/products/index.html

SPSS Inc. 2002. "Products and Solutions." [Online information; retrieved 6/30/02]. http://www.SPSS.com/products

Thing, L. 2002. *The whatis?com: Encyclopedia of Technology Terms*. Indianapolis, IN: Que Publishing.

Tietz, A., and R. Tabor. 1995. "Communicating Quality Improvement Through a Hospital Newsletter." *Journal for Healthcare Quality* 17 (4): 11–12.

Van Vliet, H. 2000. *Software Engineering: Principles and Practice*, 2nd Edition. New York: John Wiley & Sons, Inc.

Additional Readings

Blum, B. I. 1996. *Beyond Programming: To A New Era of Design*. New York: Oxford University Press.

Budd, K. W. 2000. "The Economics of Electronic Journals." *Online Journal of Issues in Nursing* 5 (1): 3.

Davis, W. S., and T. M. Rajkumar. 2001. *Operating Systems: A Systematic View*, 5th Edition. Boston: Addison Wesley.

Groothuis, S., G. G. van Merode, and A. Hasman. 2001. "Simulation as Decision Tool for Capacity Planning." *Computer Methods and Programs in Biomedicine* 66 (2001): 139–51.

Health Data Management. 2001. "2002 Resource Guide." *Health Data Management* 9 (12, supplement).

Kofler, M. 2000. *LINUX: Installation, Configuration, and Use*, 2nd Edition. Harlow, England; New York: Addison-Wesley.

Lucent Technologies. 2002. "An Overview of the UNIX* Operating System." [Online information; retrieved 6/30/02]. http://www.bell-labs.com/history/unix/tutorial.html.

O'Kane, K. C. 2001. "Migration of Legacy Mumps Applications to Relational Database Servers." *Methods of Information in Medicine* 40 (3): 225–28.

Ricadela, A. 2001. "Linux Is Useful but Still Can't Crack Windows." *Information Week* (823): 94.

Stair, R. M., and G. W. Reynolds. 2001. *Principles of Information Systems: A Managerial Approach*, 5th Edition. Boston: Course Technology.

Stallings, W. 2001. *Operating Systems: Internals and Design Principles*. Upper Saddle, NJ: Prentice-Hall.

Wagner, M. 2001. "IBM Takes Linux to Mainframes—New Software Will Move Applications to a Partition Running the OS." *Internet Week* (884): 20.

NETWORKING AND TELECOMMUNICATIONS

Today's clinicians and managers require information from a variety of sources within, as well as outside of, their organizations. As geographically separated healthcare delivery units combine to form a healthcare system, sharing information among each of the system's components becomes increasingly challenging. The implementation of computer networks and the use of telecommunications can help these organizations manage their information flow.

The technology associated with data communication systems and computer networks is relatively complex, involving the expertise of communications engineers, computer hardware specialists, and software professionals. These functional experts are the ones who assume responsibility for the design and installation of this technology. But the healthcare manager must assume responsibility for overseeing these activities and making sure that the organization's information needs can be met.

As was true in the areas of hardware and software, the manager will need sufficient understanding of networking and telecommunications concepts to work intelligently with the functional experts in these fields. The objective of this chapter is to provide such an understanding. Topics discussed in this chapter include a rationale for installing computer networks, alternative ways to distribute the processing function, the components of a network, the configuration of networks, the electronic interchange of data, the role of wireless communication, and communication via the Internet. The discussion is meant neither to be exhaustive nor to make the healthcare manager a networking or telecommunications expert but to present an introductory overview of these subjects.

A Rationale for Installing Computer Networks

Early applications of computers in hospitals, as in many other industries, consisted of a variety of financial applications like billing, payroll, and general accounting. These programs were typically run on a large mainframe computer located in the organization's data-processing department. (In some cases, a hospital might decide against owning a mainframe computer, choosing rather to have their computing performed by an outside vendor of data-processing services.) The input data for these programs were contained in handwritten documents such as charge slips, invoices, or time and attendance sheets. These documents were handed to a keypunch operator (or transferred electronically as described below) who entered the data into punched cards that were then read into the computer. The output consisted of printed reports that were distributed to the appropriate users.

Two parallel developments threatened the traditional role of the mainframe system in the healthcare setting. The first was the introduction of software systems designed to perform specific functions within hospital departments such as pharmacy, radiology, and laboratory systems. These software packages were frequently run on the then newly introduced minicomputers that could be located within close proximity of the department utilizing the system. Second, the PC was introduced. Using a PC, managers were able to analyze a variety of operational and financial data themselves. They were no longer dependent on the data-processing department to run special reports, often with considerable delay.

As department managers purchased new minicomputer-based systems and other managers became increasingly involved with personal computing, they soon realized that the programs they were running were not independent "stand-alone" modules. In fact a high level of interdependence existed among these programs. For example, the laboratory, pharmacy, and radiology systems all need information gathered by the admitting system. Similarly, many of the reports that users generated on their PC operated on data contained in a printed report generated by a mainframe financial application.

The problem grows worse in a healthcare system because data on a given patient might be found in a number of locations and a single laboratory might serve widely separated patient-care locations. Data must flow across a large area, and managers often require input from many sources to arrive at a solution to a problem. Clearly, the disparate systems throughout the organization (and even beyond) needed to be tied together to facilitate the exchange of data and the sharing of resources.

The linkage needed to facilitate this exchange of data and sharing of resources is accomplished through the construction of a network, which " . . . can be anything from a simple link between two computers in an office to a complex installation joining thousands of computers at many sites around the world" (Lee and Millman 1995, 1013). When all of the components of the network are located within relatively close proximity of one another, perhaps within a single facility, the network is known as a *local area network* (LAN). A network that extends into a broad geographical area is known as a *wide area network* (WAN).

Ways of Distributing the Processing Function

One basis for classifying networks is the way in which the processing functions are distributed among the devices comprising the network. Four configurations are in common use, ranging from a *centralized* computing environment (where the processing functions are concentrated in a single device) to a *decentralized* environment (where these functions are split or *distributed* among all of the users on the network). Decentralized networks typically create greater managerial challenges, a fact that is particularly relevant for the healthcare manager.

Terminal-Host Systems

In the most centralized computing environment, dating back to the 1960s, users work at devices known as *terminals*. Early terminals had no processing capability ("intelligence") and were often known as *dumb terminals*. Today a PC is sometimes used to mimic or *emulate* a terminal. The terminal is connected to a large central *host computer*, typically a mainframe. "Most corporations still have a large amount of their central data stored on terminal-host systems" (Panko 2001, 10). This configuration is depicted in Figure 5.1.

Depending on the level of sophistication of the program running on the host machine, the terminals allow users to perform a variety of functions, including:

- entering a set of data for a program to be run at some later time in *batch* mode—that is, as part of a sequential stream of programs from several users;
- *real-time processing* of a program immediately after entering data and/or programming commands; and
- responding to a query such as a patient account balance.

The important feature of this computing environment is that all computing is taking place on the host system.

An important subset of this computing configuration is *remote job entry* (RJE), where dumb terminals might be located at considerable distance from the host machine. Several major companies have specialized in providing computing services to hospitals on an RJE basis. Hospitals would enter their data (typically financial) into a dumb terminal (or a computer operating in a mode that emulates a dumb terminal) for processing at a remote location. Results were then mailed back to the hospital or received on their own remote printer.

Central computers with or without dumb terminals constitute the most centralized form of computing and thus are the easiest configuration for managers to control. All of the resources are close at hand and users have little potential to disrupt either program software or data files.

Client/Server Computing

Users of dumb terminals connected to a host computer easily recognized the advantage that would result from their terminals having computing capability. Data could be edited, preliminary computations could be made, and other processing could be done that did not require the power of the host machine. This early conceptualization was predictive of today's client/server computing

FIGURE 5.1
Terminal-Host
Configuration

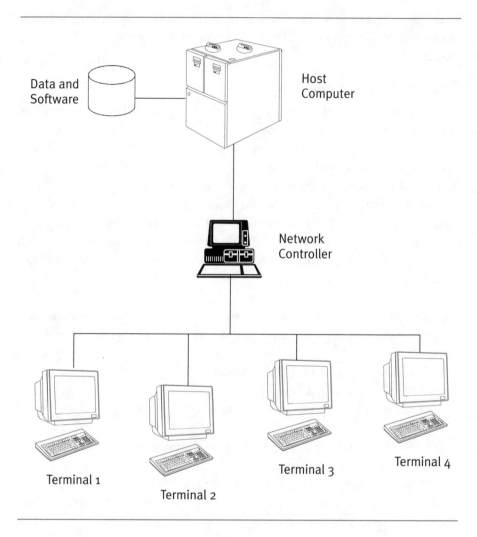

configuration, which is characterized by less centralization than a terminal-host installation (see Figure 5.2).

Client/server architecture divides applications into two components: (1) client, or *front-end* functions, which include user interface, decision support, and data processing and (2) server, or *back-end* functions, such as database management, printing, communication, and applications program execution. The server can be a personal, mini-, or mainframe computer, and multiple servers can often be found in a client/server network.

When all back-end functions are performed on a single server, the configuration is known as *two-tier* client/server architecture. "In recent years, a *three-tier* architecture has become increasingly common" (Stallings and Van Slyke 2000). In this configuration, the user interface resides on the client, the relational databases reside on one server, and the application programs reside on a second server. This configuration is easier to manage and offers

FIGURE 5.2
Client/Server
Computing
Configuration

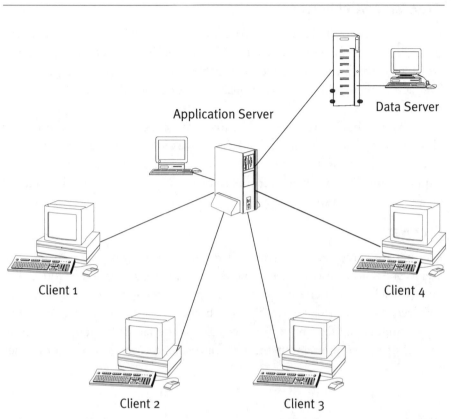

Application Server

Data Server

Client 1

Client 4

Client 2

Client 3

faster information processing and distribution. Lee et al. (2001) describe the development of a three-tier web-based physician order-entry system. The authors contrast their system with previous ones developed using two-tier client/server architecture. They claim that the system has made their clinical procedure more efficient and has reduced the chances of omission.

As managers work with their functional specialists on the implementation of client/server networks they are likely to encounter two terms. The first is *thin client*—"low-cost, centrally managed computer devoid of CD–ROM players, diskette drives, and expansion slots" (Thing 2002). These computers combine cost savings with sufficient computing power to serve as client machines. The second is *middleware*—this enables programmers to "implement the same application on a variety of server types and workstation types" (Stallings and Van Slyke 2000, 483). Client and server vendors will typically offer middleware packages as options. Chu and Cesnik (2000) report on the successful application of a three-tier system architecture in the development of a computerized clinical-pathways management system. The concept of *middleware* is explored as a solution to achieving the goals of exchanging data across different types of applications and database-management systems as well as reducing the costs of systems development and modification.

File/Server Architecture

Even less centralized than client/server installations is file/server architecture. In a file/server network, a relatively large number of network processors are able to share the data contained in files on the server (see Figure 5.3). The actual processing of data, however, is distributed across the network machines.

Many small LANs are configured with file/server architecture. The file/server typically has a large fixed-disk drive with fast disk-access time. The other computers on the network have much more modest fixed-disk drive requirements, but they benefit from fast processors to support their execution of application software.

Peer Networks

Peer networks represent a *decentralized* computing environment, where "all user workstations also handle some server functions" (Hayden 2001, 93); that is, each computer on the network has either data or some hardware resource that it can make available to the other users on the network. The key distinguishing feature of peer networks is the fact that there is no server and all of the computers on the network can be used as workstations (see Figure 5.4).

FIGURE 5.3
File/Server
Architecture

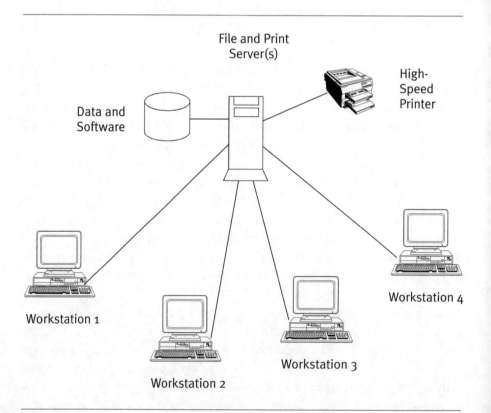

File and Print
Server(s)

High-
Speed
Printer

Data and
Software

Workstation 1

Workstation 2

Workstation 3

Workstation 4

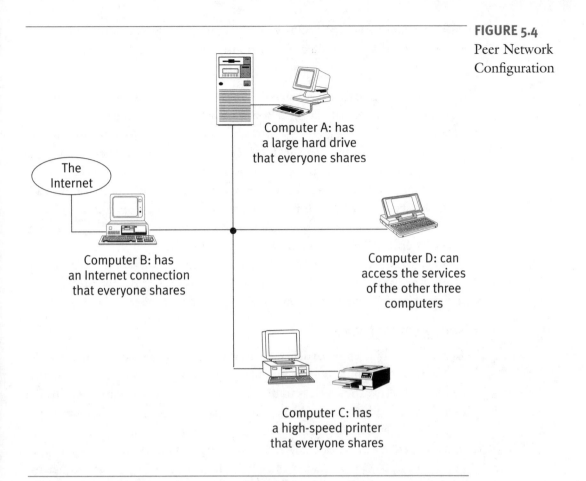

Source: M. Hayden, *Sams Teach Yourself Networking in 24 Hours*, 2/e, © 2001. Reprinted by permission of Pearson Education, Inc., Upper Saddle River, New Jersey.

Hayden (2001, 93) suggests two key advantages of a peer network: (1) ease of installation and configuration and (2) inexpensive compared to client/server networks.

In theory, as departmental systems were being installed and managers were beginning to work on their own PCs, all of the hardware could have been assembled in a peer network. This would have allowed users to share data as well as other resources. From a practical standpoint, because of software limitations and the lack of needed hardware interfaces, construction of such a network would not have been feasible.

Although the required technology for these networks is available today, peer networks are generally considered suitable only for very small installations of three or four computers. Additionally, peer networking has the following disadvantages (Hayden 2001, 93):

• *Total lack of centralized control:* This makes the network basically unmanageable

- *Tremendously insecure:* Security on a peer network is almost nonexistent
- *Unreliable:* The network can be seriously disturbed if a workstation locks up

Brailer (2001, 29) suggests that the Internet (discussed later in this chapter) provides a viable vehicle for implementing peer-to-peer technology: "Data sharing is less expensive with peer-to-peer technology because it uses public communications via the Internet, shares server time across multiple organizations and works with existing user applications." In addition to offering cost advantages, peer-to-peer networks implemented via the Internet address the security concern listed above. "Using peer-to-peer architecture . . . enables each participating organization to maintain control of its own data, which is critical because of federal regulations about privacy and access to healthcare data. Information is released only with authorization and authentication from a data originator or requestor, and is only at risk when a clinician requests specific information on a specific patient" (Brailer 2001, 29).

Management Issues

As healthcare managers participate with their functional specialists in selecting the networking configuration for their organization, several issues must be considered. First, the trend is to distribute computing capability down to the user level, as evidenced by the proliferation of microcomputers in many organizations. However, in highly complex and interrelated fields like healthcare some degree of centralization of the computing and information-storage functions is necessary. Also, the evolution of the field toward integrated healthcare systems and managed care makes information-system integration even more vital.

Second, the network configuration can affect the number of copies of application software that must be purchased, licensed, and maintained. A single "network version" of an application package can be installed on a server that is accessible to the users on the network. Individual copies of the software also can be placed on each user machine. Careful evaluation of these alternatives must consider the purchase price of the software, software licensing fees, and software maintenance costs as well as hardware costs.

Finally, many organizations are still trying to choose between maintaining an existing mainframe system and moving to client/server architecture. Not too long ago a fairly balanced debate between advocates of mainframe computing and supporters of client/server technology could be found in the literature. Currently, however, the discussion seems to focus more heavily on organizations making a transition to client/server systems. For example, Loma Linda University Medical Center, which "five years ago (was) mainframe centric," now has "more applications—especially clinical—(on) NT's client/server system" (Briggs 2000, 62). Similarly, Briggs (2001a, 53) reports that "many existing (financial) systems are 10 to 15 years old. . . . These older systems often are DOS-based mainframe systems that are labor-intensive to update because of the need to create interfaces with other systems. New financial information systems increasingly are built on client/server platforms and are . . . expected to interact with clinical information systems, perform broad analytical tasks . . . and improve workflow. . . ."

Healthcare managers are well advised to monitor closely the architecture being chosen by their functional specialists to ensure that the information system function is moving in a direction that appropriately supports the organization's strategic direction. Specification of the overall systems architecture and infrastructure is one step in the development of a strategic information systems plan (see Chapter 11).

Network Components

Creating an information network requires the assembly of a variety of hardware and software components. This section presents an overview of these components.

Transmission Media

Early in the process of designing a network, a decision must be made regarding the transmission medium to be used. The transmission medium, which carries the signal being transmitted from one location to another, can be metal wires, which carry electrical signals; fiber-optic cables, which carry optical signals; or air, through which radio waves travel. Each transmission medium is discussed below.

Wired Media

Wired media consist of one or more strands of metal, which are excellent conductors of electricity. A commonly used metal is copper. Data are transmitted along these conductors in the form of changing electrical voltages and may be represented as either a *digital* or *analog* waveform. Digital transmission involves the representation of data with binary digits or bits. Analog transmission represents data by varying the amplitude (height), frequency, and/or phase of a waveform. Traditional telephone lines carry signals in an analog format, while Integrated Services Digital Network (ISDN) lines, Digital Subscriber Lines (DSL), and the cable in a LAN carry signals digitally.

The most commonly used type of copper media is *unshielded twisted pair* (UTP). Twisted pair wiring is available in several levels, ranging from category 1 to category 5. Each successive level is used for a different application and has a higher speed rating. Hayden (2001, 86) provides details on this classification scheme. Anderson (2002) adds a description of "Enhanced Category 5" cable as well as a proposal for categories 6 and 7. Networks will typically employ category 5 UTP cable because of its ability to handle voice, video, and data.

A second type of copper media is *shielded twisted pair* (STP). The shielding consists of a special conducting layer located within the insulation that makes the cable less susceptible to interference. In addition, this shielding helps to keep the cable from emitting energy that would interfere with other nearby equipment. However, Panko (2001) suggests that the shielding increases the cost, makes the wiring thick and difficult to install, and enjoys only occasional use.

Coaxial cable is a third type of copper media that is capable of transmitting high-speed digital signals and wide-bandwidth analog signals. Panko (2001, 85) characterizes coaxial cable as "an obsolete technology" because "UTP today is less expensive than coaxial cable and now offers higher speeds." Nevertheless, because "coaxial (cable) . . . has simplicity on its side" (Hayden 2001, 84), it is likely to be found in many older, small networks.

Fiber-Optic Media

Data are carried in a fiber-optic medium in the form of light pulses. The electrical data signal is used to turn a light source on and off very rapidly. At the receiving end of the cable, an optical detector converts the light signal back to an electrical signal. Two generic types of fiber-optic cable exist. The first, *single-mode cable*, carries more information than multimode cable and incurs a lower loss of signal over the length of the cable. The second, *multimode cable*, carries less information than single-mode cable, but it is typically adequate for most LAN functions.

A number of advantages make fiber-optic cable an attractive medium (Vickers 2001), including:

- Fiber-optic cable can transmit data longer distances than copper
- Fiber-optic cable is physically thinner and more durable than copper, taking up less space in cabling ducts
- Fiber-optic cable is impervious to outside interference or eavesdropping
- Fiber-optic cable provides higher bandwidth and "future proofs" a network's cabling architecture against copper upgrades

Two disadvantages of fiber-optic cable bear mention. The first is the greater difficulty associated with its installation. Technicians must ground down the ends of the cable to a properly focusing "lens," either on site or at the manufacturing plant (Vickers 2001). The second is that fiber-optic infrastructures are still more expensive than copper. However, costs of the components associated with a fiber-optic installation have been decreasing, closing the gap between its cost and that of copper.

Radio Media

Unlike copper and fiber media, radio media utilize radio waves of different frequencies to transmit data through the air. *Broadcast radio* is used to support paging devices and cellular technology. *Microwave radio* is capable of higher data rates than broadcast radio and is used in WANs as well as wireless LANs. Because microwave signals travel in a straight line, known as *line-of-sight* transmission, they cannot follow the curvature of the earth. Transmission of these signals over long distances therefore requires the use of repeaters every

20 to 30 miles (Panko 2001, 330). Alternatively, a *satellite* can be used, which essentially serves as a "repeater in space" (Panko 2001, 331).

Some disadvantages of radio media are worth noting. First, the savings resulting from not having to install cable can often be offset by the cost of microwave and satellite transmission equipment. Second, microwave transmissions are subject to interference from adverse weather conditions as well as any objects that might interfere with its *line-of-sight* travel from transmitter to receiver. Finally, all communication using radio waves is subject to *electronic eavesdropping*, thus resulting in special security issues that must be addressed.

Transmitters/Receivers

The general process of communication consists of a transmitter sending information (or in some cases "raw data") through a transmission medium to a receiver (see Figure 5.5). When two people have a conversation, at a specific point in time the person speaking plays the role of the transmitter and the person listening has the role of the receiver. During the course of the conversation these roles alternate many times.

Similarly, in an information systems network, at any given time, one network component acts as a transmitter while a second component has the role of a receiver. Like personal conversations, the roles of these components can change frequently. The devices used to connect transmitters and receivers to the transmission media depend on the media type and data format. These devices are briefly defined below.

Network Interface Cards

A network interface card (NIC) serves as an adapter to allow a microcomputer to connect to a high-speed LAN. The specific card that is required depends on the architecture of the microcomputer and the protocol of the LAN. When an NIC is installed, it is also necessary to install appropriate software, known as the *device driver*, which allows the computer to "talk" to the NIC. Finally, one should note that every NIC is assigned a unique 48-bit number (called a media-access control) that identifies the computer to the network (Hayden 2001).

Modems

A modem (MOdulator DEModulator) is a device capable of changing signals from one format to another and then back again. Two types are available: copper-based and fiber optic. The copper-based modem converts a device's digital signals to analog signals appropriate for copper media. It can take the

FIGURE 5.5
Communication Process

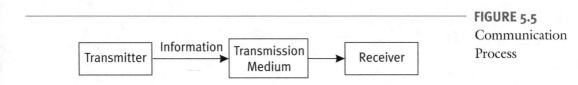

form of a card located inside the computer (internal modem) or a separate component connected to, but located outside of, the computer (external modem). Fiber-optic modems convert a device's digital signals to optical digital signals, which can then be carried over a fiber-optic network.

Multiplexers   Several devices (computer, printer, and scanner) can be connected to a multiplexer. The output of the multiplexer serves as the input to a modem, which in turn connects to the transmission medium. A multiplexer at the receiving end of the transmission medium separates the signals. Thus, the devices appear to have their own line, when in fact they are sharing the transmission medium. Figure 5.6 graphically represents the function of a multiplexer.

Bridges,   Bridges are interfaces that connect two or more networks that use similar pro-
Gateways, and   tocols (rules or conventions governing the communication process). Gateways
Routers   represent the interface between two networks that use dissimilar protocols to communicate. This allows the users to access data and programs outside of their own region. Gateways play an important role in the interconnection of the many disparate networks that comprise the Internet (discussed briefly below and in Chapter 9).

Indent   A router is a device that is located at any gateway. Its function is to manage the data flow between the networks. It decides, on the basis of its current understanding of the state of the networks, which way to send each packet of information flowing on the network.

Network Controller/Servers

A network controller is used in terminal-host networks consisting of a number of terminals connected to one or more mainframe host computers. The function of this controller, which can be a minicomputer or microcomputer, is to "direct" the communications traffic between the host and the terminals and peripheral devices.

FIGURE 5.6
Function of a
Multiplexer

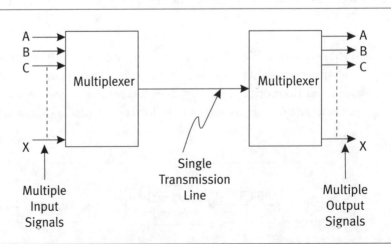

LANs do not have a network controller. Rather, communication traffic is directed by a defined protocol that depends on the network topology (described later in this chapter). The network may have one or more *servers* that provide network users with a variety of services, including access to files (file servers), help with passing files over the transmission medium (database servers), and a connection to network printers (printer servers).

Network Control Software/Network Operating Systems

Like network controllers, network control software is also associated with mainframe-based telecommunications networks. The software resides on the host (mainframe), on a small computer (front-end processor) connected to the host and dedicated to communications management, and on other processors in the network. Functions of this software include controlling access to resources, regulating data transmission to and from terminals, improving network efficiency, and detecting and correcting errors.

LANs and WANs employ network operating systems—software designed to coordinate and support the operation of the network. Functions performed by these operating systems typically include (Hayden 2001, 423):

- authenticating users,
- handling file security, and
- providing connections to network resources.

Some network operating systems serve as supplements to the computer's existing operating system, adding the network support outlined above. Others, like Windows XP, constitute comprehensive computer operating systems where the networking capabilities have been integrated into the operating system.

The IS manager, when choosing network software, must therefore consider several factors such as the number of existing or potential users, the type of network hardware available, the type of applications software programs needed, available resources (human and equipment), and network configuration costs.

Network Topologies

The configuration used to connect the computers and peripheral devices in a LAN is known as the network *physical topology*. Three alternative configurations are available to network designers: bus, ring, and star topologies. These topologies can be used singly or in combination with one another to form a *hybrid network*.

Closely related to these physical topologies are *logical topologies*, which "lay out the rules of the road for data transmission" (Hayden 2001, 36). These topologies are largely abstract and not as easily visualized as the physical topologies. This section presents an overview of four physical topologies (bus, ring, star, and hybrid) as well as four common logical topologies (Ethernet, including fast and switched Ethernet; token ring; FDDI; and ATM).

Bus Networks

In a bus network, a single circuit, or bus, is used to link the computers and other devices comprising the network (see Figure 5.7). The medium employed for this single circuit can be twisted wire, coaxial cable, or fiber-optic cable. A hardware device known as a terminator is used at either end of the bus.

Advantages of a bus network are the relative ease of wiring the network and the relatively fast communication rate. Disadvantages are limitations of length of the bus because of signal attenuation and the fact that if a break in the bus were to occur then all of the devices beyond the break are disconnected from the network.

Ethernet   A device wishing to send a message listens first to see if the bus is "busy." The message is then sent out and received by every other device. Only the intended recipient, however, pays attention to the message. If by chance two devices send out messages at the same time a "collision" will occur, which will be detected. The problem is resolved by having the two devices involved wait for a random length time interval and then send the message out again. This protocol controlling how devices send and receive messages is known as *Carrier Sense Multiple Access with Collision Detection* (CSMA/CD). (A trade name for this protocol is *Ethernet.*)

Fast Ethernet   When a large number of users are attempting to use an Ethernet network,
and Switched   a bottleneck can occur. *Fast Ethernet* and *switched Ethernet* represent two
Ethernet   possible solutions for this bottleneck. *Fast Ethernet* simply uses a higher-

FIGURE 5.7
Bus Network
Topology

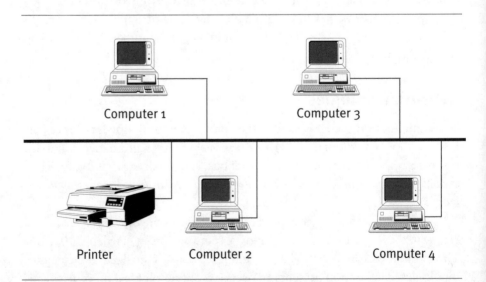

Computer 1   Computer 3

Printer   Computer 2   Computer 4

quality line and associated network components capable of operating at 100 million bits per second, ten times the speed of traditional Ethernet. *Switched Ethernet* "gives smaller segments of users access to the full bandwidth—much like today's dedicated telephone lines" (Cupito 1997, 18). "Children's Hospital in Philadelphia uses many types of networking technologies to meet the growing demand on its computer networks" (*Health Management Technology* 1997, 20). This includes fast Ethernet installed on servers and some switched 10-megabit Ethernet. Reiner et al. (2000) describe how an upgrade from Ethernet to switched Ethernet reduced their transmission failure rate by reducing the number of network collisions.

Ring Networks

A ring network can be conceptualized as a group of devices (nodes) arranged in a circle with a connection between adjacent devices to form a closed loop. (see Figure 5.8). Data travel in a single direction around the ring, and each device on the network retransmits the signal it receives from the previous device to the next device in the ring.

Ring networks offer the advantage of facilitating the construction of high-speed networks that operate over large distances. This is accomplished through the use of a fiber-optic transmission medium for the connection between adjacent nodes along with the use of an amplification device (repeater) at each node. In addition, the operation of the network is not affected by removal of a node from the ring. Disadvantages include difficulty in troubleshooting the network and adding new nodes to the ring.

A protocol often used with ring networks is known as the *token-ring* protocol. **Token Ring** Under this protocol, an electronic token is continually passed along the loop.

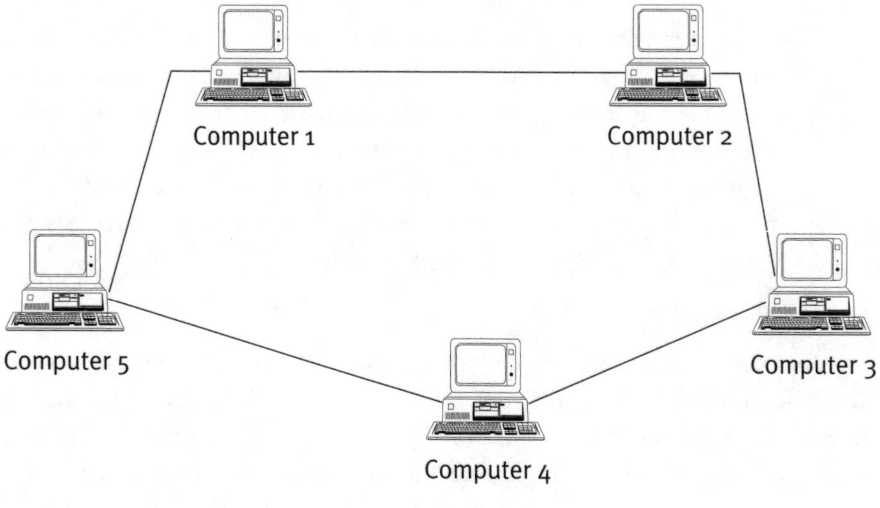

FIGURE 5.8
Ring Network
Topology

Computer 1

Computer 2

Computer 5

Computer 3

Computer 4

Only the node computer that holds the token at a given time can place a message on the network. The token is then passed on to the next node. The message passes from node to node until it reaches its destination. Because only one node can access the network at a time, the collisions that are possible with the CSMA/CD protocol (Ethernet) cannot occur here.

Fiber Distributed Data Interface

Fiber Distributed Data Interface (FDDI) is a logical topology that is based on the token-ring topology. "An FDDI network contains two token-rings, one for possible backup in case the primary ring fails" (Thing 2002, 260). If the second ring is not needed for backup and can be used to carry data, the network can operate at rates up to 200 million bits per second. Edlin (1996) describes an application of FDDI in building a network at the City of Hope Medical Center, and McDermott et al. (1999) describe an FDDI network for high-speed telemedicine communication.

Star Networks

In a star network, each of the nodes has a single point-to-point connection to a center node, called a *hub*, or *concentrator* (see Figure 5.9). When a given node wants to send a message to a second node, the message must first travel through the center node. How the message gets properly routed to its intended destination depends on the nature of the central hub.

The simplest hub, known as a *passive hub*, simply serves as a connector for the several wires coming from the various nodes. A message sent from a given node goes to every other node. The intended "recipient" node is responsible for claiming its own messages. If the hub serves not only as a connector but also regenerates message signals before sending them on to the other nodes, then the hub is known as an *active hub*. The message signal still goes to all of the nodes, and the appropriate node claims its own messages. Finally, hubs that have "reasoning" capability are able to determine the destination address for a particular message and to route the message to that address. These hubs are known as *intelligent hubs*.

Advantages of a star network include the ease with which they can be initially wired and repaired and the relative ease with which nodes can be added to an existing network. One disadvantage of a star network is the fact that a malfunctioning hub can bring the entire network "down." The use of backup hubs can help to address this difficulty. Additionally, star networks can require more cabling than networks using other topologies. Nevertheless, this topology is in wide use in many network installations.

Hybrid Networks

Two or more of these network topologies are often combined into a single network known as a *hybrid network*. One example is a WAN formed by linking several LANs having different topologies. Another example is the Internet (discussed briefly later in this chapter and in Chapter 9), which consists of an interconnection of a variety of network types.

FIGURE 5.9
Star Network
Topology

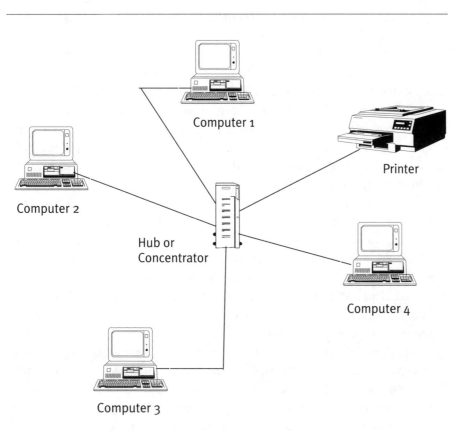

Computer 1

Printer

Computer 2

Hub or
Concentrator

Computer 4

Computer 3

ATM

Asynchronous Transfer Mode (ATM) refers to a logical network topology that segments data to be transmitted into small packets called *cells*, directs the cells through switches to the appropriate destination node, and then reassembles the data. It allows voice, data, and video to be mixed over the network, and it can run at speeds up to 1.5 billion bits per second (Hayden 2001, 40). Several applications of ATM topology have been reported, including a dedicated ATM service to facilitate transcontinental telesurgery (Marescaux et al. 2002) and the transmission of radiographic images over ATM networks (Krupinski et al. 2000; Gomez et al. 2001).

Electronic Data Interchange

The networks described in this chapter can serve as the medium for transferring structured information from one computer to another without human intervention. Such a transfer is known as *electronic data interchange* (EDI). This process needs to incorporate standards and procedures so that the "receiving" computer will be able to interpret the output of the "sending" computer. The fact that the information is structured serves to differentiate

EDI from electronic communication such as e-mail in which unstructured text is transferred in the form of messages.

The use of EDI dates back to the 1980s when it was employed in a number of settings such as the shipping and automotive industries. Early applications in the healthcare field involved the electronic processing of health insurance claims, and claims processing remains an important role for EDI today. Topel and Mullen (2002) report on the conversion to EDI by a 40-physician group practice. A commercially available product offered the practice a central hub that connected them to 44 individual payers, with the potential to expand to 1,000 payers. The practice is now able to process up to 1,000 claims daily, send more than 75 percent of their claims electronically, and reduce their average turnaround time from 14 to 10 days.

At a general medical practice in East London, "all of the National Health Service (NHS) administrative tasks connected with the registration of patients and the claiming of payments for medical services are handled with electronic data exchange (EDI) links to the local health authority" (Dobbing 2001, 197). In addition, the practice uses EDI links to the local hospital to transmit the results of laboratory tests and other procedures.

EDI can also play a part in a healthcare organization's supply chain management. Haavik (2000) describes how vendor-managed inventory (VMI) software can help these organizations obtain significant cost savings in their supply chains by monitoring utilization, forecasting demands, and generating orders. "The VMI-based system sends and receives its information via standard electronic data interchange (EDI) documents that can be made compatible with a hospital's materials management information system" (Haavik 2000, 56).

Wireless Communication

In each of the computing configurations described earlier, users interact with the information system at a fixed location, often called a *workstation*. But healthcare practitioners deliver their expertise at the site of the patient, and at that site is where they must be able to retrieve needed information and record newly acquired patient data. Mobile computing and wireless communication make this flow of data at the point of care possible.

Mobile Computing Versus Wireless Communication

Mobile computing and wireless communication are in fact two separate concepts. *Mobile computing* refers to the use of a portable computing device such as a laptop, notebook, or palmtop computer (introduced in Chapter 3). For example, home health care nurses can *download* the records of their patients for a given day from a central database into their laptop computer's hard disk, enter new data and notes into their laptop computer over the course of the day, and then *upload* the newly acquired information back to the central system at the end of the day.

Although this procedure is workable, it creates the very difficulty that led hospitals to adopt networking technology. Because the laptops function as stand-alone computers, the information in the central database (see Chapter 6) is not current until data collected by the portable devices are uploaded back to the central system. If a second provider, say a physical therapist, calls on the patient later in the day, the nurse's notes, collected earlier but not yet uploaded, will not be available to the therapist.

Even within an inpatient setting, similar problems result when independent mobile computers are used. Until newly acquired information within the hard disk of the mobile computer is transmitted back to the central database or information from the central computer is sent to the mobile computer, a discrepancy remains between two or more databases relative to a given patient. This "mismatch" is not always considered to be a serious problem. For some applications, merely updating the wireless device on a periodic basis is sufficient. For example, physicians at a Tulsa, Oklahoma, hospital are using personal digital assistants (PDAs) at the bedside. The PDAs contain a subset of clinical data, including basic patient data, lab results, and medications prescribed and administered. Data available to the PDAs are updated hourly, and most physicians download the data from syncing stations (Briggs 2002a, 46). A syncing station is a cradle that is wired to a PC. When the PDA is placed in the cradle, data and systems are updated on the PDA and the PC.

On the other hand, the combination of mobile computing and *wireless communication* enables portable computers to be connected to an established information systems network. In this way, the computing activities performed on the portable devices occur in real time, and the central database, as well as the mobile device, always stay current. A Minnesota medical center wanted to bring clinical information directly to the point of care and wanted the information available in real time. They decided to install a wireless network, a solution that is considerably less costly than installing additional cabling to create a hard-wired system (Sislo 2002).

As healthcare managers develop plans within their organizations to implement wireless networks, they are likely to receive support from clinicians. "Wireless technology and health care to many industry observers seem like a match made in heaven. One of the reasons is that physicians, who often can be resistant to information technology, many times are the biggest proponents of wireless systems" (Gillespie 2001a, 27).

Wireless Topologies

Three wireless communication topologies are commonly used in networks. Two are typically associated with LANs, while the third is used in a WAN. Each is briefly described below.

Spread Spectrum   Spread spectrum is a type of radio frequency (RF) technology that is widely used in healthcare today for wireless communication between devices on a LAN. An adapter card is added to each portable computer and to the fixed server(s) to provide the needed radio equipment. Two forms of spread spectrum are available: (1) frequency hopping spread spectrum (FHSS) and (2) direct sequence spread spectrum (DSSS), the more commonly used form in wireless LANs. DSSS has a throughput of 2 to 8 million bits per second (Hayden 2001, 393).

Healthcare managers overseeing wireless LAN installations should be aware of three characteristics of spread spectrum equipment:

1. *Range:* The distance covered by the transmitted signal. This will determine the required number of *access points* into the network.
2. *Frequency:* The goal is to avoid interference problems with other systems in the hospital. Spread spectrum equipment typically operates at a frequency of 2.4 gigahertz (1 gigahertz = 10^9 hertz).
3. *Aggregate throughput:* The rate with which data can be transferred by the wireless medium.

Infrared Technology   Because infrared technology is "line-of-sight" and cannot pass through walls, it can only be used in a single room. It has found common use in wireless keyboards and mouse devices, remote control units, and cordless modems.

Cellular Digital Packet Data   *Cellular Digital Packet Data* (CDPD) is a WAN architecture whose systems and communications protocols "make the transmission of data across cellular networks possible" (Wu et al. 1996, 178). CDPD network users are "serviced by the same cell sites as cellular telephone users and their calls are handed off just like the calls of cellular telephone users. The difference is that the CDPD user is transmitting or receiving data rather than a voice message. . . ." and data are "transmitted in well-defined packets of information rather than a continuous . . . voice signal" (Wu et al. 1996, 179). Hayden (2001, 393) characterizes CDPD as "currently in a state of flux." Although CDPD is "the fastest wireless networking protocol available, . . . it's limited to a 19.2 kilobits-per-second data transmission speed—quite a bit slower than today's regular wired modems and an order of magnitude slower than an Ethernet connection. Nevertheless, the allure of being able to connect to a network without a phone jack is difficult to resist, and many corporate networkers are cautiously testing CDPD networking for their remote users."

Communicating Via the Internet

The LANs described in this chapter can be connected to form larger networks, known as internets (observe the use of a lowercase i). For example, the LANs within each institution comprising an integrated delivery system can be linked to form an internet known as an enterprise computer network. (Enterprise systems are discussed in Chapter 8.) In the past, attempts were made to interconnect these enterprise networks to create another internet, designated as a *community health information network*, which would link the networks of all of the healthcare delivery institutions and/or systems in a given region. Although some successes were reported, interest in creating or maintaining such community-based internets seems to have subsided.

The largest interconnection of networks in the world today is known as the Internet (note the uppercase I). The Internet began in 1969 as a Defense Department project designed to connect various government laboratories and contractors. However, as the "Net" began to be used, it was soon recognized that a data link between researchers was indispensable. Briggs (2002b, 50) suggests that the public is "infatuated with the medium. The Internet is absorbing some two million new users per month . . . (which) translates to 143 million Americans, or about 54% of the population, online as of September 2001. Among those users, about 35% are looking for health information." The World Wide Web (www), developed in 1991, is a collection of electronic resources distributed over the Internet that combine text, graphics, sound, and video.

Not only have individuals found the Internet and the www to be valuable tools, but a wide spectrum of businesses has also developed numerous applications utilizing these resources. The healthcare field is no exception, and Chapter 9 is devoted to a survey of the applications on the Internet directly applicable to healthcare organizations. This section provides an overview of the technology issues associated with communication on the Internet, including connecting to the Internet, the concept of a web site, the role of an intranet, and the notion of a network computer.

Connecting to the Internet

Except for the very few institutions with a staff of in-house engineers, computer specialists, and networking experts who are capable of connecting directly to the Internet, the majority of healthcare organizations will obtain their Internet services through an intermediate provider. This provider can be an *online service connection* (OLSC) such as America Online, which provides an array of information services, or an *Internet service provider* (ISP) whose function is to provide users with a link to the Internet. A list of these ISPs can be obtained on the Internet at http://www.thelist.com. The Internet provider can be reached using a dial-up connection or a direct network connection.

Users of dial-up services typically have a high-speed modem (56 kilobits per second) connected to a standard telephone line, or they make use of an Integrated Services Digital Network (ISDN) line with an appropriate card to connect their computer to the line. The data transfer rate is typically 64 or 128 kilobits per second. Hayden (2001, 112) suggests that telephone companies *Dial-Up Services* have "begun aggressively marketing ISDN as an alternative connection for smaller businesses."

Direct Network Connections

A direct network connection uses dedicated digital telephone lines that go directly from the computer to the ISP. They can be fractional T1 lines (about 1 megabit per second) or T3 lines (45 megabits per second). Telephone companies now offer Digital Subscriber Line (DSL) service. "DSL is at least as fast as T1, but unlike T1, DSL runs over standard two-wire telephone wire" (Hayden 2001, 113). It is priced affordably and can be found in many home-computing environments.

Many cable companies are offering direct connections between a computer and the cable television network. The cable company then provides a connection between its cable network and an ISP or the company might serve as the ISP. A cable modem must be added to the computer to facilitate making a connection into the cable network. Bennett et al. (2000) report on the use of a cable modem to access the radiology web server in a picture archiving and communications system at an Ohio medical center.

Once a connection has been made between a computer and the Internet, a program is needed to manage the assembly and routing of the messages being transmitted. This *Transmission Control Protocol/Internet Protocol (TCP/IP)* is such a program. Although the IP takes care of handling the actual delivery of the data, the TCP takes care of keeping track of the individual units of data (called packets) that a message is divided into for efficient routing through the Internet.

The Concept of a Web Site

The connection to the Internet described above is sufficient if the goal is to simply utilize the array of information available on the Internet. Many organizations (and individuals), however, want their own "presence on the Web," known as a web site. This presence enables these organizations to provide other Internet users with an array of e-health applications (see Chapter 9).

A web site consists of one or more web "pages" that a user can display using software known as a *browser*. Creating the web site requires the talents of graphic designers and programmers with knowledge of specialized languages that create the text, graphics, sound, and animation that many users expect to be present in today's web sites. A language that is basic to creating these pages is *Hypertext Markup Language* (HTML). HTML "tells the Web browser how to display a Web page's words and images for the user" (Thing 2002, 325). Other software is available that is designed to simplify the creation of web pages.

A unique *Uniform Resource Locator* (URL) is used to identify each web site. For example, the URL for the American College of Healthcare Executives (ACHE) is www.ache.org.

The *org* is known as the "top-level domain" (TLD) name of this web site and indicates that ACHE is a nonprofit organization. Other domain names that have been in common use are *com* (commercial organization), *gov* (government organization), and *edu* (educational institution). In November 2000, seven new TLDs were selected (ICANN 2002):

TLD	Purpose
.aero	Air-transport industry
.biz	Businesses
.coop	Cooperatives
.info	Unrestricted use
.museum	Museums
.name	Registration by individuals
.pro	Accountants, lawyers, physicians, other professionals

Creation of the web pages is just the beginning of establishing a web site. Hardware specialists must set up "space" on the computer that will house the web pages. This computer is known as the *host computer*. Software known as a *web server* serves the files that form the web page. Special attention must be paid to security issues so that information contained in the web pages can be restricted, if necessary, to only those individuals authorized to access it.

Finally, the web pages must be maintained. Of particular importance is keeping the content of the pages current. Out-of-date information on a web page creates a negative image for the organization. In addition, the usual hardware and software updates required by any computer installation are required.

Like other information technology implementations, alternative approaches exist for a healthcare organization to establish a Web presence. These range from completing the entire project "in-house" to turning the entire project over to an outside firm. Florida Hospital, a 2,048-bed facility, teamed with IBM Corporation to develop its Web applications (Gillespie 2001b). However, Gillespie (2001b, 48) suggests that "most hospitals are going to rely on their vendors to come up with Web solutions, and because the big, established vendors haven't come up with anything new for Web sites, it's frozen the whole market."

The Role of an Intranet

Once the technology necessary to allow employees to access the Internet is in place, the healthcare manager might wonder why that infrastructure cannot support communication *within* the organization. In fact it can, and this use of the Internet technology is known as an intranet. "An intranet is a private network that is contained within an enterprise" (Thing 2002, 363). It uses the same protocols as the Internet and in general "looks like a private version of the Internet." Thing (2002) indicates that in many cases intranet users can access the public Internet through *firewall* servers that provide security against outside users entering the intranet. "When part of an intranet is made accessible to customers, partners, or others outside the company, that part becomes part of an *extranet*" (Thing 2002, 363).

The firewall server can also contain software that establishes a *virtual private network* (VPN). A VPN allows organizations to maintain privacy while sharing public networks for transmission of their data. Data are encrypted before they are sent through the public network and then decrypted at the receiving end. This methodology makes customers feel more comfortable about providing credit card information "online." Transmission of sensitive patient information can utilize this same protocol.

The development of intranets in healthcare settings began primarily with "content-based" sites. For example, a Wisconsin hospital, "like most other health care organizations with intranets, . . . initially created static pages for its intranet that contained only nonsensitive information, such as organizational policies and procedures, physician credentials, and cafeteria menus" (Kelly 2000, 56). But, as Briggs (2001b, 59) points out, "intranets have been branching out to more sophisticated administrative and clinical applications."

As developments in intranet applications continue, healthcare managers should monitor how their organizations are utilizing this technology. Special attention should be directed toward the security and confidentiality issues created by intranets. Chapter 13 is devoted to this topic.

Thin Clients and the Internet

Thin client computers are minimally configured PCs that were described earlier in the chapter as suitable client machines in a client/server network. These machines can also serve as user workstations on the Internet. The healthcare manager will encounter a variety of terminology associated with this type of installation, including thin client, network computer (NC), net PC, and proprietary names like Windows Terminal or Winterm.

Two major advantages result from the use of thin clients rather than fully configured PCs. The first, and obvious advantage, is cost. Thin clients carry a lower purchase price that can become significant as the number of computers connected to the Internet in typical healthcare settings continues to increase. A second, and somewhat related, advantage relates to the maintenance of these machines. The typical PC has a number of applications packages residing on its hard drive. As software changes, the information technology (IT) department has a formidable task of updating all of the machines. In an environment where thin clients are used, the software resides on the web server and can be updated quite easily.

A disadvantage that the manager will face in moving toward the use of thin clients is a cultural one. Users have become accustomed to the power of a fully configured PC on their desk. Making a change to thin clients could face opposition from these users. Second, like in all networking situations, when the server is "down," the user of a thin client is also "down."

In this area, like all decisions concerning information-systems acquisition and installation, the healthcare manager is well advised to be aware of all alternatives and select the one best suited for his or her organization.

Summary

The trend toward the creation of integrated health systems and other environmental changes have made the information needs of healthcare organizations increasingly complex. Among the strategies necessary to respond to these changes are the development of computer networks and the use of telecommunications. A network can be a local area network (LAN) or a wide area network (WAN), depending on how narrowly or broadly dispersed are the components that comprise the network.

Networks can also be classified according to the manner in which the processing function is distributed among the devices comprising the network. Four alternative configurations are (1) terminal-host systems, in which all of the processing is concentrated in a single machine—typically a mainframe computer—and dumb terminals are connected to the host; (2) a client/server network that divides the computing function between two or more machines; (3) a file/server configuration, in which most processing takes place on the user's computer and the server is used to store the files; and (4) a peer network, in which processing is done on all of the computers, and each computer's resources are available to other computers on the network. Each alternative has its own strengths and weaknesses, and the appropriate configuration is dependent on the organization's strategic direction.

A variety of components comprise an information network. Transmission media include wired media, fiber-optic media, and radio media. Transmission and receiving components include network interface cards, modems, multiplexers, bridges, gateways, and routers. Network controllers and protocols associated with the network servers help to direct the communication traffic on the network. Finally, network control software and network operating systems control the accessing and use of network resources and help improve network efficiency.

The configuration with which devices are connected to form a network is known as the network physical topology. Three alternative configurations, each with pros and cons, are a bus, ring, or star topology. Two or more topologies can be combined to form a hybrid network. Networks also have logical topologies that guide data transmission. Four logical topologies are

Ethernet (including fast and switched Ethernet), token ring, Fiber Distributed Data Interface (FDDI), and Asynchronous Transfer Mode (ATM).

The transfer of structured information between computers is known as electronic data interchange (EDI). The healthcare field employs EDI for a number of important applications, including claims processing, electronic enrollment, and materials management.

Mobile computing makes information available at the point of care. The addition of wireless communication to the mobile computing device allows the transfer of information between the device and central database to occur in real time. Spread spectrum technology serves as the basis for wireless LANs. Cellular digital packet data (CDPD) is a WAN architecture that makes data transmission across cellular networks possible.

The Internet is evolving into an important resource for healthcare organizations. It provides access to a wide range of information, allows the organization to achieve a presence on a worldwide information network, and provides an infrastructure for communication within the organization.

Networking and telecommunications are highly technical and rapidly changing areas. Gaining a basic understanding of these areas, staying abreast of the changes, and knowledgeably interacting with the technical specialists in the field are ongoing challenges for the healthcare manager.

Discussion Questions

5.1 Describe how the development of integrated healthcare systems has created an impetus for installing computer networks.

5.2 Name and describe the computer environment that offers the highest degree of centralization.

5.3 Explain the difference between a two-tier and a three-tier client/server architecture.

5.4 What is the difference between digital and analog waveforms?

5.5 Name and describe the two types of copper media in common use.

5.6 What are the advantages of fiber-optic media compared with copper media?

5.7 Describe the function of a modem.

5.8 Describe the functions of a network operating system.

5.9 Name and describe the three physical network topologies.

5.10 Describe some important applications of electronic data interchange in the healthcare field.

5.11 Explain the notion of a wireless local area network.

5.12 What is the difference between mobile computing and wireless communication?

5.13 Define the concept of cellular digital packet data.

5.14 Explain the difference between internet and Internet.

5.15 What is meant by the term web site?

5.16 Explain the role of an intranet.

Problems

5.1 The executive suite of your hospital is contained in a contiguous space on a single floor. It has a total of 12 computers currently functioning independently. Each is a 2.0 Ghz Pentium IV machine, with 256 Mb memory and an 80 GB hard drive. All of the computers are running under Windows XP. The furthest distance between any two machines is about 70 feet. Discussions are under way to link these computers into a LAN. Determine the specific additional hardware and software required and the approximate cost of this hardware and software. (Assume that the building has been prewired with appropriate cabling and that each computer is no more than six feet from a cable connection.)

5.2 Use the Internet to obtain a list of the Internet Service Providers in your zip code. Contact at least one of these providers to obtain details about available Internet service and the associated cost. Recommend an appropriate level of service for a three-physician medical office wishing to have access to the Internet for medical research purposes.

5.3 Interview one or more hospital chief information officers in your area to find one who has evaluated taking their institution from a mainframe configuration to client/server architecture. Indicate whether they decided to keep their mainframe and/or to install a client/server system. Describe clearly the logic they used to reach their decision.

5.4 Contact the telephone company in your area to determine their cable offerings for data services in your home. For each type of cable, indicate the transmission speed and the price. Suppose you are an independent healthcare consultant operating from your home and that access to the Internet is important for your work. Specify the cable option that would seem to make the most sense.

5.5 The chief financial officer (CFO) of your hospital has just returned from a conference where healthcare claims clearinghouses were discussed. She wonders if the use of such a clearinghouse would be beneficial for your institution. Using the library, interviews of CFOs, and other appropriate sources, do sufficient research to determine the following:
- What is a claims clearinghouse
- What is the scope of services provided
- What is the relationship between claims clearinghouses and electronic data interchange
- What hardware and/or software is required to utilize the services of a claims clearinghouse

- What is the financial viability of utilizing a claims clearinghouse

Write a report to your CFO describing your findings.

5.6 The areas of mobile computing and wireless communication are dynamic fields. You have been hired by a home health agency to investigate the feasibility of equipping their home health nurses with laptop computers capable of utilizing cellular digital packet data (CDPD) technology. They want you at a minimum to determine:

- whether new technology (if any) exists that should be considered as an alternative to CDPD technology;
- what specific benefits result from the real-time transmission of data;
- the feasibility of the home health nurse to transmit the data back to a central computer from a fixed telephone location after each home health visit; and
- any additional information relevant to the question of whether to adopt the CDPD technology.

Write a report to the CEO of the home health agency describing your findings and document your recommendation(s).

References

Anderson, D. 2002. "Communications/Networking: Cabling." [Online article on PCTechGuide web site; retrieved 6/30/02]. http://www.pctechguide.com/29network.htm#cabling.

Bennett, W. F., D. G. Spigos, K. V. Vaswani, and J. E. Terrell. 2000. "Cable Modem Access to Picture Archiving and Communication System Images Using a Web Browser Over the Internet." *Journal of Digital Imaging* 13 (2, Supplement 1): 93–96.

Brailer, D. J. 2001. "Connection Tops Collection. Peer-to-Peer Technology Lets Caregivers Access Necessary Data, Upon Request, Without Using a Repository." *Health Management Technology* 22 (8): 28–29.

Briggs, B. 2000. "Network Operating Systems. Is There a Final Answer? A. Unix, B. Windows, C. Novell, D. Linux." *Health Data Management* 8 (10): 62, 63, 66, 68, 70, 72.

———. 2001a. "Aging Bean Counting Systems Run Out of Gas." *Health Data Management* 9 (6): 52–54, 56, 58, 60.

———. 2001b. "Advanced Intranets Can Bring Good Fortune." *Health Data Management* 9 (10): 58–60, 62, 64, 66.

———. 2002a. "Is the Future in the Palm of Your Hand?" *Health Data Management* 10 (1): 44–46, 48, 50, 52, 54, 56, 58, 60, 62.

———. 2002b. "Internet Helps Whittle Down Transactions Costs." *Health Data Management* 10 (4): 46–48, 50, 51.

Chu, S., and B. Cesnik. 2000. "A Three-Tier Clinical Information Systems Design Model." *International Journal of Medical Informatics* 57 (2–3): 91–107.

Cupito, M. C. 1997. "Widening the Pipe: Plain Talk About Fast and Switched Ethernet." *Health Management Technology* 18 (1): 18, 21–22.

Dobbing, C. 2001. "Paperless Practice—Electronic Medical Records at Island Health." *Computer Methods & Programs in Biomedicine* 64 (3): 197–99.

Edlin, M. 1996. "HOPENET Puts Center on Path for Year 2000." *Health Management Technology* 17 (11): 13–14, 16.

Gillespie, G. 2001a. "Wireless Catching Up, Catching On in Health Care." *Health Data Management* 9 (8): 26–28, 30, 32, 34.

Gillespie, G. 2001b. "Hospital Web Sites Face an Unpredictable Future." *Health Data Management* 9 (5): 46–53.

Gomez, E. J., P. J. Caballero, N. Malpica, and F. del Pozo. 2001. "Optimisation and Evaluation of an Asynchronous Transfer Mode Teleradiology Co-operative System: The Experience of the EMERALD and the BONAPARTE Projects." *Computer Methods & Programs in Biomedicine* 64 (3): 201–14.

Haavik, S. 2000. "Building a Demand-Driven, Vendor-Managed Supply Chain." *Healthcare Financial Management* 54 (2): 56, 57, 59–61.

Health Management Technology. 1997. "At Children's Hospital of Philadelphia, the 'Layered Look' in Networks Is in Style." *Health Management Technology* 18 (1): 20.

Hayden, M. 2001. *Sams Teach Yourself Networking in 24 Hours.* Indianapolis, IN: Sams Publishing.

The Internet Corporation for Assigned Names and Numbers (ICANN). 2002. "New TLD Program." [Online article; retrieved 6/30/02]. http://www.icann.org/tlds/.

Kelly, B. 2000. "Intranets Succumb to Irresistible Pull of e-Health." *Health Data Management* 8 (12): 56–58, 60, 62, 64.

Krupinski, E., M. Gonzales, C. Gonzales, and R. S. Weinstein. 2000. "Evaluation of a Digital Camera for Acquiring Radiographic Images for Telemedicine Applications." *Telemedicine Journal & E-Health* 6 (3): 297–302.

Lee, N., and A. Millman. 1995. "ABC of Medical Computing: Hospital Based Computer Systems [Education & Debate]." *British Medical Journal* 311 (7011): 1013–16.

Lee, Y. L., C. Y. Hsu, D. Hsieh, and Y. C. Li. 2001. "Development and Deployment of a Web-Based Physician Order Entry System." *International Journal of Medical Informatics* 62 (2–3): 135–42.

Marescaux, J., J. Leroy, F. Rubino, M. Smith, M. Vix, M. Simone, and D. Mutter. 2002. "Transcontinental Robot-Assisted Remote Telesurgery: Feasibility and Potential Applications." *Annals of Surgery* 235 (4): 487–92.

McDermott, W. R., J. L.Tri, M. P Mitchell, S. P. Levens, M. A. Wondrow, L. M. Huie, B. K. Khandheria, and B. K. Gilbert. 1999. "Optimization of Wide-Area ATM and Local-Area Ethernet/FDDI Network Configurations for High-Speed Telemedicine Communications Employing NASA's ACTS." *IEEE Network* 13 (4): 30–38.

Panko, R. R. 2001. *Business Data Communications and Networking,* 3rd Edition. Upper Saddle River, NJ: Prentice-Hall.

Reiner, B., E. Siegel, P. Kuzmak, and S. Severance. 2000. "Transmission Failure Rate for Computed Tomography Examinations in a Filmless Imaging Department." *Journal of Digital Imaging* 13 (2, Supplement 1): 79–82.

Sislo, W. 2002. "What Works: Reaping the Benefits of Wireless." *Health Management Technology* 23 (2): 50.

Stallings, W., and R. Van Slyke. 2000. *Business Data Communications,* 4th Edition. Upper Saddle, NJ: Prentice-Hall.

Thing, L. 2002. *The whatis?com: Encyclopedia of Technology Terms.* Indianapolis, IN: Que Publishing.

Topel, K., and H. Mullen. 2002. "At the Speed of EDI." *Health Management Technology* 23 (2): 26.

Vickers, L. 2001. "Emerging Technology: Is Fiber Optic Destined for the Desktop?" [Online article on *Network Magazine* web site; retrieved 6/30/02]. http://www.networkmagazine.com/article/NMG20010103S0004.

Wu, J. B., J. Colon, J. Lauer, and J. Kromelow. 1996. "Wireless Data Transmission: How to Implement Remote Data-Access." In *Proceedings of the 1996 Annual HIMSS Conference,* March 3–7, 1996, Atlanta, Georgia, Volume 2, pp. 175–87. Chicago: Health Care Information and Management Systems Society.

Additional Readings

Branger, P. J., A. van Hooft, J. C. van der Wouden, J. S. Duisterhout, and J. H. van Bemmel. 1998. "Shared Care for Diabetes: Supporting Communication Between Primary and Secondary Care." *Medinfo* 9 (Part 1): 412–16.

Briggs, B. 2000. "No Time to Plan for Intranets." *Health Data Management* 8 (12): 48–50, 52, 54.

Dombkowski, K. J., M. Charles, and R. L. Uren. 1996. "Using Electronic Data Interchange in Managed Care Performance Measurement." In *Proceedings of the 1996 Annual HIMSS Conference,* March 3–7, 1996, Atlanta, Georgia, Volume 1, pp. 159–76. Chicago: Health Care Information and Management Systems Society.

Gandsas, A., K. Montgomery, K. McIntire, and R. Altrudi. 2001. "Wireless Vital Sign Telemetry to Hand-Held Computers." *Studies in Health Technology & Informatics* 81: 153–57.

Gillespie, G. 2000. "A Recipe for Tomorrow's Intranets." *Health Data Management* 8 (12): 34–36, 38, 40, 42, 44.

Goldman, J. E., and P. T. Rawles. 2001. *Applied Data Communications: A Business-Oriented Approach,* 3rd Edition. New York: Wiley.

Held, G. 2000. *Understanding Data Communications: From Fundamentals to Networking,* 3rd Edition. Chichester, England: Wiley.

Hill, C. A. 2000. "Information Technology and Supply Chain Management: A Study of the Food Industry." *Hospital Materiel Management Quarterly* 22 (1): 53–58.

Krohn, R. 2001. "On the Verge of a Unifying Link: Wireless Technologies Close in on the Data Gap." *Healthcare Informatics* 18 (9): 45, 46, 48, 50.

Oberson, J. C., R. Welz, and L. Bovisi. 2000. "Development of an Electronic Radiologist's Office in a Private Institute." *Radiographics* 20 (2): 573–80.

Papadakis, I., V. Chrissikopoulos, and D. Polemi. 2001. "Secure Medical Digital Libraries." *International Journal of Medical Informatics* 64 (2–3): 417–28.

Subramanian, M. 2000. *Network Management Principles and Practice.* Reading, MA: Addison-Wesley.

Sveum, M. E. 2000. *Data Communications: An Overview.* Upper Saddle, NJ: Prentice-Hall.

Weinstein, R. S., and K. M. McNeill. 2001. "What Works: Powering the Arizona Telemedicine Program." *Health Management Technology* 22 (6): 46–47.

Wilkinson, E. P., R. Shahidi, B. Wang, D. P. Martin, J. R. Adler, Jr., and G. K. Steinberg. 1999. "Remote-Rendered 3D CT Angiography (3DCTA) As an Intraoperative Aid in Cerebrovascular Neurosurgery." *Computer Aided Surgery* 4 (5): 256–63.

DATA MANAGEMENT

The application of information technology to the healthcare field is characterized by a high degree of complexity and interdependence among users and applications. The formation of healthcare systems and the growth in managed care have served to add to this complexity. As a result, multiple users often require access to the same data, data collected in one institution are often needed by a user in another location, and newly acquired data must be merged into existing data. Providing a linkage to facilitate the exchange of data is a key rationale for the installation of computer networks. (See Chapter 5.)

However, even when computers have been networked, users will not be able to easily access the data they need unless care has been given to the organization of the data and to the development of software for storing, modifying, deleting, and disseminating the data. A collection of data carefully organized to be of value to the user is called a *database,* and the associated software used to manipulate the database is commonly known as a *database-management system* (DBMS). The development of database technology has provided much improvement over previous data-storage methodologies.

Because the healthcare field is so dependent on the timely availability of data, the appropriate implementation of database technology is particularly important. Healthcare managers must have sufficient understanding of this technology to oversee its implementation. This chapter is designed to help the manager develop this understanding. Specific topics that are covered include a review of computer files as a data-storage approach, the improvement offered by databases, an overview of database models, the notion of database-management systems, issues surrounding data security, developments in database technology, and the role of data warehouses in healthcare.

Computer Files

Long before electronic computing and storage devices were introduced, organizations maintained data in paper files. Filing cabinets containing one or more drawers were designed to "hold" the data in file folders, which were arranged alphabetically, numerically, or according to some predefined sequence. By placing a document or other "piece" of data into the proper folder when the data item was received, it ensured that the user could retrieve the item when it was needed.

The secondary storage devices described in Chapter 3 provide an electronic alternative to the filing cabinet. These can be either sequential devices or direct-access storage devices. The type of storage device has an impact on the format of the files maintained on it.

Sequential Computer Files

The tape drive allows users to create one or more tape *files*. Each file, roughly equivalent to a file drawer, contains a series of *records*. The record is essentially equivalent to a file folder, and each record consists of a number of *fields* corresponding to the data items stored within the file folders of a paper-based system. As an example, an early hospital personnel system typically utilized a tape file in which each record stored information on a given employee. Within the record were multiple fields containing specific data about the employee— that is, date of hire, Social Security number, date of birth, address, foreign language skills, etc. Figure 6.1 depicts the hierarchy of a field, a record, and a file for this application.

The hospital either developed or purchased software that was capable of adding new employees to the file, modifying one or more fields in an employee's record, or deleting an employee from the file. This software might also produce one or more reports such as an alphabetical listing of the employees, a list of employees in descending order of years of affiliation with the hospital, or a list of employees fluent in Spanish. The fact that a tape drive is a *sequential* storage device creates challenges for the software developer. The simple task of changing an employee's address requires reading through the entire file to find the employee's record. Adding several new employees to a file maintained in alphabetical order requires sorting the employees to be added, creating a transaction file containing the new employees, reading the

FIGURE 6.1

Hierarchy of a Field, Record, and File

	Employee Name	Date of Hire	Social Security No.	Language Fluency
FILE	Ken L. Watt	03/03/86	111-23-3223	None
	Jane Sargent	11/10/90	356-29-0588	German
	Mary Smith	05/05/97	334-44-9876	Spanish
	⋮	⋮	⋮	⋮
	Robert Cardin	09/12/92	056-88-4848	French

	Employee Name	Date of Hire	Social Security No.	Language Fluency
RECORD	Mary Smith	05/05/97	334-44-9876	Spanish
FIELD	Mary Smith		(Employee Name Field)	

old employee file, merging the records from the transaction file where applicable, and writing a new employee file. Computer code had to be developed to accomplish these tasks.

Direct-Access Computer Files

When disk files, which are *direct-access* storage devices (DASD), were introduced, a major difficulty was addressed. To update a given employee's record, reading through the entire employee file was no longer necessary. Rather, the program could "go directly" to that employee's record and make the necessary corrections.

In fact, the ability of the file maintenance program to directly access a given employee's record depends on the program's "knowing" the *record number* containing that employee's data; that is, the software developer was responsible for creating a system for keeping track of the location of each employee's record within the file. One approach commonly used was to develop an algorithm that converted the employee number to a unique record number. Alternatively, an index file could be maintained whose records contain either the employee name or number along with the number of the record in the employee file containing that employee's data. If no means is provided for determining the record number associated with a given employee, then the file could only be processed sequentially.

Problems of Computer Files

The need for the programmer to design a means for identifying the number of a desired record in a direct-access file is just one of several problems associated with traditional computer files. Other problems include program/file dependence, data redundancy, and data inconsistency. Each of these problems is briefly described below.

Program/File Dependence

The notion of program/file dependence refers to the fact that a given computer-based data file is typically associated with a specific application program. Thus, when developing a hospital billing system using, for example, COBOL, a programmer would also design and implement the related data file using the same language.

This dependence has several implications. First, a second application program written in another language—for instance, Pascal—cannot practically access the billing system file. Second, even when another application program is written in COBOL, its developer needs detailed information about the file structure to be able to use the file for the second application. And finally, even though the billing file contains valuable detailed information about the resources consumed by all of the inpatients, retrieving this information can be a very difficult task requiring development of a custom program. The impact of this difficulty on the development of decision-support and executive information systems is discussed in Chapter 10.

The close linkage between a given application program and its associated data files is easy to understand within the healthcare field. Each application was often developed independently of other applications, taking the form of a stand-alone module. Thus, an admissions/discharge/transfer (ADT) program, an order-entry and results-reporting program, a radiology program, and a laboratory program all have data files that could potentially be shared but instead function independently. This situation is portrayed graphically in Figure 6.2.

Data
Redundancy
As its name implies, data redundancy refers simply to the situation in which the same data item appears in several files within the healthcare organization's computer system. (The same data item can also occur redundantly within a single data file.) For example, the files used by the ADT program contain the name, address, telephone number, and other patient-demographic data. But the computer program used by the radiology department will likely have associated files whose fields include similar patient-demographic information. Patients are all too familiar with the fact that they are typically asked for the same demographic information by multiple persons during their inpatient stay or outpatient encounter.

FIGURE 6.2

Linkage
Between
Application
Programs and
Associated Data
Files

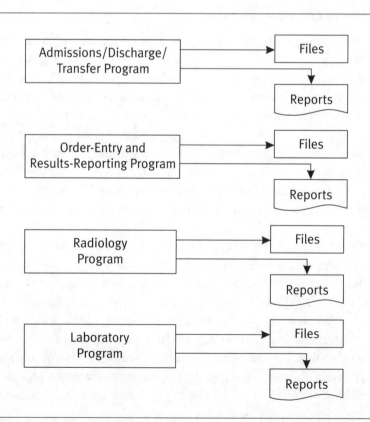

Similarly, the results of laboratory tests will be stored in a file associated with the laboratory computer system and will also be sent back to the patient floor. There, the information will be added either to a computer record (if one is in place) or filed in the patient's paper chart. In any event, the same patient information will be stored in multiple locations.

This duplication of information wastes resources such as personnel, time, and computer storage. As healthcare organizations expand into large health systems, one begins to see the potential for significant data redundancy. Each time a patient receives care from another entity within the system, a conventional file-based computer system will require the creation of a new record, many of whose fields duplicate those existing in files within other system entities.

The redundancy described above creates the potential for data inconsistency as *Data* well. For example, an address change between encounters can cause a patient *Inconsistency* to have an address in the file of one entity that is different from the address contained in another entity's file. Perhaps even more significant is the situation where the patient's name appears differently in different computer files. This can result from a typing error, use of a middle initial on one occasion but not on another, or a name change associated with marriage. A task as simple as searching for all of the records associated with a specific patient can become quite difficult when patient name inconsistencies exist.

Data redundancies can also lead to data inconsistencies when changes are made in a file field. Consider the patient billing system. Suppose that the pharmacist has discovered that the wrong price has been quoted on a given pharmaceutical item. All of the fields recording the dispensing of that pharmaceutical item must now be changed to correct the error. Failure to change *all* of the fields will lead, of course, to inconsistencies. If it were possible to store the price of the item in a single location to which reference would be made as the statement is generated, this chance of data inconsistency would be greatly reduced. The database technology discussed below provides such a possibility.

Databases

A number of difficulties associated with the use of traditional computer files were described in the previous section. Database technology does an excellent job of addressing these difficulties. Among the benefits offered by using the database approach (see, for example, Connolly and Begg 2002, 26–29) are the following:

1. *Redundancy can be reduced.* Although not all data redundancy is eliminated, the redundancy is *controlled.* This results in efficient data storage as well as data processing.

2. *Inconsistency can be avoided.* This is accomplished either by storing a given data item only in one place or by making the system aware of redundancies so that they can be properly handled.

3. *Data can be shared.* An important benefit of the database approach is the ability to make data available to many applications, both existing as well as new applications. Thus, the sharing of data allows a decision-support system (discussed in Chapter 10) to utilize data generated by a number of the applications running within the organization. When data are shared, careful attention must be paid to how the information resource is managed, such as the development of standards.

4. *Data integrity can be maintained.* The reduction in inconsistencies increases the users' confidence in the integrity of the data. In addition, the manager in charge of the centralized data resource can define rules, which are imposed when the database is updated. Adherence to these rules will also help to maintain data integrity.

5. *Security restrictions can be applied.* Again, this benefit is made necessary by the centralization of the information resource. Users can be required to use a password to gain access to data, and security levels can be defined so that data are made available only to users having a legitimate "need to know."

6. *Standards can be enforced.* The centralization of the information resource affords the opportunity to enforce standards. (Of course, the centralization itself is responsible in part for the need for standards.) Three important areas of standardization are:

   • data representation;
   • naming of variables; and
   • documentation.

7. *Conflicting requirements can be balanced.* The centralization of the data resource will result in a system that attempts to globally optimize the value of that resource enterprisewide. This is in contrast to a noncentralized configuration that works well for one department but not for any others.

8. *Data independence.* The tight coupling between the data file and the application program no longer exists. Thus, changes in the structure of the data file or of techniques for accessing the file do not affect the application program. This independence is, of course, related to the benefit of sharing data.

Although database technology is the preferred approach for an organization to meet its data storage needs, this technology presents several challenges, including:

1. Database technology is complex. Typical installations will require a database administrator responsible for maintaining the database.

2. Database systems are costly to purchase and install.
3. Conversion from the present system to the database system can be costly.
4. Because the database system must have sufficient generality to support an array of applications, the performance of a specific application might be slightly worse than its file-based predecessor.
5. Because the database system constitutes a centralized function, its failure has a high impact on the entire organization. (Distributed database systems, discussed later in the chapter, can help to address this problem.)

Database Models

Healthcare managers will typically use databases whose logical structure follows one of three models: hierarchical, network, or relational. A simple database application will be used to illustrate each of these models. A large medical center has many departments, each of which has a variety of equipment. Technicians from the biomedical engineering department are assigned the task of providing scheduled maintenance on this equipment as well as servicing the equipment when it breaks down. The medical center wishes to develop a database system to support this equipment-maintenance process. The database will maintain a profile of the equipment as well as the employees in each department, the technician assigned to each piece of equipment, and a detailed description of each maintenance procedure performed on the equipment.

Hierarchical Data Model

The hierarchical data model stores data as nodes in a *tree* structure. Figure 6.3 illustrates the application of this model to the equipment-maintenance process. The node "Department" is called the *root*—a special node always drawn at the top of the diagram. "Department" has two *child nodes*: "Employees" and "Equipment." Similarly, "Equipment" is the *parent node* of

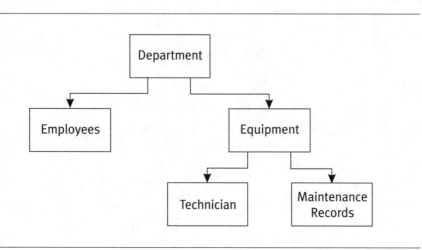

FIGURE 6.3
Hierarchical
Data Model:
Equipment
Maintenance
Database

"Technician" as well as "Maintenance Records." Thus, each node can have only one *parent node*, but it may have multiple *child nodes*. This property is referred to as a "one-to-many" relationship, a characteristic of the hierarchical database model. A node having no branches leaving it is known as a *terminal node*. "Employees," "Technician," and "Maintenance Records" are terminal nodes.

Network Data Model

The network data model, as its name suggests, stores data as nodes in a network. The parent nodes and children nodes defined in the hierarchical data model become *owners* and *members*, respectively, in the network data model. The model uses links, called *pointers*, to connect the owners and members, forming a relationship called a *set*. Unlike the hierarchical model where a node can have only one parent, in the network data model a member can have more than one owner. As a result, "many-to-many" relationships are possible, which result in reduced data redundancy. The network data model for the equipment-maintenance process is shown in Figure 6.4.

Relational Data Model

The relational data model stores data in individual files, or *tables*, with data items arranged in rows and columns. The application of this model to the equipment-maintenance process is illustrated in Figure 6.5. Three tables have been defined—DEPTABLE, EMPTABLE, and EQTABLE—that store data on departments, employees, and equipment, respectively. These two-dimensional tables are also known as *relations* (from which the name *relational model* is derived).

Each row, or *tuple*, normally includes data for a single data *record* (e.g., a department), with each column, or *field*, of the table containing one piece of data. The fields in the department relation, for example, are DEPT_NO,

FIGURE 6.4
Network Data Model: Equipment Maintenance Database

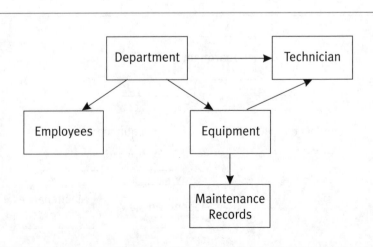

DEPT_NAME, and DEPT_MGR (see Figure 6.5). At least one field of the table should be a key field used for searching and retrieving records, with each record having a unique value. An example of a key field in a department record is the department number, DEPT_NO.

A Comparison of the Three Data Models

Advantages and disadvantages are associated with each of these three data models. Both the hierarchical and network models have predefined links, or pointers, that define *explicit* relationships. These links provide efficient processing in high-volume applications, so long as the search follows a path through the data that was specified in advance. However, although the network structure is somewhat more flexible than the hierarchical structure, both models tend to be limiting with respect to the searches that can be easily performed.

　　Although network data models appear to have achieved little popularity in healthcare management computer applications or among PC users, healthcare applications of hierarchical data models have been described. For

FIGURE 6.5
Relational Data Model: Equipment Maintenance Database

DEPTABLE:

DEPT_NO	DEPT_NAME	DEPT_MGR
12	Telecommunications	Hendrickson
15	Radiology	Jones
18	Nursing	Smith
19	Office equipment	Johnson
23	Admitting	O'Riley
⋮	⋮	⋮
37	Physical therapy	Krusher

EMPTABLE:

EMP_NO	EMP_NAME	DEPT_NO
3021	Lynn Francis	19
3034	Harry Kildare	23
3049	Michael Cruse	22
⋮	⋮	⋮
3812	Fran Simmons	18

EQTABLE:

EQUIP_NO	EQUIP_NAME	DEPT_NO
803	Pocket pager	12
844	Laptop computer	19
850	Cart	23
852	Portable x-ray	15
863	Personal digital assistant	19
⋮	⋮	⋮
879	Respirator	28

example, Partners HealthCare System in Boston reports finding that "the flexible hierarchical data structures of M technology remain the most efficient way to store and manipulate complex clinical data" (Flammini 2001, 33). For applications such as budget planning, data mining, or human resources they do indicate a preference for relational databases "because the data they need falls naturally into rows and columns. But simple tabular data is the exception for healthcare applications" (Flammini 2001, 34).

Mavroudis and Jacobs (2000) describe a project organized to standardize congenital heart surgery nomenclature and reporting strategies as the foundation for an international database. Participants in the project determined that a hierarchical database scheme would best meet their needs for several levels of reporting based on the data input. A tertiary care teaching hospital developed an in-house hierarchical database of drug costs. Using the database, the hospital was able to track and report drug costs according to patterns of clinical use (Chaffee et al. 2000).

Relational data models, the newest of the three database models, "are the dominant paradigm for new applications and have been used for most applications developed within the past decade" (Blaha 2001, 37). The strengths of the relational model lie in its ability to handle ad hoc queries, the ease with which it can be created and maintained, and its ability to easily interface with a variety of systems in the organization (Sherr 1995). A disadvantage of the relational data model is the relatively slower processing time compared to the other two models, a result of the relational model's greater flexibility and ad hoc query capability. Blaha (2001, 37) suggests that "in practice, slow performance is usually a result of poor implementation, rather than an intrinsic (relational database) problem."

A variety of applications using relational database models have been reported in the literature. A relational database serves as an electronic logbook in an Australian advanced surgical training program (Brouwer and Kiroff 2002). The database provides trainees with a convenient and versatile record of their experience while meeting Royal Australian College of Surgeons (RACS) requirements for documentation of surgical experience. Manley et al. (2001) describe the relational database structure used to manage clinical, pathology, and molecular data on more than 1,300 prostate cancer patients from a university cancer and geriatrics center. All of the databases were created in Microsoft® Access. Unique identifier fields joined the several database tables comprising the system.

Daumit et al. (2001) incorporated a literature-abstraction tool into a PC-based relational database to better synthesize evidence on preventive behavioral interventions. The database contained information abstracted from 100 studies reported in the literature on behavioral interventions for hypertension management.

Blaha (2001) provides a useful characterization of the kinds of applications for which relational database models are most appropriate to use:

- *Ordinary Business Applications:* applications where the data naturally conform to the notion of tables
- *Conservative Applications:* applications where the developer feels more comfortable using the mature relational database technology with proven administration, error handling, and security features
- *Decision-Support Applications:* applications that require a powerful query language

Query languages are discussed in the next section, and the role of relational databases in decision-support systems is discussed further in Chapter 10.

Database-Management Systems

The discussion thus far has focused on the advantages of databases over traditional files and an overview of three alternative database models. But conceptualizing about the data elements that will support the operations and management of a healthcare organization is not enough. Organizations must be able to actually build and maintain the database as well as to easily extract desired information from it. These tasks are accomplished with a *database-management system* (DBMS), the software used to manipulate the database. This section provides more detail about the specifics of this software. In particular, two languages and a special file are introduced: (1) the *data definition language* (DDL) used to define and describe the data in the database; (2) the *data manipulation language* (DML) used to access, edit, and extract information from the data contained in the database; and (3) the *data dictionary* used to store a detailed description of the data in the database.

The Data Definition Language

The computer views data stored on a secondary storage device as a given number of bytes located at a specific location on the disk. This perspective, known as the *physical view* of the database, may be appropriate for the computer, but it is anything but satisfactory for the user. The healthcare manager prefers a *logical* or *user* view of the data in which a data item is known by some "logical" name, typically one that suggests the quantity being stored. The DDL is used to create the link between the user view and the physical view of the database.

The user begins the process by defining his or her view, or *schema*, of the database. In those cases where multiple users will be accessing portions of the same database, each user's view will be known as a *subschema*. The schema can be stored as part of the database or in a separate file. Among the items included in the schema (or subschema) are a description of the file; a description of the record; and information about the data fields, including field name, type of quantity stored in the field (numeric, logical, text, etc.), and length of the field. In addition, the DDL is used to define relationships among the records, allow relationships among data to be defined, and establish data-security access.

The Data Manipulation Language

Because programming skills are typically required to extract information from a traditional file, managers have generally been unable to easily interact with this form of data storage. A major benefit of database technology is that interaction with the data does not require a high level of computer programming proficiency. This ease of interaction with data results from the inclusion with the DBMS of a *data manipulation language* (DML).

The DML allows users to perform a variety of operations, including adding new data; sorting, deleting, editing, or displaying data; and generating reports. Two basic methods for interacting with the database are available: (1) "embedded statements," which can be added to an application program to instruct the database to find certain data and return it to the program, or (2) the user can issue a command through a workstation in a special language to find a certain data item and return it to the screen. Use of the DML for direct interaction with the database gives rise to the notion of a *query language*.

To illustrate a direct query to a database, consider a user who wants to generate a list of the number and name of all pieces of equipment associated with department number 19 as well as the name of this department. The query might be handled in at least three ways.

Natural Language Queries

Perhaps the ultimate way for a user to query a database is in simple English words. For this approach, the sample query might be "Please give me the number, name and department name of all pieces of equipment that are associated with the department having the number 19." Notice that the use of a natural language query requires very little new vocabulary to be learned. The computer processes the request by looking for key words in the sentence. If a key word cannot be found, the user might be asked to rephrase the request.

Even better than typing natural language requests into the computer is the ability to make English language requests verbally. Such a system would combine natural language query with voice recognition technology, as discussed in Chapter 3, and would undoubtedly be well received by the community of database users. However, the technical limitations of natural languages query and voice recognition technology make the implementation of this ideal system impractical at this time.

Query-by-Example

A very common and easy to use query method is known as query-by-example (QBE). Many microcomputer database systems employ this method, in which the system "builds" the query based on selections made by the user from a list of tables and fields.

Figure 6.6 illustrates how the QBE function in Microsoft® Access can be used to print the number, name, and department name of all equipment in department 19. The checkmarks in the row labeled "Show" indicate the fields that will be printed, while the "19" in the row labeled "Criteria" indicates that only records having a department number of 19 are to be included

FIGURE 6.6

Illustration of
Use of Query-
by-Example

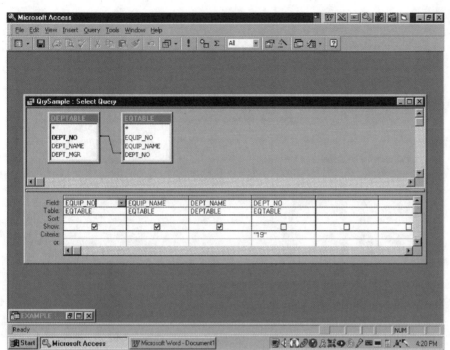

in the output. Fields have been selected from two tables—DEPTABLE and
EQTABLE—and the line connecting them indicates that the field DEPT_NO
has been used to establish a relationship between the two tables. More complex criteria involving logical "ANDs" and "ORs" can be programmed with
little difficulty. Running this query generates the output shown in Figure 6.7.

Structured query language (SQL) is a query language that combines elements
of both a DDL and a DML. It was developed in the 1970s and adopted as a
standard relational language in 1986. Because it is a standard, programmers
familiar with the language can use it on a number of hardware platforms from
microcomputers to mainframes. As with other DMLs, a user can invoke SQL
statements either interactively or from within an application program.

***Structured
Query
Language***

    Many of the language statements consist of verbs like "Create," "Up-
date" "Select," or "Delete," along with appropriate modifiers describing the
nature of the desired action to be taken. For example, to accomplish the sample inquiry (obtaining a list of the number, name, and department name of the
equipment in department 19), one might issue the following SQL command:

```
SELECT EQUIP_NO, EQUIP_NAME, DEPT_NAME
FROM EQTABLE, DEPTABLE
WHERE DEPTABLE.DEPT_NO=EQTABLE.DEPT_NO
AND DEPT_NO=19
```

FIGURE 6.7
Results of
Query

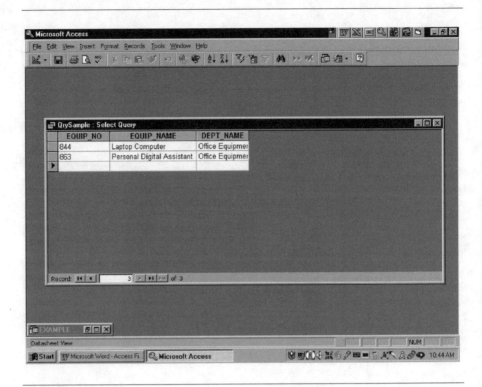

Remember that EQUIP_NO, EQUIP_NAME, DEPT_NO, and DEPT_NAME are the "logical" names for the number of the piece of equipment, the name of the piece of equipment, the department number, and the department name, respectively (refer to Figure 6.5).

A number of database applications described in the literature specifically indicate the use of SQL. Examples include the formulation of queries in radiology information systems (Tamm, Kawashima, and Silverman 2001); in an information system for a surgical practice (Oyama, Tannas, and Moulton 2002); and in an anesthesia information system (Benson et al. 2000).

The Data Dictionary

The data dictionary is a file that stores detailed information about the data elements used in a database, including:

- the name of the data element;
- the type of element (numeric, alphanumeric, logical, etc.);
- the amount of storage allocated to the data element;
- the person in the organization authorized to change the element;
- the date the element was last changed;
- the programs that use this element; and
- the reports that use this data element.

This information is quite useful to programmers developing applications that will use the associated database.

Data dictionaries can be *passive* or *active*. A passive data dictionary simply provides documentation about the data elements within the database in the form of a report. When changes are made to an active data dictionary, these changes can automatically be used by the applications that utilize the database.

Data Security

Healthcare information systems typically contain data that are highly critical and sensitive. Therefore, data security becomes a particularly important issue in this environment. The healthcare manager must ensure that at least three areas of data security have been addressed: privacy/confidentiality protection, virus protection, and data backup/recovery procedures. Each is briefly outlined below and discussed in more detail in Chapter 13.

Privacy/Confidentiality Protection

Patient-data privacy is a very important concern. At least two levels of confidentiality issues will need to be considered by healthcare organizations implementing database technology: (1) individual patient records used by healthcare providers and (2) aggregate databases used by planners and managers.

In the clinical setting, user access codes and password procedures must be established and enforced so that only users with a legitimate "need to know" can obtain specific patient information. For example, the financial portion of the database might be made available to billing personnel, demographic information to a registration clerk, and full clinical data to physicians for their own patients.

In addition to supporting clinical care, patient data serve as the basis for a variety of analyses such as outcomes research, resource planning, and managed care contracting. For the most part, these analyses are based on aggregate patient data so that the identity of individual patients is not really necessary. In these cases, masking all patient identifiers is important, including name, patient number, Social Security number, and any other field that would allow the researcher or analyst to identify the patient.

Virus Protection

Computer users and information system (IS) staff must also protect software from computer viruses, programs that intentionally try to alter or destroy data, programs, or operating system files on computer hard drives or floppy disks. A virus may be unintentionally passed from one computer to another by floppy disk or through a network. The healthcare IS manager must have security procedures to prevent viruses from infecting computers, including:

- not allowing the use of any bulletin board or other unauthorized software that has not first been checked out with an antivirus program;
- employing and enforcing effective security codes and passwords for users on networks; and

- purchasing, installing, and periodically running antivirus software programs on network servers and other computers.

Data Backup/Recovery Procedures

The healthcare manager should make sure that effective data backup and recovery procedures are implemented on a regular basis across the organization. At the central processing site, daily, weekly, and other periodic backups to removable disk packs or tape must be performed. Duplicated data should be secured and stored in a separate location away from the central site, preferably in a different building if possible.

Individual sites also need to have regular and effective backup procedures, especially for microcomputers and workstations. Disk or tape backup and software should be used to automate data backup and recovery. Also, data at individual sites that also reside on the main processor or at other individual sites must be correctly updated at all locations.

The IS manager must also be able to trace data transactions on distributed systems in case of data corruption, loss, or tampering. The IS manager can use these audit trails to recover data in a timely and effective manner. Transaction auditing procedures must be an integral part of the database management system design. IS and other authorized personnel must maintain accurate, up-to-date, secure transaction logs, both at the central IS site as well as at individual sites.

Developments in Database Technology

The information demands of the healthcare field often require database technologies beyond those discussed thus far. Three additional technologies offer potential advantages that the healthcare manager should understand: (1) *object-oriented databases* and (2) *hypermedia databases*, both of which are capable of storing multimedia data, and (3) *distributed databases*, which allow data to be stored in multiple physical locations.

Object-Oriented Databases

The relational databases described earlier contain text fields stored in rows and columns. Many of these databases have a feature known as binary large objects (BLOBs) that allows them to link to graphic images. However, such linkages are somewhat clumsy; cannot be "searched" to locate records having certain defined properties; and do not support other media, such as audio or video, which are gaining increasing importance in today's medical record. One approach to addressing these deficiencies is object technology.

Introduced in the late 1980s, object-oriented databases can be defined as "an information retrieval system that manages complex objects containing both data (referred to as properties) and procedures for manipulating this data (called methods)" (Dyck 1996). Thing (2002, 490) suggests that "there is currently no widely agreed-upon standard for what constitutes an OODBMS (object-oriented data-base management system), and OODBMS products are considered to be still in their infancy."

The healthcare manager should be aware that object-oriented databases offer both advantages and disadvantages (Blaha 2001, 40). On the positive side, these databases

- are purported to navigate data structures more quickly than relational databases;
- support "rich data types" (videos, images, or audio recordings); and
- cleanly integrate with at least one programming language.

On the other hand, disadvantages associated with these databases include

- the lack of a theoretical basis,
- a tendency for them to have weak security, and
- the fact that query optimizers associated with these databases are inferior to those for relational databases.

Applications of object-oriented database technology have been reported in the healthcare literature. An online genetic information resource has been implemented as an object-oriented database containing a combination of data and semi-structured text for publishing a given "disease profile" on the Internet (Tarczy-Hornoch et al. 2000). An academic medical center implemented a multi-tiered telemedicine system based on the programming language *Java* and an object-oriented database (Dionisio et al. 1999). The telemedicine system provided insight into this technology's effectiveness and suitability as the implementation basis for a healthcare infrastructure. Schacherer et al. (2001) describe an information system on gene-regulatory pathways. Elements of the relevant signal transduction pathways and their states are stored with information about their interaction in an object-oriented database.

Hypermedia Databases

To understand the concept of a hypermedia database, one needs first to be familiar with a *hypertext database*. A hypertext database consists of a network of *nodes*, each of which stores text. The user defines the *links* between the nodes. Users of the World Wide Web are familiar with this database structure. As readers scan a paragraph of text on a particular topic, they observe that certain words are highlighted in a different color from the rest of the text. By clicking the cursor on one of these highlighted words, users can cause the program to branch to another node where text on this new topic can be accessed.

In a *hypermedia database*, the *nodes* can store a variety of media—that is, text, graphics, motion pictures, audio, or programming code. As in the hypertext database, the nodes in the network are connected by *links* that can be defined by the user. In this way, a multimedia patient record can be constructed in which text fields can have audio or video fields linked to them. For example, a brief textual summary of the results of a cardiac catheterization procedure can be associated with a video of the actual procedure. By clicking on the text of the report, the user can "branch" to the video and see the actual catheterization displayed on the screen.

Chun et al. (2001) describe the design of a medical teleconferencing system that is integrated with a multimedia patient database. The system incorporates easy-to-use tools and functions that support collaborative work between physicians in remote locations. Physicians have real-time access to the database during the conference sessions.

Distributed Databases

The processing function within a computer network can be concentrated in a single computer, often a mainframe, or it can be split among all of the network workstations, typically microcomputers (see Chapter 5). The former approach represents a *centralized* computing environment, while the latter is known as *distributed processing*. In a similar fashion, an organization can choose to store its data in a single, centralized database or to spread the data across several smaller databases. This latter data-storage configuration is known as a *distributed database*.

Distributed systems allow extensive data storage and processing at multiple departments within the same building, in several buildings on a single campus, or on several campuses separated by significant distances. In a modest-sized, stand-alone healthcare facility, it is frequently possible to maintain a single database to support all of the organization's data needs. However, in today's large integrated healthcare systems, this single database concept becomes impractical for at least two reasons:

1. the use of distributed databases within each of the geographically dispersed entities comprising the system is more practical than the use of a single centralized database; and
2. the use of a single database to support both clinical operations as well as database searches results in unacceptable time delays for users of the information system.

Blaha (2001, 187) cites the following benefits associated with distributed databases:

- *Synergy:* Individual databases can be coordinated
- *Modular growth:* Database capacity can be incrementally increased
- *Fault tolerance:* Data remain available even if an individual database fails
- *Cheaper computing:* The configuration of computing resources is more flexible

Pogash et al. (2001) describe a distributed database-management system that was developed by the data-coordinating center of the Asthma Clinical Research Network. The system, consisting of modular applications for separate data processing activities, was used to enter, track, verify, validate, and edit collected data.

The use of distributed databases has disadvantages as well. As Blaha (2001, 187–188) indicates, the management of distributed databases is more complex, the communication network on which the distributed database is built can be prone to security breaches, and a potential for loss of data synchronization among the various databases exists. Therefore, provisions must be made to maintain the overall integrity of the organization's data, including specific details for sharing and controlling the data.

One final challenge resulting from the use of distributed databases bears mention. Although users in a particular entity can more easily interact with the databases located within their facility, gaining access to information distributed among databases in several entities of an integrated system can be difficult. This same difficulty presents itself to corporate executives wishing to do systemwide planning or to a physician wanting to gather information about a patient who has received treatment in several of the system's facilities. This challenge is being addressed through the development of data warehouses.

Data Warehouses

As noted, many occasions exist when managers and physicians have a need for an aggregate view of the data contained in the distributed databases of their system. Constructing such a view on an "as-needed" basis can be time consuming and inefficient. A better approach is to maintain this aggregate view in one or more databases called *data warehouses*. A data warehouse is "a central repository for all or significant parts of the data that an enterprise's various business systems collect" (Thing 2002, 170).

Clinicians use this aggregate view to obtain a profile of past data for a given patient. For example, a physician might want to compare a current blood pressure reading with those obtained over the past three years. Investigators can use the data warehouse to perform outcomes research, evaluate alternative treatment modalities, and focus on quality improvement (Goldstein 2000). Managers need aggregate patient and financial data to support a variety of planning, marketing, contracting and decision-making activities.

Clinical Data Repositories

The *clinical data repository (CDR)* is a data warehouse specific to healthcare organizations. Einbinder et al. (2001) describe a CDR implemented at the University of Virginia. It provides users with direct access to detailed, flexible, and rapid retrospective views of clinical, administrative, and financial patient data. The University's CDR draws data from four independent systems and includes:

- inpatient and outpatient visits,
- professional billing data,
- laboratory results, and
- cardiac surgery data.

Data are retrieved using a "Guided Query" function that automatically generates structured query language (SQL) statements.

Pates et al. (2001) describe the methodology and impact of merging detailed statewide mortality data into the master patient-index tables of the University's CDR. (Master Patient Index is discussed later in this chapter). The authors indicate they were able to update their CDR with 97 percent of the deaths from the state source and that this approach provides an efficient and inexpensive way to enrich hospital data with important outcomes information.

Data Marts

Although the term data mart is often used synonymously with the term data warehouse, an important distinction exists between the two concepts. Whereas the data warehouse is typically an enterprisewide repository, "the emphasis of a data mart is on meeting the specific demands of a particular group of knowledge users in terms of analysis, content, presentation, and ease of use. Users of a data mart can expect to have data presented in terms that are familiar" (Thing 2002, 169).

Isken, Littig, and West (2001) describe the evolution and architecture of a data mart developed by the management engineering department at William Beaumont Hospital. The data requirements of this department could not be met simply by accessing existing transaction systems. Rather, their data mart includes a number of complex, precalculated fields, data structures, and function libraries that are specific to the needs of operations analysts. Healthcare managers should understand the relationship between data marts and data warehouses. On the one hand, data marts can evolve from an organization's existing data warehouse. For example, Intermountain Health Care of Salt Lake City had a successful data warehouse in place (Warner 2001). A team of multidisciplinary participants from throughout the organization focused on developing data marts from data currently in the data warehouse. These data marts consolidate, integrate, and index data that support a single domain area with specific reporting requirements.

Conversely, individual data-mart projects in an organization can eventually evolve into the development of a data warehouse. In summarizing the development of the management engineering department's data mart described above, Isken, Littig, and West (2001, 144) suggest that "very useful and valuable data marts can be incrementally developed with widely available, low cost tools. A departmental data mart can provide a 'quick win' that spurs further data warehouse development efforts throughout the organization as awareness of the value of a well-designed data mart increases."

Data Warehouse Design Issues

Several issues associated with the design and implementation of data warehouses can affect the resources consumed by these efforts. These issues are discussed below.

Separate Transactional and "Research" Platforms

Because the goal of implementing a data warehouse is to make aggregate data from across the system available in a single location, a single database appears to be the most appropriate. However, the transactional needs of clinicians and operating personnel and the "research" needs of managers and investigators can often be a source of conflict. As a result, performance issues will often cause separate operational/transactional and query/reporting data platforms to be maintained. Sederholm (2002) describes the software product used by a health plan to "off-load queries and reports from the production server and maximize operational efficiency." This software tool helped ensure that the plan's data were available in real time for both operational as well as reporting purposes.

Master Patient Index

Because each of the entities within an integrated system frequently use a different patient-numbering system, linking data on a given patient uploaded from the various entity computer systems can be difficult. Because of spelling errors, omission of middle initials, or legal name changes, even the use of the "Name" field may not totally solve the problem. One possible solution is the use of a *master patient index* (MPI)—a relational database containing all of the identification numbers that have been assigned to a patient anywhere within the system. The MPI "assigns a global identification number as an umbrella to all patient numbers. Database queries go through the master patient index so that all appropriate data in the repository are retrieved" (Siwicki 1996, 58). The global identification number must be matched to all of the records associated with the given patient, a process made particularly difficult because the match must be made in real time.

Mays, Swetnich, and Gorken (2002) report on the efforts of a 12-facility, 3,000-bed enterprise in Southwest Florida to attack duplicate records with MPI software. Their initial plan was to have the medical records department produce reports to identify potential duplicates and then merge the records post discharge if the duplicate represented a risk to patient care. They revised this plan to focus on process: understand how duplicates were created, identify and eliminate them, and finally prevent creation of new duplicates at the source. They now report on creating about 140 duplicates a month (an improvement over their performance without the software), and they are in fact able to identify and eliminate these 140 duplicates before they "snowball."

Hall (2001, 50) suggests that "the focus of the master patient index (MPI) has shifted recently to the concept of an enterprise-wide master person index (EMPI)." Operated in passive mode, the EMPI interacts with admission, discharge, and transfer transactions to produce a database where all patients in the enterprise have a unique patient identifier. In active mode, the EMPI is connected with all systems, acting as "an enabler of other enterprise systems and (creating) a standardized way for collecting, transferring and reporting information."

Standardization of Terminology and Data Format

In addition to differences in a patient's name, variations can also be found in the format and terminology within the various computers of an integrated delivery system. As a result, one can experience difficulty in uploading data from these computers to a data warehouse as well as in using the data in the warehouse to draw comparisons among the entities of the healthcare system. One resolution of this dilemma is the development of standards to guide both the format and substance of the data. A number of such standards exist, two of which are described below.

1. *Health Level-7 (HL7)*. This is a set of standards designed to develop a cost-effective approach to system connectivity. The HL7 standard is supported by most system vendors and is used in the majority of large hospitals in the United States. Thus, each of the health system entities can implement the software of their choice and can transfer data from one system to another so long as the software is HL7-compliant. The HL7 standard is discussed further in Chapter 11.

2. *SNOMED*. Of course, even when the system entities adhere to the HL7 standard, the system still "must tackle the challenge of making sure all users use the same terms the same way. This is a particularly important issue for integrated delivery systems attempting to share clinical data among multiple sites" (Anderson and Bunschoten 1996, 41). This challenge is addressed by a standard vocabulary known as the *Systematized Nomenclature of Medical Reference Terminology*. The newest release, SNOMED CT, combines the efforts of an earlier version of SNOMED created by The College of American Pathologists (based in Northfield, Illinois) with the United Kingdom National Health Service's Clinical Terms Version 3 (healthdatamanagement.com 2002). "Cedars-Sinai Medical Center in Los Angeles is using SNOMED CT because it is the most clinician-friendly clinical terminology. . . . Clinicians (can) use real terms, such as 'chest pain' or 'fever without a source,' rather than diagnosis or procedure codes to code problems or diagnoses." Further information is available at www.snomed.org.

The success of the HL7 and SNOMED standards clearly requires the cooperation of the entities. In a health system with a large number of legacy computer systems and a heritage of "independent thinkers," enforcing a policy that requires adherence to these standards can be difficult. An alternative approach is to feed the output of the entity systems to a translator interface, which standardizes the content before passing the information to the data repository. The translator might even be capable of recognizing non-HL7-compliant data from the existing systems, and only future systems will be required to adhere to HL7 standards.

More details of the uses of data warehouses are given in Chapter 10, and computer-based patient records (CPRs) are discussed in Chapter 7.

Concluding Comments

Many healthcare organizations have been said to be drowning in data and starving for information. Healthcare managers must assume responsibility for ensuring that their organizations have in place the appropriate databases to provide the needed information. In carrying out this important function, the managers should bear several points in mind.

First, many users of the information, both inside as well as outside of the organization, will access the databases via the Internet. The networking concepts discussed in Chapter 5 are helpful when formulating plans for incorporating databases into the networking structure.

Second, the organization's ability to interface clinical and financial data continues to be important. The subject of clinical databases frequently receives a great deal of attention, and little attention is paid to the development of financial data repositories. The collection of financial data has always been an important role of computer systems in the healthcare setting, and many early installations were justified on the basis of their ability to significantly reduce the loss of charge slips. But the need persists for an accurate and detailed accounting of the resources consumed by a given patient and the associated costs of these resources.

Third, the pressure for improved quality and fewer errors that many healthcare organizations are feeling creates a need for more information about the organizations' processes. This includes data on time spent by patients in various phases of the delivery process, data on time spent by caregivers in various activities, data on patient severity on nursing units by shift, etc. "Reinventing the wheel" is too often necessary each time an improvement study is performed. The collection of these kinds of data has not been a routine activity of healthcare organizations and certainly merits the healthcare manager's encouragement.

Finally, steps should be taken to ensure that outcome data are also included in the organization's databases. Clearly, decision makers must know the type of care given, the value traditionally placed on that care, and the cost of that care. But they also need to associate an outcome, or "benefit," with the episode so that the healthcare system can demonstrate a cost benefit for the care offered by their delivery system.

Summary

As healthcare computer systems increase in complexity, the IS manager must choose new database-management systems (DBMSs) with care, taking into account patient-data security and privacy versus user access to data, distributed or centralized systems, and data accuracy and quality. These DBMSs offer a number of advantages over traditional file storage methods.

The three main database models are the hierarchical, network, and relational models. The model most used today is the relational, although the hierarchical model is also used for some applications. Network data models appear to have achieved little popularity in healthcare management computer applications.

DBMSs allow users to fully utilize the power of databases. These systems consist of (1) a data definition language (DDL), used to define and describe the data in the database; (2) a data manipulation language (DML), used to access, edit, and extract information from the data contained in the database; and (3) a data dictionary that stores a detailed description of the data in the database.

Use of the DML for direct interaction with the database gives rise to query languages, which allow the database user to easily and efficiently extract data records and fields. These queries can take the form of a natural language query, a query-by-example, or a structured language query. The database designer must decide how data will be used in designing a good DBMS.

Data security is an important issue and one that database designers and users must constantly address. At least three areas to be considered are privacy/confidentiality protection, virus protection, and data backup/recovery procedures. Only users with a genuine "need to know" should have access to individual patient data where the identity of the patient can be determined. In other cases, aggregate data with masked identifiers should be used. Passwords should be implemented that help to ensure that only authorized users can gain access to the system. Deliberate steps should be taken to reduce the potential impact of viruses on the database, particularly in light of the increased vulnerability created by greater use of the Internet and other external data sources. Backup and recovery procedures are an essential component of data security, including the use of audit trails.

Healthcare managers will find increasing use of object-oriented, hypermedia, and distributed technologies, and they are well advised to become familiar with how these approaches can benefit their database applications. In fact, distributed systems are now used at many healthcare units with multiple processing sites. The IS manager must take into account several factors in deciding to use distributed systems, including the type of data to be distributed, data security and quality, protection and privacy of patient data, and user security training procedures.

Although distributed systems are being increasingly used, managers and physicians in integrated delivery settings require aggregate views of data distributed throughout the system. As a result, healthcare organizations are building data warehouses to support clinical care, outcomes research, and managerial decision making. The success of these warehouses can be enhanced with use of a master patient index and the adoption of data standards such as HL7 and SNOMED.

Without question, healthcare management and delivery have been and continue to be a data-driven endeavor. The skill with which healthcare managers lead the process of developing and managing database technology within their enterprise will have a great influence on the ultimate quality of the healthcare services offered.

Discussion Questions

6.1 Name and explain three problems associated with traditional computer files.

6.2 Name and describe the three most widely used database models.

6.3 Define *schema,* and name the items typically included within a schema.

6.4 Explain the function of a data manipulation language.

6.5 Describe three ways of handling a direct query to a database.

6.6 What is a *data dictionary file?*

6.7 Explain how security issues dealing with accessing aggregate patient data differ from security issues associated with accessing individual patient records.

6.8 Give an advantage and a disadvantage offered by object-oriented databases.

6.9 Describe a hypermedia database.

6.10 Define the concepts of distributed databases and centralized databases, and indicate the strengths and weaknesses of each.

6.11 Explain the function of a master patient index.

6.12 Why is standardization of terminology so important in developing a data warehouse within integrated delivery systems?

6.13 What is the difference between a data warehouse and a data mart?

6.14 What is the advantage of maintaining separate transactional and reporting data platforms?

Problems

6.1 Set up a sample patient record with pertinent data fields using both relational and hierarchical database models.

6.2 Obtain a copy of the schema that is employed in an electronic medical record system. Prepare a brief presentation that outlines how the schema supports the query capability of this system.

6.3 Identify an integrated delivery system that has developed, or is developing, a data warehouse. Determine the data fields that comprise this database, the composition of the committee who decided on the structure of the database, and the mechanism by which the decision regarding the structure was made. In addition, determine who has access to the data and what specific security measures are in place. Write a brief report of your findings.

6.4 Interview a chief information officer in a nearby healthcare organization or system. Determine the role that data standards such as HL7 and SNOMED play in their selection and purchase of software. Summarize your findings in a memo.

6.5 Prepare an annotated bibliography of articles from the literature that describe the use of SQL in application software written for the healthcare field.

6.6 Identify an ambulatory care facility in your area. Arrange an interview with the executive director of this facility to determine the extent to which data are used by this executive director. Determine the database(s) maintained by the facility. Write a report describing your findings.

References

Anderson, H. J., and B. Bunschoten. 1996. "Creating Electronic Records: A Progress Report." *Health Data Management* 4 (9): 36–38, 41–42, 44.

Benson, M., A. Junger, A. Michel, G. Sciuk, L. Quinzio, K. Marquardt, and G. Hempelmann. 2000. "Comparison of Manual and Automated Documentation of Adverse Events with an Anesthesia Information Management System (AIMS)." *Studies in Health Technology and Informatics* 77: 925–29.

Blaha, M. R. 2001. *A Manager's Guide to Database Technology: Building and Purchasing Better Applications.* Upper Saddle River, NJ: Prentice Hall.

Brouwer, R., and G. Kiroff. 2002. "Computer-Based Logbook for Surgical Registrars." *ANZ Journal of Surgery* 72 (1): 57–61.

Chaffee, B. W., K. A. Townsend, T. Benner, and R. F. de Leon. 2000. "Pharmacy Database for Tracking Drug Costs and Utilization." *American Journal of Health-System Pharmacy* 57 (7): 669–76.

Chun, J., H. Kim, S. Lee, J. Choi, and H. Cho. 2001. "A DBMS-Based Medical Teleconferencing System." *Journal of the American Medical Informatics Association* 8 (5): 460–67.

Connolly, T. M., and C. E. Begg. 2002. *Database Systems: A Practical Approach to Design, Implementation, and Management,* 3rd Edition. Harlow, England; New York: Addison-Wesley.

Daumit, G., L. E. Boulware, N. R. Powe, C. S. Minkovitz, K. D. Frick, L. A. Anderson, G. R. Janes, and R. S. Lawrence. 2001. "A Computerized Tool for Evaluating the Effectiveness of Preventive Interventions." *Public Health Reports* 116 (Supplement 1): 244–53.

Dionisio, J. D., U. Sinha, B. Dai, D. B. Johnson, and R. K. Taira. 1999. "Initial Experiences with Building a Health Care Infrastructure Based on Java and Object-Oriented Database Technology." Proceedings/AMIA Annual Symposium, pp. 515–19.

Dyck, T. 1996. "Relational Model's Limits Fuel Move to Object Databases." [Online article on *PC Week*; retrieved 6/30/02]. http://www.pcweek.com/archive/1345/pcwk0078.html.

Einbinder, J. S., K. W. Scully, R. D. Pates, J. R. Schubart, and R. E. Reynolds. 2001. "Case Study: A Data Warehouse for an Academic Medical Center." *Journal of Healthcare Information Management* 15 (2): 165–75.

Flammini, S. 2001. "The Remedial Power of MUMPS." *Healthcare Informatics* 18 (8): 33, 34, 36.

Goldstein, R. 2000. "Data Warehousing Solution Focuses on Quality Improvement." *Health Management Technology* 21 (8): 46.

Hall, L. K. 2001. "Unlocking the Power of Your EMPI." *Health Management Technology* 22 (4): 50.

healthdatamanagement.com. 2002. "New Clinical Terminology Available from SNOMED." [Online article; retrieved 6/30/02]. http://www.healthdata management.com/html/NewProdStory.cfm?DID=7841.

Isken, M. W., S. J. Littig, and M. West. 2001. "A Data Mart for Operations Analysis." *Journal of Healthcare Information Management* 15 (2): 143–53.

Manley, S., N. R. Mucci, A. M. De Marzo, and M. A. Rubin. 2001. "Relational Database Structure to Manage High-Density Tissue Microarray Data and Images for Pathology Studies Focusing on Clinical Outcome: The Prostrate Specialized Program of Research Excellence Model." *American Journal of Pathology* 159 (3): 837–43.

Mavroudis, C., and J. P. Jacobs. 2000. "Congenital Heart Surgery Nomenclature and Database Project: Overview and Minimum Dataset." *Annals of Thoracic Surgery* 69 (4 Supplement): S2–17.

Mays, S., D. Swetnich, and L. Gorken. 2002. "Toward a Unique Patient Identifier: Florida IDN Attacks Duplicate Records with MPI Software, Consultation and a Shift in Organizational Philosophy." *Health Management Technology* 23 (3): 42–44.

Oyama, L., H. S. Tannas, and S. Moulton. 2002. "Desktop and Mobile Software Development for Surgical Practice." *Journal of Pediatric Surgery* 37 (3): 477–81.

Pates, R. D., K. W. Scully, J. S. Einbinder, R. L. Merkel, G. J. Stukenborg, T. A. Spraggins, C. Reynolds, R. Hyman, and B. P. Dembling. 2001. "Adding Value to Clinical Data by Linkage to a Public Death Registry." *Medinfo* 10 (Part 2): 1384–88.

Pogash, R. M., S. J. Boehmer, P. E. Forand, A. M. Dyer, S. J. Kunselman, and The Asthma Clinical Trials Network. 2001. "Data Management Procedures in the Asthma Clinical Research Network." *Controlled Clinical Trials* 22 (6 Supplement): 168S–80S.

Schacherer, F., C. Choi, U. Gotze, M. Krull, S. Pistor, and E. Wingender. 2001. "The TRANSPATH Signal Transduction Database: A Knowledge Base on Signal Transduction Networks." *Bioinformatics (Oxford)* 17 (11): 1053–57.

Sederholm, K. 2002. "Centralized Health Data: A Multiplatform Problem Is Solved." *Healthcare Informatics* 19 (3): 48.

Sherr, B. 1995. "Flexibility, Access Give RDBMS the Edge." *Health Management Technology* 16 (9): 38.

Siwicki, B. 1996. "Data Repository: Early Users Learn Valuable Lessons, Reap Benefits." *Health Data Management* 4 (10): 57, 58, 60, 61.

Tamm, E. P., A. Kawashima, and P. Silverman. 2001. "An Academic Radiology Information System (RIS): A Review of the Commercial RIS Systems, and How an Individualized Academic RIS Can Be Created and Utilized." *Journal of Digital Imaging* 14 (2, Supplement 1): 131–34.

Tarczy-Hornoch, P., P. Shannon, P. Baskin, M. Espeseth, and R. A. Pagon. 2000. "Gene Clinics: A Hybrid Text/Data Electronic Publishing Model Using XML Applied to Clinical Genetic Testing." *Journal of the American Medical Informatics Association* 7 (3): 267–76.

Thing, L. 2002. *The whatis?com: Encyclopedia of Technology Terms.* Indianapolis, IN: Que Publishing.

Warner, H., Jr. 2001. "Mining the Gems: Strategies to Help CIOs Effectively Use Clinical Databases While Avoiding the Data Warehouse Pit." *Health Management Technology* 22 (10): 3–32.

Additional Readings

Barry, D. K. 1996. *The Object Database Handbook: How to Select, Implement, and Use Object-Oriented Databases.* New York: John Wiley and Sons.

Briggs, B. 2001. "Easy Access Is Key with Data Repositories." *Health Data Management* 9 (8): 36–40.

Connolly, T. M., and C. E. Begg. 2000. *Database Solutions: A Step-by-Step Guide to Building Databases.* Harlow, England; Reading, MA: Addison-Wesley.

Date, C. J. 2002. *An Introduction to Database Systems,* 7th Edition. Reading, MA: Addison-Wesley.

Foster, N. L., E. Gombosi, C. Teboe, and R. J. Little. 2000. "Balanced Centralized and Distributed Database Design in a Clinical Research Environment." *Statistics in Medicine* 19 (11–12): 1531–44.

Gillespie, G. 2000. "There's Gold in Them Thar' Databases." *Health Data Management* 8 (11): 40–44, 46, 48–52.

Gu, H., Y. Perl, J. Geller, M. Halper, L. M. Liu, and J. J. Cimino. 2000. "Representing the UMLS as an Object-Oriented Database: Modeling Issues and Advantages." *Journal of the American Medical Informatics Association* 7 (1): 66–80.

Juzoji, H., I. Nakajima, M. Hata, K. Tanabe. 2001. "Design of an SHD-Distributed Database Over IP to Support Telemedicine." *Journal of Medical Systems* 25 (5): 285–95.

Keener, R. E. 2000. "Bridge the Patient-Provider Gap: Link to a More Complete Patient Record with EMPI." *Health Management Technology* 21 (11): 44, 46, 49.

Kelly, B. 2001. "Stacking the Shelves with Data." *Health Data Management* 9 (2): 122–24, 126.

Machtynger, J., and D. M. Shotton. 2002. "VANQUIS, A System for the Interactive Semantic Content Analysis and Spatio-Temporal Query by Content of Videos" [Letter; comment]. *Journal of Microscopy* 205 (Part 1): 43–52.

Mattison, R., and B. Kilger-Mattison. 1999. *Web Data Warehousing and Knowledge Management.* New York; London, England: McGraw-Hill.

O'Kane, K. C. 2001. "Migration of Legacy Mumps Applications to Relational Database Servers." *Methods of Information in Medicine* 40 (3): 225–28.

Oberson, J. C., R. Welz, and L. Bovisi. 2000. "Development of an Electronic Radiologist's Office in a Private Institute." *Radiographics* 20 (2): 573–80.

Rob, P., and C. Coronel. 2002. *Database Systems: Design, Implementation, and Management,* 5th Edition. Cambridge, MA: Course Technology.

Sakamoto, N. 1998. "A Practical Object-Oriented Approach to a Development of a Next Generation Hospital Information System." *Medinfo* 9 (Part 2): 957–61.

Shams, K., and M. Farishta. 2001. "Data Warehousing: Toward Knowledge Management." *Topics in Health Information Management* 21 (3): 24–32.

Sternberger, C., and L. Meyer. 2001. "Hypermedia-assisted Instruction: Authoring with Learning Guidelines." *Computers in Nursing* 19 (2): 69–74.

Applications

PATIENT CARE APPLICATIONS

Development of clinical information systems has become a top priority for healthcare organizations. Clinical systems provide direct support to the patient care process and establish data repositories that are essential for quality-improvement and cost-control programs.

Clinical information systems support diagnosis, treatment planning, and evaluation of medical outcomes across the continuum of care. They offer the potential for quality improvement and cost control by documenting that medically necessary procedures have been followed and that unnecessary tests and procedures have been avoided. In programs of evidence-based medicine, treatment patterns for individual patients are planned and compared against regimens for a large number of similar patients using information obtained from a clinical database. Risk is reduced through demonstration that medically necessary and historically mandated procedures have been followed.

Clinical systems also facilitate cost control. Clinical justification is required for tests and procedures that go beyond the patterns suggested by the clinical database. Generalized protocols are developed (nursing care, medical treatment, follow-up) that are both clinically effective and cost efficient.

Surveys of healthcare managers confirm the importance that is placed on development of clinical information systems. Respondents to the 2002 Annual Leadership Survey conducted by the Healthcare Information and Management Systems Society (HIMSS) gave high priority to implementing computer-based patient records and upgrading clinical system. Respondents to a survey of healthcare managers in November 2000 indicated that information technology "will lead to clinical improvements such as the use of best practices" and "will help reduce medical errors" (*Modern Healthcare* 2000). Marhula (2001, 90) states that healthcare organizations are allocating budget dollars toward clinical information systems: " . . . the fundamental kernel to improving healthcare in the United States is patient-specific clinical information. Vendors focused on clinical solutions are likely to be the primary beneficiaries of IT spending over the next year."

This chapter discusses specific patient care systems and their application across the continuum—that is, ambulatory care, acute care, critical care, home care, rehabilitation, and long-term care.

Computer-Based Patient Records

The medical record is central to all patient care activities, serving several important functions. The medical record is a guide to, and continuous record of, treatment for active patients. For patients not currently receiving treatment, it serves as an archival record. Medical records also are working documents for medical audit, utilization review, quality improvement, and cost control. In many healthcare organizations, particularly teaching hospitals, the depository of medical records serves as a database for research studies.

A 1991 report by the Institute of Medicine (IOM), provided major impetus to efforts aimed at the development of electronic medical records. The IOM's Committee on Improving the Patient Record called for "the prompt development and implementation of computer-based patient records (CPRs)" on a national basis to "improve the care of individual patients and populations and, concurrently, to reduce waste through continuous quality improvement" (Dick and Steen 1991, v). Key attributes of the CPR as defined by the IOM committee include the following:

- The CPR includes a problem list that clearly delineates the patient's clinical problems and current status of each.
- It encourages and supports the systematic measurement and recording of the patient's health status and functional levels.
- It documents the clinical rationale for all diagnoses or conclusions.
- It links to clinical records from various settings and time periods to provide a longitudinal record of events that have influenced a person's health.

The IOM report called for the development of CPRs by all healthcare organizations, from large medical centers to solo practice physician offices. National standards for content of the CPR are under development by a follow-on, nonprofit organization—the Computer-Based Patient Record Institute.

Although progress over the last ten years has been slow, many health-care organizations are moving forward with plans to develop and implement CPR systems. The status of these efforts can be summarized as follows:

- Many healthcare organizations have partially automated records that include items such as laboratory results, summaries of radiology procedures, current medications, and diagnostic and treatment summaries.
- Integrated delivery systems have developed master patient indexes that provide common patient identifiers for all patients in the system and that facilitate electronic exchange of information among all providers in the network.
- An increasing number of physician offices and group practices have installed practice management systems and ambulatory care records systems.
- A small number of organizations, often university medical centers, are working on the development of complete electronic medical record systems, including the storage and retrieval of medical images as well as digital information.

Despite these efforts, development of a computer-based patient record as envisioned in the 1991 IOM report has been an elusive goal. Drazen (2001) has been actively involved in CPR development; she now believes that "a CPR is neither necessary nor sufficient on its own as a tool for improving care" (p. 94). She argues that only information needed to improve the care process should be included in electronic records, with special focus on clinical decision support to reduce medical errors and development of disease registries that include the key data needed for disease-management programs. Waegemann (2001) agrees with this assessment, and states that the CPR should be replaced by a component electronic health record (EHR). The EHR will consist of many components, will focus on the enterprise rather than on the patient, and will be implemented in steps with components selected according to their return on investments.

Kaiser Permanente of Cleveland, Ohio, won a national award for its CPR system. However, Kaiser decided not to pursue a totally electronic record. Rather, it chose to scan paper images into the electronic record and code only the data elements needed to support disease-management and wellness programs (Drazen 2001).

The Patient Safety Institute, a nonprofit consortium of hospitals, medical groups, and consumer organizations, has raised funds for a system of medical-information sharing. The system will track information on prescriptions, allergies, immunizations, lab tests, and diagnoses. Access will be available by handheld devices and PC terminals. System designers believe that it will reduce medical errors while still protecting patient privacy (Reuters Medical News 2001a). Saint Alphonsus Regional Medical Center in Boise, Idaho, has developed an enterprisewide master person index (EMPI) that provides access to a database of patients across all units of the organization. Clinicians have access to medical records, inpatient histories, prescriptions, lab results and orders at their desktops (Hall 2001).

Small organizations are also pursuing electronic records. Piedmont Urology Associates is a two-physician practice in Gastonia, North Carolina. The practice implemented an electronic medical record system in 1999 that has improved documentation and lowered transcription costs and chart costs. Physicians enjoy remote access to these records from their homes (Mildon and Cohen 2001). Health Management Technology's 2002 Resource Guide lists 175 companies that provide products in this area.

Order Entry and Results Reporting

Clinical information systems, whether operated in a single healthcare organization (e.g., hospital, ambulatory care center, etc.) or across an integrated network of care, require software for efficient entry of orders for diagnostic tests and patient treatments and subsequent reporting of test results back to caregivers. Order-entry and results-reporting software systems are designed to meet this need. These systems provide computerized telecommunication of information throughout the various service areas of a healthcare organization. Physician orders are entered and transmitted to the appropriate clinical service units. Test results and treatment summaries are transmitted back for entry into patient charts, and records of charges for services provided are transmitted electronically to the appropriate business office for processing and entry into the accounting system.

When installing order-entry systems, healthcare organizations must decide whether physicians will enter their own orders directly at computer terminals or whether clerical personnel will make the entries by transcribing physician paper notes. User-friendly operation is an essential element in the selection of order-entry systems, particularly if physicians are to enter their own orders. Physicians and other caregivers will resist the use of systems that are time consuming and difficult to understand. Commitment to successful use of these systems must be obtained through well-planned orientation and training programs. Based on a comprehensive review of the literature, Sittig and Stead (1994, 108) conclude:

> Key ingredients for successful implementation [of physician order-entry systems] include: the system must be fast and easy to use, the user interface must behave consistently in all situations, the institution must have broad and committed involvement and direction by clinicians *prior to* implementation, the top leadership of the organization must be committed to the project, and a group of problem solvers and users must meet regularly to work out procedural issues.

The Leapfrog Group for Patient Safety, a voluntary organization of large purchasers of healthcare, lists computer physician order entry (CPOE) as one of the three most important elements of a hospital patient-safety program. The group's studies show that CPOE of prescriptions can reduce serious medication errors by up to 86 percent (Leapfrog Group 2002).

Wilson, Bulatao, and Rascati (2000) studied user satisfaction with computerized order entry at two military healthcare facilities. Satisfaction was correlated most strongly with the perceived efficiency of the system. Another study was conducted on the use of a direct physician order-entry system at 11 primary care internal medicine practices. Results indicated that physicians believed that the system improved their patient care. Physicians with experience using the system did not spend any more time writing orders than did physicians who used paper-based methods (Overhage et. al. 2001). Kuperman et al. (2001) studied the effects of computerized medication ordering on patient safety. They concluded that computerized physician order entry combined with clinical decision-support tools increased patient safety by decreasing the frequency of serious medication errors.

Clinical Services Applications

Given the complexity of the modern medical environment, many healthcare organizations and integrated delivery systems operate separate clinical service information systems, particularly in areas such as pharmacy, clinical laboratory, and radiology. Advances in microcomputer technology and the availability of an extensive array of packaged software have facilitated the development of these decentralized departmental systems. As discussed in Chapter 11, corporatewide or institutionwide planning is essential when individual departmental systems are being installed to ensure system integration and the ability to transmit data across organizational units both for medical and administrative purposes. This section presents an overview of some of the clinical service applications in common use in healthcare organizations.

Laboratory Automation and Laboratory Information Systems

Laboratory systems constitute one of the most common clinical computer applications in healthcare organizations. Clinical laboratory systems have two phases: automation of the test processes and processing of laboratory data. Automation of test processing involves linking laboratory instruments directly to a computer. Signals from the test instruments are first converted to digital form (if not already digitized) for computer processing. For example, chemical auto-analyzers generate analog signals in which slide wire potentiometers are attached to continuous strip chart recorders. The same signals that drive the chart recorders are captured and converted to digital form. The computer then carries out calculations that would be made by the lab technician in a manual system. Computer calculations include determination of peak values and computation of the concentration of the unknown patient sample. The final results are then stored in a patient laboratory data file, and test results are printed.

In a comprehensive review of laboratory automation, Markin and Whalen (2000) state that the design of automated testing systems has evolved from hardware-based to software-based approaches. Cost-containment pressures have forced changes in laboratory operations to reduce the average cost per test. Aultman Hospital in Canton, Ohio, recorded cost measurements before and after implementation of clinical laboratory automation. The unit costs of laboratory procedures were reduced, and payback from the automation project was projected to occur in 2.5 years.

Although laboratory automation is most advanced in the clinical chemistry area, information systems are used extensively in other laboratory operation such as blood banks, microbiology, and virology.

Laboratory information systems can be used independently of, or in conjunction with, laboratory automation systems. A laboratory information system includes

1. recording of test requisitions,
2. scheduling of specimen collection and test processing,
3. recording of the results of completed tests,
4. preparing test reports for immediate return to the nursing units or outpatient department,
5. periodically preparing summary reports of all tests run for a given patient,
6. preparing statistical reports for the laboratory, and
7. record keeping for quality control and administrative control of laboratory operations.

Workman, Lewis, and Hill (2000) describe the implementation of a laboratory information system in a multi-institutional integrated delivery system. Reported benefits include control of operating expenses and expansion of the hospital network through an outreach program.

Some hospital emergency departments face a special problem with laboratory test results that arrive after a patient has been discharged. In 2000, Children's Hospital of the Harvard Medical School installed a system of computerized alerts for use by emergency department physicians for patient follow-up when late arriving results are received (Greenes, Fleisher, and Kohane 2000). Asare and Caldwell (2000) describe a system for laboratories that perform clinical molecular diagnostic and cytogenetic testing. The system automates results reporting, quality assurance, and specimen tracking. Technologist productivity increased and gains were realized in quality improvement. The Mayo Clinic operates a CPR and electronic results-inquiry system. A review of five years experience with the system demonstrated a 68 percent reduction in telephone inquires for test results using the electronic inquiry capabilities. The system handles 56,000 results and 170,000 inquiries each day (Forsman 2000).

Collaboration between private laboratories and public health agencies is essential for disease prevention and surveillance. The State of Washington Clinical Laboratory Initiative has "increased interaction, collaboration, and communication between health practitioners, health plans, hospitals, laboratories, government agencies, and academicians" (Counts 2001).

Health Management Technology's 2002 Resource Guide lists 50 vendors that provide software products for laboratory automation and information processing.

Pharmacy Information Systems

The pharmacy is one of the most informationally complex departments in the healthcare organization. Good records must be maintained to carefully control the ordering, stocking, and distribution of drugs and to avoid medication errors to the maximum extent possible. Accurate records are also important for billing and revenue generation purposes.

The two basic approaches to the design of computer applications in the pharmacy include (1) the development of stand-alone pharmacy systems and (2) the integration of pharmacy activities with a larger institutional information system. Stand-alone pharmacy systems are available for control of dangerous drugs (particularly narcotics), drug ordering and inventory control, control of drug distribution to patients, storage and retrieval of drug information, the construction of patient drug profiles, the maintenance of the organization's formulary, and generation of charges for patient billing.

Pharmacy systems integrated into an enterprisewide information system will typically involve the entering of medication orders on computer terminals at nursing units and outpatient treatment centers. These orders are then communicated automatically to the pharmacy, where worksheets are generated, patient profiles are updated, and labels are prepared. Such systems often include automatic updating of the drug inventory and automatic generation of patient charges from the medication orders.

Computer systems are used to check prescriptions and monitor medications administered to patients. Current drug orders and prescriptions are checked against patient profiles to ensure proper dosage, monitor contraindications, and protect against drug allergies and sensitivities.

Medication errors constitute the largest percentage of medical errors discussed in the IOM's 2000 report, *To Err Is Human: Building a Safer Health System*. Findings of the report include:

* Physicians do not routinely screen for potential drug interactions
* Errors can occur in the dispensing of drugs by pharmacists
* Errors in the ordering and administration of medications are common in hospitals

The report calls for the use of computerized information and decision-support systems in reducing medication and other types of medical errors.

Barcia (2001) states that major differences exist in the quality of screening carried out by pharmacy information systems. The screening should include drug-drug interactions, drug-food interactions, dose range checking, screening for allergies, duplicate drug protection, geriatric and pediatric specific screens, IV compatibility checks, and others.

The Maine Medical Center reports that direct physician order entry combined with improved use of medical protocols in its medical information system has helped to reduce medication errors in the facility (Cox, D'Amato, and Tillotson 2001). In a comprehensive literature review of electronic prescribing in ambulatory care practice, Papshev and Peterson (2001) conclude: "Electronic prescribing can eliminate the time gap between point of care and point of service, reduce medication errors, improve quality of care, and increase patient satisfaction."

Liu et al. (2000) evaluated the use of prescription order-entry systems by physicians in 80 university hospitals in Japan. Seventy-eight percent of those surveyed were positive about the benefits of direct order entry. The greatest concern was that input procedures took too much time and reduced communication with the patient. Goldblum (2001) studied the use of hand-held devices for electronic prescribing. Results demonstrated that the system was user-friendly and successfully connected with a commonly used practice management system.

Barcoding of unit doses of pharmaceuticals facilitates automation in the pharmacy. However, only about 60 percent of drugs arrive barcoded from the manufacturers, and calls are being made for the Food and Drug Administration to exert pressure for expanded use of barcodes in the industry (Stammer 2001).

A wide array of pharmacy software products is available in the market. Health Management Technology's 2002 Resource Guide lists 53 vendors that provide products, including general pharmacy systems, archival, drug data services, inpatient, outpatient/retail, packaging/distribution, and pharmacy interface systems.

Medical Imaging and Radiology Information Systems

Radiology systems fall into two general categories. *Medical imaging systems* use computer technology for image processing and enhancement. *Radiology information systems* include recording test requisitions, scheduling procedures, recording and reporting test results, reporting charges to the business office, and preparing management reports for the department.

Image enhancement by computer has become an extremely important component of modern medical technology, particularly in the fields of radiology and nuclear medicine. Major diagnostic advancements have occurred as a result of the development of computerized image enhancement in computed tomography, gamma cameras, ultrasound scanners, digital subtraction angiography, and magnetic resonance imaging.

Computers are used extensively in the field of radiation treatment planning as well. Computerized treatment planning permits the preparation and evaluation of individual patient treatment plans utilizing complex mathematical models in conjunction with image enhancement of the treatment site. Given data about a patient and the location and size of a tumor, the computer determines the exact dosage to be applied at various treatment sites while minimizing the exposure to unaffected regions of the body.

Development of picture archiving and communications systems (PACS) is an active area in radiology systems planning and implementation. PACS involve online storage and rapid retrieval of images transmitted over communications networks to user workstations that can display both digital information and images. Benefits of PACS include faster turnaround of images and reports, elimination of lost films, reliable retrieval of archived films, and reduced storage space requirements.

PACS are often used in conjunction with teleradiology communications systems to bring images from remote facilities to a central site for reading and interpretation. Teleradiology also provides the ability for physicians to call up images at workstations in remote locations, including their own homes. Use of teleradiology and medical imaging systems in conjunction with emerging telemedicine programs are discussed later in this chapter.

Elmhurst Hospital, a 534-bed urban hospital in Queens, New York, replaced its existing radiology information system with an upgraded system in 1998. A hospitalwide PACS system was added in late 1999. The hospital was able to convert to filmless radiography (with the exception of mammography) in 60 days. The objectives of maintaining control over all films and improving the reporting process have been realized, with 99 percent of all examinations now formally reviewed and reported (Hayt et al. 2001).

Staff members at MD Anderson Cancer Center in Houston, Texas, reviewed radiology information systems available from vendors. They found that many older systems are designed for scheduling, billing, charge collection, and reporting only. Newer systems provide the capability for customized searches and reporting and included data collection for quality-assurance purposes (Tamm, Kawashima, and Silverman 2001).

Texas Children's Hospital in Houston was an early adopter of PACS technology. A long-range strategy was needed to ensure that electronic images would be available for viewing 23 years in the future. Concerns include the long-term stability of digital media, frequent changes in software systems for maintaining electronic files, and rapid development of new storage media coupled with obsolescence of existing media and hardware. The hospital is now working with a third-generation archive based on a helical tape library (Blado 2001).

Health Management Technology's 2002 Resource Guide lists 44 vendors that provide radiology information systems and 51 vendors that offer PACS products.

Other Service Department Systems

In addition to laboratory, pharmacy, and radiology systems as described above, software is available for most other clinical departments and service areas of healthcare organizations. Systems are available to support clinical care and departmental management in physical therapy, pulmonary, emergency room, operating rooms, labor and delivery, and critical care units to mention only a few. For references on systems such as these, consult the Additional Readings section at the end of this chapter.

Ambulatory Care Information Systems

Increasingly, healthcare is being delivered in outpatient and ambulatory care settings. The number of physicians in solo private practice is declining, consolidation of small practices into larger, multispecialty groups is increasing, and mergers of hospitals and clinics into integrated delivery systems has become commonplace. Increased emphasis is being placed on computer systems that support ambulatory care and assist physicians and dentists in their practices. The availability of powerful and inexpensive microcomputer and office practice software packages has brought this technology within the reach of small medical groups and solo practitioners.

For larger clinics and group practices, typical computer applications include but are not limited to

• patient scheduling and appointment systems,
• electronic medical records and medical management systems,
• patient and third-party billing,
• managed care contract management, and
• electronic communications with other providers in an integrated delivery system.

A typical practice management system for a solo or small group practice includes such functions as: (1) patient registration and scheduling; (2) billing and accounts receivable; (3) and limited medical records and document-maintenance capabilities, including transcription and word processing.

Office practice computers can be linked to local hospitals in addition to serving the management needs of the practice. Many hospitals or integrated delivery systems have developed computer linkages to physician offices to enable clinicians to preadmit patients, order tests, and inquire into patient files for lab results, nursing notes, and other current clinical information. Healthcare organizations use such linkages as incentives to attract physicians to use their facilities in a highly competitive environment.

Anderson (2000) conducted a literature review of some of the major ambulatory information systems studying costs, benefits, effect on quality of care, and physician acceptance: "The evidence suggests that computer-based information systems can increase access to clinical information, improve physician performance, enhance quality of care, and facilitate outcomes research."

Rogoski (2001a) states that most practice management systems can handle administrative and financial functions but have limited clinical capabilities. Some efforts are underway to design practice management systems with an electronic medical record component. He believes that a better solution is to select separate practice management and electronic records systems and integrate the two.

Lee (2000) studied the attitudes of ambulatory care staff and physicians toward the adoption of an electronic medical record system at the Medical University of South Carolina in Charleston. The attitudes of potential users were generally positive or neutral, with nonphysician professional staff members more enthusiastic than their physician counterparts.

Mead, Powell, and Sevilla (1996) describe the development of an automated outpatient scheduling system at the University of Rochester Medical Center in Rochester, New York. The in-house developed system handles scheduling of some 400,000 annual outpatient visits and is linked to the

Medical Center's patient registration and billing system, which contains over 1.6 million patient records. Benefits reported include increased efficiency, reduction in no-shows, and improved patient tracking.

Acharya (2000) reports on his experiences in installing a practice management system for a small practice in California. Substantial benefits were realized from electronic phone messaging, handling of prescriptions, reviewing of documents, and communicating with patients. The system is reported to have saved $45,000 per year in administrative costs.

An increasing number of practicing physicians are using Internet services. A survey of physicians in medium and large practice organizations revealed that 85 percent of the medical groups used one or more Internet-enabled services, including both business and clinical applications. Internet applications are discussed in more detail in Chapter 9.

Health Management Technology's 2002 Resource Guide lists 135 vendors that offer practice management systems.

Nursing Information Systems

Information systems have become an essential component of nursing practice in most healthcare organizations. Computer systems have been developed to assist in patient care planning, critical care monitoring, and nursing unit management.

Protocol-based nursing care systems are available to assist in the planning and administration of patient care. Uniform standards of nursing care are programmed and stored in the computer's memory. When the nurse enters a specific care initiator code into the system, the computer responds with specific nursing orders and lists of interventions to be considered

PeaceHealth, an integrated delivery system in the Northwest, provides regional health services in facilities located in Alaska, Washington, and Oregon. Nurses at PeaceHealth facilities use a comprehensive clinical and nursing information system to support patient care. The clinical system was implemented as a "cross-continuum patient record to make information available to all caregivers, regardless of location" (Rewick and Gaffey 2001, 25). Nurses can now view information in ways that are not possible with paper charts. Nursing modules include automated tools for patient assessments, charting tools including standardized charting and data entry by exception, medication administration tools, shift reporting, standards of care for disease management, and support for outcomes analysis and improvement.

Cottage Health System in Santa Barbara, California, is implementing an automated nursing documentation system that will replace 57 paper forms with three electronic forms—that is, patient history and intake, patient assessment, and progress notes (Hagland 2001a).

A before-and-after study was conducted of a nursing information system installed at a 100-bed urban hospital in West Tennessee. System implementation did not improve documentation within the first six months. However, after additional training and longer experience in use of the system, significant improvements were noted in nurse assessments, achievement of patient outcomes, and nursing interventions (Larrabee 2001).

Information systems are used to support nursing service management as well as clinical care. The University of Oslo, Norway, developed a decision-support system to assist nurse managers in financial management, resource allocation, activity planning, and quality control (Ruland 2001).

Point-of-care information processing has been a goal of many health-care organizations for several years. During the 1990s, a number of organizations experimented with the use of fixed computer terminals at patient bedsides. Mobile devices have replaced these fixed units in providing point-of-care information. Potential advantages for point-of-care nursing systems include the following.

1. *Reduction in nursing service costs.* Recording patient data at the bedside can improve nursing efficiency by cutting down travel time to the nursing station and decreasing the amount of time spent recording patient data.
2. *Improved quality of care.* Because nurses are able to record and retrieve data at the bedside, they can spend more time with the patient and less time at the nursing station.
3. *More timely access and improved recording of information.* The patient record is updated at the bedside, and nurses do not tie up the chart when documenting their care. Because information is entered immediately as it is received, the patient record is more accurate.
4. *Overall cost reduction.* Bedside patient information systems can result in fewer lost charges because information is entered immediately after completion of a patient care activity. Length of stay could be reduced because every patient service will be delivered faster and better. The point-of-care system permits more accurate logging of nursing activity, thereby producing better data on nursing staff productivity and costs related to patient diagnosis.

Schou (2001, 51) states that "the nursing shortage, along with increased scrutiny on reducing medical mistakes, has dramatically increased the rate at which hospitals are adopting mobile computing technology to enhance productivity and improve patient outcomes."

Mobile computer workstations and portable laptop computers are being used for point-of-care information processing. Duke University Medical Center in North Carolina uses mobile workstations in the emergency department, patient admitting department, and selected hospital nursing stations. The mobile units have worked extremely well in the emergency department, but receptivity of nurses at the nursing stations has been mixed, with younger nurses more likely to use them (Rogoski 2001b).

Young et al. (2001) compared the utility and efficiency of keyboard-based and pen-based portable devices used by nurses in six specialty areas of an acute care hospital. Nurses preferred pen-based devices for working with structured data, but keyboards were preferred for entering textual information.

Health Management Technology's 2002 Resource Guide lists 45 vendors that provide nursing information systems.

Clinical Decision-Support Systems

Clinical decision-support systems (CDSS) are computer-based information systems designed to assist physicians in diagnosis and treatment planning. CDSS fall into two categories: (1) passive systems that collect, organize, and communicate patient data to the physician, including data on the patient's medical history, physical examinations, and diagnostic tests performed, and (2) active decision-support systems that utilize medical data stored in the computer to suggest diagnoses and treatment protocols.

Passive systems use the computer to organize clinical data for interpretation and analysis by the physician. They make clinical information more readily available and useable but do not process the information for further analysis. The clinical information systems described earlier in this chapter (computer-based patient records, laboratory, pharmacy, radiology, and other clinical services applications) are examples of passive CDSS in that they capture clinical data and make them available to caregivers. These applications become more useful to clinicians for decision support when they are fully integrated and can provide complete medical information (both current data and historical information on the patient) through simple, user-friendly access from a computer workstation.

Active CDSS employ the computer to provide direct assistance to the physician in diagnosis and treatment planning. They combine patient-specific data with generalized medical knowledge to reach a conclusion or make a recommendation to the caregiver. Active clinical decision-support systems generally fall into three categories: expert systems, systems that employ probabilistic algorithms, and reminder/alert systems (Elson and Connelly 1995).

Expert systems contain three major components. A *general knowledge base* of medical information is obtained from a panel of experts in a given medical specialty. This knowledge base is matched against *patient-specific information* retrieved from the healthcare organization's clinical database. A *rule-based inference engine* generates conclusions for consideration by the physician. The system is dependent on the quality of the expert knowledge base and the "reasoning power" of the rules used by the inference engine.

Probabilistic algorithms use statistical information "on the prevalence of diseases in the domain of interest . . . as well as [information] on the specificity and sensitivity of symptoms and the findings associated with those diseases"

(Elson and Connelly 1995, 370–371). These systems differ from expert systems in that they employ statistical probabilities rather than knowledge collected from expert human beings.

Clinical reminders and alerts are incorporated into clinical computer applications to alert the caregiver to potential medical conditions or other problems that should be given attention. Examples include pharmacy systems that alert the physician to potentially negative interactions between two drugs prescribed for the same patient and systems that suggest that certain drugs or treatments should not be employed when specific laboratory results contraindicate their use.

Studies of Computerized Decision-Support Systems

Payne (2000) has prepared a comprehensive review of computerized decision-support systems. Computers can aid decision making by simplifying access to data needed to make decisions, providing reminders and prompts, assisting in order entry, assisting in diagnosis, and reviewing new clinical data to issue alerts when important patterns are recognized. Systems are more likely to be successful when they give patient-specific suggestions, save time, and are incorporated into the regular workflow of the organization. Payne (2000) describes two examples of successful systems. In the treatment of HIV-infected patients, Beth Israel Hospital in Boston demonstrated that clinicians who received patient-specific alerts and reminders instituted treatment far more rapidly than clinicians who did not. At LDS Hospital in Salt Lake City, a computer-assisted management program for antimicrobials has reduced excessive drug dosage and drug allergies. The system has resulted in shorter length of stay and lower hospital costs for patients treated with the program.

In a comprehensive literature review, Weiner and Piper (2000, 50) conclude: "Clinical computing tools are most successful when their role is to ensure that basic care is not overlooked while the physician focuses on more acute issues. Where the diagnosis is certain, decision-support tools can also assist the physician to choose an appropriate therapeutic course and to ensure that standards of care for the particular disease are being met."

Kaplan (2001) is skeptical about the effectiveness of clinical decision-support systems. He believes the systems have the potential to improve care, but that evidence of their effectiveness is equivocal. Riesenberg and Riesenberg (2001, 163) do not agree: "Diagnostic decision-support systems are ready for prime time. We used them in a general medical clinic and found that they could suggest new diagnostic possibilities, focus thinking about clinical problems, and serve as a tool for recertification preparation."

The intensive care unit provides fertile ground for employment of computerized protocols because of the large amount of information produced in a complex environment (Morris 2001; Hanson and Marshall 2001). Software systems are available to support critical care (Sakallaris, Jastremski, and Von Rueden 2000). Kaushal, Barker, and Bates (2001) reviewed the literature on the use of information technology to reduce medication errors in pediatric practice. They conclude that decision-support systems can reduce the number of errors and that the benefits may be greater with children rather than adults because of the need for weight-based dosing.

Clinical decision-support tools are becoming available through the Internet (Portela 2000). See Chapter 9 for more discussion of e-health applications. Health Management Technology's 2002 Resource Guide lists 103 vendors that provide clinical decision-support software products.

Evidence-Based Medicine and Disease-Management Systems

Evidence-based clinical practice guidelines were developed in the 1990s to assist clinicians and healthcare organizations. Woolf and George (2000) state that early enthusiasm for use of these guidelines has been tempered by an understanding of their limitations. Managed care organizations and health insurers have used such guidelines "with considerable success in reducing costs, lengths of stay, and utilization rates" (Woolf and George 2000, 761).

Disease-management information systems and software products are designed to assist healthcare organizations in providing quality care at the most reasonable cost possible. For the most part, they are disease specific and focus on high-volume, high-cost conditions such as asthma, diabetes, and congestive heart failure. Empire Blue Cross and Blue Shield, a large managed care organization in New York, has taken a different approach to disease management. Empire's Systematic Analysis Review and Assistance (SARA) program focuses on the patient and uses computer software to identify potential problems before they occur (Stocker 2000). The system examines claims information (lab, pharmacy, hospital admissions, etc.) to identify signs of potential risk for serious medical conditions. When such signs appear, the treating physician is notified. In 1999, SARA recommended medical intervention for more than 3,400 patients to help avert potentially serious consequences.

The National Committee for Quality Assurance has developed standards for accreditation and certification of disease-management programs. The standards cover a full range of disease-management functions and evaluate an organization's effectiveness in using disease-management tools (Reuters Medical News 2001b).

Health Management Technology's 2002 Resource Guide lists 79 vendors that provide disease-management software systems.

Computer-Assisted Medical Instrumentation

Computers have become an important component of many sophisticated pieces of medical equipment being utilized for instrument control, image enhancement, and processing of medical data in conjunction with a broad array of diagnostic and therapeutic protocols.

Computer systems have been interfaced directly with patient-monitoring devices in critical care units of the hospital. Patient-monitoring systems employ the computer for continuous surveillance of a patient's vital signs and periodic display of physiological data for use by trained monitoring personnel. The first step in the process is acquiring data from monitoring equipment attached to the patient and converting the data for computer processing and display. Data are then stored and made available for periodic display or display on demand. Computer programs enhance the measured data through structured analysis of clinical data in accordance with programmed decision rules. Trend data are also followed to monitor changes in patient vital signs over time. Patient-monitoring systems can operate at the individual patient bedside, at a central station designed to monitor a small number of intensive care beds, or at a remote location linked back to the critical care unit by telecommunication equipment. Many of these systems also have electronic linkages for transmission of clinical data to the centralized computer-based medical record.

Computerized monitoring is an essential tool used by anesthesiologists in the operating room. The department of anesthesiology at Mount Sinai School of Medicine in New York has developed computer algorithms that detect critical conditions during surgery: "The complexity of modern anesthesia procedures requires the development of decision-support systems functioning in a smart-alarm capacity" (Krol and Reich 2000, 141).

Computer systems have been designed for processing and interpretation of data from various diagnostic devices. Computerized signal processing is used in such areas as interpretation of electrocardiograms, analysis of electroencephalograms, and testing of pulmonary function. In addition to the devices mentioned above, virtually every piece of modern medical equipment used for diagnostic testing and treatment now contains a microprocessor that helps control, enhance, and interpret the results of the testing or treatment process.

Other Clinical Applications

Telemedicine and Teleradiology

Telemedicine is the application of computer and communications technologies to support healthcare provided to patients at remote locations. Telemedicine often involves online communication between a family practice physician, nurse practitioner, or physician's assistant treating patients in a rural area and specialty physicians located at a distant medical center. Audio communications and video conferencing equipment are used in conjunction with computer access to patient records online. The systems often employ *teleradiology* for transmission of medical images for review by specialty physicians.

The University of Arizona Medical Center in Tucson operates an extensive telemedicine program serving rural areas of the state. As of June 2001, 96 physicians representing 60 medical subspecialities had seen more than 11,000 patient cases. The system has been used to provide primary diagnoses, expert consultation, and second opinions. Using the system at a rural location is estimated to save over $400, compared with the cost at an urban health center (Weinstein and McNeill 2001).

The University of California Davis Medical Center is engaged in a demonstration project that serves patients with congestive heart failure. Patients use a portable telemedicine unit in their homes connected by telephone lines to a terminal at the medical center some ten miles away. A nurse at the center listens to heart and lungs, monitors blood pressure and pulse, and checks for ankle swelling. Each home unit costs about $5,000, which is less than the average cost of one hospital admission that could be avoided by use of the system (Sandberg 2000). Telemedicine is being used at the National Science Foundation research facility at the South Pole, where physician consultations are obtained from a medical center in Colorado via telemedicine (Tabor 2001).

Although telemedicine applications have increased in recent years, there are still issues related to reimbursement for remote services, state licensure of health professionals when the system crosses state borders, patient-privacy protection, and government regulation (Curtin and Simpson 1999).

Mair and Whitten (2000) conducted a literature review of studies of patient satisfaction with telemedicine. Thirty-two studies were reviewed, and all reported good levels of patient satisfaction. Hersh et al. (2001) reviewed 25 studies to evaluate health outcomes of telemedicine in home-based and office/hospital-based settings. The authors state that "the strongest evidence for the efficacy of telemedicine in clinical outcomes comes from home-based telemedicine in the areas of chronic disease management, hypertension, and AIDS. . . . There is also reasonable evidence that telemedicine is comparable to face-to-face care in emergency medicine and is beneficial in surgical and neonatal intensive care units as well as patient transfer in neurosurgery" (Hersh et al. 2001, 1). The British National Health Service studied the use of telemedicine in treating dermatology patients. One hundred and two patients receiving traditional outpatient consultations were compared to 102 patients with teledermatology consultations. No major differences were found in clinical outcomes (Wootton et al. 2000).

Health Management Technology's 2002 Resource Guide lists 65 vendors that provide telemedicine systems.

Long-Term Care Information Systems

The long-term care industry has been slower to implement computer systems than have other components of the healthcare delivery system. Software vendors have been slow to develop products tailored to the needs of nursing homes and continuing care communities. This situation is changing as more and more care is being delivered in subacute and post-acute care facilities. "Providers who were once steadfast in their refusal to participate in the computer revolution are now eager converts, implementing innovative information and clinical technologies to operate more efficiently and improve quality of care" (Weiss 1999, 37).

Park Vista at Morningside in Fullerton, California, is a continuing care community with a nursing home, assisted living facility, and a senior apartment complex. Long-term care residents need to be checked routinely for health status indicators to help prevent common problems such as infections and skin problems. One of the problems faced was reducing the time between data collection and charting. Park Vista uses wireless technology with specialized personal digital assistants (PDAs) that transmit data so that charts can be updated electronically within minutes after residents are checked (Hagland 2001b).

Otterbein Homes in Lebanon, Ohio, operates six continuing care retirement communities with care ranging from independent living to skilled nursing and dementia. The organization determined that it needed an integrated clinical and financial information system to identify costs and link them with episodes of care (Marietti 1999). Leatham (1996) describes the development of an integrated long-term care information system in a 157-bed skilled nursing facility operated by the Group Health Cooperative of Puget Sound. Systems requirements include census management, resident care documentation and assessment, documentation of physician orders, menu planning in the dietary department, and pharmacy applications.

As more long-term care facilities become components of larger integrated delivery systems, electronic sharing of clinical and administrative information with hospitals, clinics, ambulatory care facilities, and other system components will be essential.

Home Health Care Information Systems

Home health services have expanded rapidly in recent years as an alternative to more costly institutional care. Information systems have been developed to support home care.

Many home health agencies are using laptop computers and other remote access devices for on-site documentation of patient care. Home health nurses and other caregivers enter information directly at the treatment sites. These systems reduce the amount of administrative work needed to document care, allowing visiting nurses and home health aides to spend more time with patients.

Telemedicine systems are also used to support home health care. Chae et al. (2001) conducted a pilot study of telemedicine in home health services for the elderly. A computer-based patient record was developed to allow caregivers to view patient summaries and document home encounters. The system was shown to be effective in reducing the number of clinic visits required and in achieving patient satisfaction.

Health Management Technology's 2002 Resource Guide lists 50 vendors that provide home health software systems.

Computer Applications in Medical Research and Education

Information systems and medical databases are used extensively to support biomedical education and research. Computerized patient records serve as the basis for epidemiological studies of a variety of diseases and their potential linkages to social and environmental factors. In addition, computers are used to support medical, dental, nursing, and allied health education using such techniques as computer-aided instruction (CAI) and patient-management simulation.

Computers are an integral component of most medical research projects. Effective project design requires close collaboration among clinicians, biostatisticians, and information systems specialists. Some research projects would not be possible without the high-speed computational capabilities and data storage capacity of large computer systems. A prime example is the Human Genome Research Project, which "would provide a new understanding of the genetic contributions to human diseases and help in the development of rational strategies to minimize or prevent diseases in the future" (Panchal and Brandt 2001, 155).

Hospitals, medical libraries, and many individual clinicians utilize microcomputers to access references to the medical literature. The most widely used system is MEDLINE, developed at the National Library of Medicine. Articles from thousands of biomedical journals are indexed, stored in computer files, and available for searching and retrieval using standard medical subject headings and key word searches. The Internet is used extensively to retrieve clinical information from a wide variety of specialty databases. (See Chapter 9 for more detail on Internet applications.)

Computers are an important tool for the education of clinicians. Computer-based medical education is designed to involve the student actively in the learning process. Projects range from presentation of information to students at computer terminals to sophisticated simulations of clinical problems. Microcomputer-based simulation programs are used to teach clinical problem solving. Students are presented initial cues and additional information on request as they proceed through a diagnostic process. Final diagnosis, patient management, and follow-up plans selected by the students are entered, and the system responds with a comparison to the "ideal" solution and critiques the process followed.

Summary

Clinical information systems support diagnosis, treatment planning, and evaluation of medical outcomes across the continuum of care. The number of clinical systems installed has increased as governing boards and healthcare managers recognize their importance for continuous improvement of patient-care quality, cost control, and reduction of medical errors.

Medical records are central to all patient care activities. However, the development of a completely electronic medical record remains an elusive goal. A 1991 report by the Institute of Medicine recommended the development of a national system of computer-based patient records (CPR). Many healthcare organizations are moving forward with plans to develop and implement CPR systems.

Order-entry/results-reporting systems provide computerized telecommunication of information throughout the various service areas of a healthcare organization. User-friendly design of these systems is essential because physicians and other clinicians will resist using them if they are difficult and time consuming.

Clinical services applications support the various clinical service departments of a healthcare organization or integrated delivery system. Common clinical services applications include laboratory information systems, pharmacy systems, and radiology information systems. Picture archiving and communications systems (PACS) provide online storage and retrieval of medical images transmitted to user workstations. Information systems also support clinical care and departmental management in areas such as physical therapy, pulmonary medicine, emergency room, operating rooms, labor and delivery, and critical care.

As more and more care is delivered in clinics and outpatient settings, development of ambulatory care information systems has accelerated. Typical functions include (1) patient scheduling and appointments, (2) electronic medical records and medical management, (3) patient and third-party billing, (4) managed care contract management, and (5) electronic communication with other providers in a network of care.

Nursing information systems support patient-care planning, critical care monitoring, and nursing unit management. Use of point-of-care terminal devices for data entry and retrieval has become common. Well-planned bedside systems have been shown to improve patient-care quality and efficiency.

Clinical decision-support systems (CDSS) are computer-based systems designed to assist physicians in diagnosis and treatment planning. Two types of CDSS exist. Passive CDSS systems organize clinical data for interpretation and analysis by the physician. Active CDSS combine patient-specific information with generalized medical knowledge to reach a conclusion or make a recommendation to the caregiver. The categories of active CDSS are expert systems, systems that employ probabilistic algorithms, and reminder/alert systems.

Evidence-based medicine programs compare treatment plans for individual patients with regimens for a large number of similar patients using information from a clinical database. Disease-management software has been developed to guide clinical care at the most reasonable cost possible. For the most part, these systems focus on specific high-volume, high-cost conditions such as asthma, diabetes, and congestive heart failure.

Computers have become an integral component of many pieces of medical equipment. They are used for instrument control, image enhancement, and medical data processing. Patient-monitoring systems employ the computer for continuous surveillance of a patient's vital signs and display of physiological data for use by trained monitoring personnel.

Telemedicine is the application of computer and communications technology to support patient care at remote locations. Primary care practitioners and patients in rural areas are linked to specialty physicians at distant medical centers through audio communications, video conferencing, and online computer access. These systems often employ teleradiology for transmission of medical images.

As more care is delivered outside of the hospital, information systems have been developed to support long-term care and home health services. Long-term care systems support census management, residential care documentation, pharmacy, and other areas of operation in skilled nursing facilities. Home health nurses often use laptop computers or other remote-access devices to document care at the location where it is provided.

Information systems are used extensively to support biomedical education and research. Automated databases of patient records support epidemiological studies of disease linkage to social and environmental factors. Computer-assisted instruction and patient-management simulation programs support the education of physicians, dentists, nurses, and other allied health personnel. National databases of bibliographic information and other clinical knowledge can be accessed for searching and retrieval through personal computers located in hospitals, medical center libraries, and individual physician offices.

Discussion Questions

7.1 Why has implementation of clinical information systems become a high priority for many healthcare organizations?

7.2 In your opinion, when will the fully electronic medical record be a reality? What are some of the problems that must be overcome for this milestone to be reached?

7.3 Why is involvement of physicians important to successful implementation of clinical information systems? What are some ways to achieve this involvement?

7.4 What are clinical decision-support systems (CDSS)? What is the difference between a passive and an active CDSS? Discuss some specific applications.

7.5 What kinds of information systems have been developed in the clinical laboratory? Describe typical applications.

7.6 Define evidence-based medicine. What role do information systems play in the implementation of evidence-based medicine programs?

7.7 How are computers being used to support disease-management programs in healthcare organizations?

7.8 Discuss the application of computers in a hospital pharmacy.

7.9 Give examples of information systems being used in (1) ambulatory care, (2) long-term care, and (3) home health care.

7.10 Discuss the application of computers and information systems to biomedical education and research.

7.11 What is telemedicine? How is it being used? What are some of the barriers to more extensive application of telemedicine?

Problems

7.1 Interview the chief information officer and medical director of a hospital or medical center in your area. Determine plans (if any) for development of a computer-based patient record system for this organization. Write a report of your findings.

7.2 Conduct an Internet search and develop information about five software vendors that offer products in the following areas:
- Laboratory information systems
- Order-entry systems
- Pharmacy systems
- Radiology information systems
- Ambulatory care information systems
- Home health care information systems
- Disease-management systems

In your report, include the name and address of each vendor; the number of years in business; the size of the vendor's business (e.g., total revenue, number of employees, etc); and a profile of the software product offered.

References

Acharya, S. 2000. "Practice Makes Perfect." *Health Management Technology* 21 (8).

Anderson, J. G. 2000. "Computer-based Ambulatory Information Systems: Recent Developments." *Journal of Ambulatory Care Management* 23 (2): 53–63.

Asare, A. L., and C. W. Caldwell. 2000. "An Information System for Improving Clinical Laboratory Outcomes." Proceedings from AMIA Symposium, pp. 22–26.

Barcia, S. M. 2001. "Reducing Medication Errors." *Health Management Technology* 22 (1): 26.

Blado, M. E. 2001. "Management of the Picture Archiving and Communications System Archive at Texas Children's Hospital." *Journal of Digital Imaging* 14 (2, Supplement 1): 84–88.

Chae, Y. M. et al. 2001. "Patient Satisfaction with Telemedicine in Home Health Services for the Elderly." *International Journal of Medical Informatics* 61 (2–3): 167–73.

Counts, J. M. 2001. "Washington Clinical Laboratory Initiative: A Vision for Collaboration and Strategic Planning for an Integrated Laboratory System." *Clinical Leadership Management Review* 15 (2): 97–100.

Cox, P. M., S. D'Amato, and D. J. Tillotson. 2001. "Reducing Medication Errors." *American Journal of Medical Quality* 16 (3): 81–86.

Curtin, L., and R. Simpson. 1999. "Telemedicine Tangles with Red Tape." *Health Management Technology* 20 (10): 48–49.

Dick, R. S., and E. B. Steen (eds.). 1991. *The Computer-based Patient Record*. Washington, DC: National Academy Press.

Drazen, E. 2001. "Is This the Year of the Computer-based Patient Record?" *Healthcare Informatics* 18 (2): 94, 96, 98.

Elson, R. B., and D. P. Connelly. 1995. "Computerized Decision Support Systems in Primary Care." *Primary Care* 22 (2): 365–84.

Forsman, R. 2000. "The Electronic Medical Record: Implications for the Laboratory." *Clinical Leadership Management Review* 14 (6): 292–95.

Goldblum, M. D. 2001. "Electronic Prescribing: Criteria for Evaluating Handheld Prescribing Systems and an Evaluation of a New, Handheld, Wireless Wide Area Network (WWAN) Prescribing System." *Dermatology Online Journal* 7 (1).

Greenes, D. S., G. R. Fleisher, and I. Kohane. 2000. "Potential Impact of a Computerized System to Report Late-Arriving Laboratory Results in the Emergency Department." *Pediatric Emergency Care* 16 (5): 313–15.

Hagland, M. 2001a. "Nursing IS on the Leading Edge." *Healthcare Informatics* 18 (2): 24–25.

———. 2001b. "Automation Improves Nursing Home Care." *Healthcare Informatics* 18 (7): 16–17.

Hall, L. K. 2001. "Unlocking the Power of your EMPI." *Health Management Technology* 22 (4): 50.

Hanson, C.W., and B. E. Marshall. 2001. "Artificial Intelligence Applications in the Intensive Care Unit." *Critical Care Medicine* 29 (2): 427–35.

Hayt, D. B. et al. 2001. "Filmless in 60 Days: The Impact of Picture Archiving and Communications Systems within a Large Urban Hospital." *Journal of Digital Imaging* 14 (2): 62–71.

Health Management Technology. 2002. Resource Guide. [Online resource]. www.healthmgttech.com.

Healthcare Information and Management Systems Society. 2002. *Thirteenth Annual Leadership Survey*. Chicago: HIMSS.

Hersh, W. R. et al. 2001. "Clinical Outcomes Resulting from Telemedicine Interventions: A Systematic Review." *BMC Medical Informatics and Decision Making* 1 (November): 5.

Institute of Medicine. 2000. *To Err Is Human: Building a Safer Health System*. Washington, DC: National Academy Press.

Kaplan, B. 2001. "Evaluating Informatics Applications: Clinical Decision Support Literature Review." *International Journal of Medical Informatics* 64 (1): 15–37.

Kaushal, R., K. N. Barker, and D. W. Bates. 2001. "How Can Information Technology Improve Patient Safety and Reduce Medication Errors in Children's Health Care?" *Archives of Pediatric Adolescent Medicine* 155 (9): 1002–7.

Krol, M., and D. L. Reich. 2000. "Development of a Decision Support System to Assist Anesthesiologists in Operating Room." *Journal of Medical Systems* 24 (3): 141–46.

Kuperman, G. J. et al. 2001. "Patient Safety and Computerized Medication Ordering at Brigham and Women's Hospital." *Joint Committee Journal of Quality Improvement* 27 (10): 509–21.

Larrabee, J. H. 2001. "Evaluation of Documentation Before and After Implementation of a Nursing Information System in an Acute Care Hospital." *Computers in Nursing* 19 (2): 56–65.

Leapfrog Group. 2002. [Online information; retrieved 6/30/02]. www.leapfrog group.org/consumer_intro2.htm.

Leatham, P. 1996. "Information Systems for Long Term Care." *HIMSS News* 7 (10): 10–13.

Lee, F. W. 2000. "Adoption of Electronic Medical Records as a Technology Innovation for Ambulatory Care at the Medical University of South Carolina." *Topics in Health Information Management* 21 (1): 1–20.

Liu, Z. et al. 2000. "Evaluations of the Prescription Order Entry System for Outpatient Clinics by Physicians in the 80 University Hospitals in Japan." *Medical Informatics Internet Medicine* 25 (2): 123–32.

Mair, F., and P. Whitten. 2000. "Systematic Review of Studies of Patient Satisfaction with Telemedicine." *BMJ* 320: 1517–20.

Marhula, D. C. 2001. "Clinically Oriented Solutions in Healthcare." *Healthcare Informatics* 18 (2): 90–92.

Marietti, C. 1999. "In for the Long Term." *Healthcare Informatics* 16 (4): 97–99, 102, 104–6.

Markin, R. S., and S. A. Whalen. 2000. "Laboratory Automation: Trajectory, Technology, and Tactics." *Clinical Chemistry* 46 (5): 764–71.

Mead, A., D. J. Powell, and C. Sevilla. 1996. "Automated Outpatient Scheduling: A Step Toward the Integrated Delivery System." *Journal of the Healthcare Information and Management Systems Society* 10 (3): 11–21.

Mildon, J., and T. Cohen. 2001. "Drivers in the Electronic Medical Records Market." *Health Management Technology* 22 (5): 14–16, 18.

Modern Healthcare. 2000. "Technology in Healthcare." [Online survey; retrieved 6/30/02]. www.modernhealthcare.com.

Morris, A. H. 2001. "Rational Use of Computerized Protocols in the Intensive Care Unit." *Critical Care* 5 (5): 249–54.

Overhage, J. M. et al. 2001. "Controlled Trial of Direct Physician Order Entry: Effects on Physicians' Time Utilization in Ambulatory Primary Care Internal Medicine Practices." *Journal of the American Medical Informatics Association* 8 (4): 361–71.

Panchal, J., and E. N. Brandt. 2001. "The Human Genome Research Project: Implications for the Healthcare Industry." *Journal of the Oklahoma Medical Association* 94 (5): 155–59.

Papshev, D., and A. M. Peterson. 2001. "Electronic Prescribing in Ambulatory Practice: Promises, Pitfalls, and Potential Solutions." *American Journal Of Managed Care* 7 (7): 725–36.

Payne, T. H. 2000. "Computer Decision Support Systems." *Chest* 118: 472–52S.

Portela, A. 2000. "Clinical Decision Support via the Internet." *Health Management Technology* 21 (2): 43.

Reuters Medical News. 2001a. "Non-Profit Consortium at Work on Electronic Patient Information System." *Reuters Health* (December 11).

———. 2001b. "NCQA Releases Standards for Disease Management Programs." *Reuters Health* (December 18).

Rewick, D., and E. Gaffey. 2001. "Nursing System Makes a Difference." *Health Management Technology* 22 (8): 24–26.

Riesenberg, L. A., and D. Riesenberg. 2001. "Diagnostic Decision Support Systems." *Journal of Medical Practice Management* 17 (3): 163–65.

Rogoski, R. R. 2001a. "Integration Crossroads." *Health Management Technology* 22 (10):14–16, 20.

———. 2001b. "Mobile Computing." *Health Management Technology* 22 (1): 44–46.

Ruland, C. M. 2001. "Developing a Decision Support System to Meet Nurse Managers' Information Needs for Effective Resource Management." *Computers in Nursing* 19 (5): 187–93.

Sakallaris, B. R., C. A. Jastremski, and K. T. Von Rueden. 2000. "Clinical Decision Support Systems for Outcomes Measurement and Management." *AACN Clinical Issues* 11 (3): 351–62.

Sandberg, L. 2000. "Managing Congestive Heart Failure with Telemedicine." *Health Management Technology* 21 (7).

Schou, J. 2001. "Information Where It's Needed." *Health Management Technology* 22 (10): 48, 51.

Sittig, D. F., and W. W. Stead. 1994. "Computer-based Physician Order Entry the State of the Art." *Journal of the American Medical Informatics Association* 1 (2): 108–23.

Stammer, L. 2001. "The Slow Road to Barcoding." *Healthcare Informatics* 18 (3): 48.

Stocker, M. A. 2000. "A Blue's Approach to Disease Management." *Health Management Technology* 21 (4): 32, 37.

Tabar, P. 2001. "On Call at the South Pole." *Healthcare Informatics* 18 (7): 14.

Tamm, E. P., A. Kawashima, and P. Silverman. 2001. "An Academic Radiology Information System (RIS): A Review of the Commercial RIS Systems, and How an Individualized Academic RIS Can Be Created and Utilized." *Journal of Digital Imaging* 14 (2, Supplement 1): 131–34.

Waegemann, C. P. 2001. "An Electronic Health Record for the Real World." *Healthcare Informatics* 18 (5): 55–58, 60.

Weiner, M. G., and M. D. Piper. 2000. "Computerized Decision Support and the Quality of Care." *Managed Care* 9 (5): 41–42, 44–46, 48–51.

Weinstein, R. S., and K. M. McNeill. 2001. "Powering the Arizona Telemedicine Program." *Health Management Technology* 22 (6): 46–47.

Weiss, G. 1999. "Senior Living Technology." *Contemporary Longterm Care* 22 (10): 37–37, 41, 45 passim.

Wilson, J. P., P. T. Bulatao, and K. L. Rascati. 2000. "Satisfaction with a Computerized Order-entry System at Two Military Health Care Facilities." *American Journal of Health System Pharmacy* 57 (23): 2188–95.

Woolf, S. H., and J. N. George. 2000. "Evidence-based Medicine: Interpreting Studies and Setting Policy." *Hematology Oncology Clinics of North America* 14 (4): 761–84.

Wootton, S. E. et al. 2000. "Multicentre Randomized Control Trial Comparing Real Time Teledermatology with Conventional Outpatient Dermatological Care: Societal Cost-benefit Analysis." *BMJ* (May): 1252–56.

Workman, R. D., M. J. Lewis, and B. T. Hill. 2000. "Enhancing the Financial Performance of a Health System Laboratory Network Using an Information System." *American Journal of Clinical Pathology* 114 (1): 9–15.

Young, P. M. et al. 2001. "An Evaluation of the Use of Hand-held Computers for Bedside Nursing Care." *International Journal of Medical Informatics* 62 (2–3): 189–93.

Additional Readings

Adhami, T., and J. E. Richter. 2001. "Twenty-four Hour pH Monitoring in the Assessment of Esophageal Function." *Seminar in Thoracic Cardiovascular Surgery* 13 (3): 241–54.

Alexander, S. R. 2001. "Radiology Goes Filmless." *Healthcare Informatics* 18 (4): 65–68, 70.

Arnaert, A., and L. Delesie. 2001. "Telenursing for the Elderly. The Case for Care Via Video-telephony." *Journal of Telemedicine and Telecare* 7 (6): 311–16.

Ash, J. S. et al. 2000. "Multiple Perspectives on Physician Order Entry." Proceedings from AMIA Symposium, pp. 27–31.

Bagshaw, B. A., and K. M. Neill. 2000. "Nurse Practitioners and the Internet." *Clinical Excellence in Nursing Practice* 4 (4): 245–49.

Bailey, T. C., and S. Troy McMullen. 2001. "Using Information Systems Technology to Improve Antibiotic Prescribing." *Critical Care Medicine* 29 (4 Supplement): N87–91.

Becich, M. J. 2000. "The Role of the Pathologist as Tissue Refiner and Data Miner: The Impact of Functional Genomics on the Modern Pathology Laboratory and the Critical Roles of Pathology Informatics and Bioinformatics." *Molecular Diagnosis* 5 (4): 287–99.

Benson, M. et al. 2000. "Comparison of Manual and Automated Documentation of Adverse Events with an Anesthesia Information Management System (AIMS)." *Studies of Health Technology Information* 77: 925–29.

Benson, M., A. Junger, L. Quinzio, C. Fuchs, A. Michel, G. Sciuk, K. Marquardt, J. Dudeck, and G. Hempelmann. 2001. "Influence of the Method of Data Collection on the Documentation of Blood-pressure Readings with an Anesthesia Information Management System (AIMS)." *Methods of Information in Medicine* 40 (3): 190–94.

Blignaut, P. J., T. McDonald, and C. J. Tolmie. 2001. "Predicting the Learning and Consulation Time in a Computerized Primary Healthcare Clinic." *Computers in Nursing* 19 (3): 130–36.

Burrillo, J. M., F. B. Diez, and S. Perez-Hoyos. 2001. "Use of Different Hospital Data Bases in the Estimation of the Relation Between Air Pollution and Chronic Obstructive Pulmonary Disease." *Epidemiology* 12 (2): 280.

Bussmann, J. B. et al. 2001. "Measuring Daily Behavior Using Ambulatory Accelerometry: The Activity Monitor." *Behavioral Research Methods And Instrument Computing* 33 (3): 349–56.

Carter, J. 2000. "What Works: Timing Is Everything in the OR." *Health Management Technology* 21 (4): 80–81.

Chamorro, T. 2001. "Computer-based Patient Record Systems." *Seminar in Oncology Nursing* 17 (1): 24–33.

Coye, M. J., G. Jacks, W. E. Everett, and L. Akay. 2001. "Medical Group Adoption of Internet Services." *Journal of Ambulatory Care Management* 24 (4): 67–75.

Dayhoff, J. E., and J. M. DeLeo. 2001. "Artificial Neural Networks: Opening the Black Box." *Cancer* 91(8 Supplement): 161–65.

Delaney, C. 2001. "Health Informatics and Oncology Nursing." *Seminar in Oncology Nursing* 17 (1): 2–6.

Dexter, F., A. Macario, and R. D. Trash. 2000. "Statistical Method Using Operating Room Information System Data to Determine Anesthetist Weekend Call Requirements." *AANA Journal* 68 (1): 21–26.

Espinosa, A. 2000. "Implementing an ICU-CIS Integrated to a HIS in Latin America." *Studies in Health Technology Information* 77: 916–20.

Farbstein, K., and J. Clough. 2001. "Improving Medication Safety Across a Multihospital System." *Joint Committee on Quality Improvement* 27 (3): 123–37.

Fontaine, B. R., S. Speedie, D. Abelson, and C. Wold. 2000. "A Work-sampling Tool to Measure the Effect of Electronic Medical Record Implementation on Health Care Workers." *Journal of Ambulatory Care Management* 23 (1): 71–85.

Frank-Stromberg, M., A. Christensen, and D. Elmhurst. 2001. "Nurse Documentation: Not Done or Worse, Done the Wrong Way—Part I." *Oncology Nursing Forum* 28 (4): 697–702.

Freburger, J. K. 2000. "An Analysis of the Relationship Between the Utilization of Physical Therapy Services and Outcomes of Care for Patients After Total Hip Arthroplasty." *Physical Therapy* 80 (5): 448–58.

Gandsas, A. et al. 2001. "Wireless Vital Sign Telemetry to Hand Held Computers." *Studies in Health Technology Information* 81: 153–57.

Gaynor, J. W., N. D. Bridges, and T. L. Spray. 2000. "Congenital Heart Surgery Nomenclature and Database Project: End-stage Lung Disease." *Annals of Thoracic Surgery* 69 (4 Supplement): S308–18.

Gaytos, B. 2001. "Developing Policies and Procedures for a Picture Archiving and Communications System." *Journal of Digital Imaging* 14 (2, Supplement 1): 44–47.

Gutierrez, G. 2001. "Medicare, the Internet, and the Future of Telemedicine." *Critical Care Medicine* 29 (8 Supplement): N144–50.

Hanson, C. W., and B. E. Marshall. 2001. "Artificial Intelligence Applications in the Intensive Care Unit." *Critical Care Medicine* 29 (2): 427–35.

Hardin, W. D. 2000. "Clinical Information Systems." *Seminar in Pediatric Surgery* 9 (1): 35–39.

Henricks, W. H. 2000. "Information System Issues Facing Clinical Laboratories Serving Complex Integrated Delivery Systems." *Journal of Healthcare Information Management* 14 (3): 55–67.

Hilz, L. M. 2000. "The Information Nurse Specialist as Change Agent: Applications of Innovation-Diffusion Theory." *Computers in Nursing* 18 (6): 272–78.

Hirschorn, D. S., C. R. Hinrichs, D. M. Gor, K. Shah, and G. Visvikis. 2001. "Impact of a Diagnostic Workstation on Workflow in the Emergency Department at a Level I Trauma Center." *Journal of Digital Imaging* 14 (2, Supplement 1): 199–201.

Hooper, G. S., P. Yellowlees, T. H. Marwick, P. J. Currie, and B. P. Bidstrup. 2001. "Telehealth and the Diagnosis and Management of Cardiac Disease." *Journal of Telemedicine and Telecare* 7 (5): 249–56.

Huber, J. T., and D. W. Huggins. 2000. "Assessing Electronic Information Access and Use in Long-term Care Facilities in North Texas." *Bulletin of the Medical Library Association* 88 (2): 187–89.

Humbertson, S. K. 2001. "Management of a Point-of-care Program: Organization, Quality Assurance, and Data Management." *Clinical Laboratory Medicine* 21 (2): 255–68.

Inumpudi, A., M. Srinivas, and D. K. Gupta. 2001. "Telemedicine in Pediatric Surgery." *Pediatric Surgery International* 17 (5–6): 436–41.

Johnston, R. C. 2000. "Implementation of a Computer-based Patient Record and an Outcomes Data-collection System at the Department of Orthopaedic Surgery, University of Iowa." *Journal of Bone and Joint Surgery* (October): 82-A.

Kerr, P. 2000. "Comparing Two Nursing Outcomes Reporting Initiatives." *Outcomes Management in Nursing Practice* 4 (3): 144–49.

Kornhoven, I., M. van Gils, and J. Gade, J. 2001. "The Challenges in Creating Critical-care Databases." *IEEE Engineering in Medicine and Biology* 20 (3): 58–62.

Lapinsky, S. E., J. Weshler, S. Mehta, M. Varkul, D. Hallett, and T. E. Stewart. 2001. "Handheld Computers in Critical Care." *Critical Care* 5 (4): 227–31.

Lovis, C. et al. 2001. "Evaluation of a Command-line Paper-based Order Entry Pathway for the Department of Veteran Affairs Electronic Patient Record." *Journal of the American Medical Informatics Association* 8 (5): 486–98.

Marietti, C. 2001. "Lab's Labor Lost." *Healthcare Informatics* 18 (10): 25–26, 28, 30.

McClatchey, S. 2001."Disease Management as a Performance Improvement Strategy." *Topics in Health Information Management* 22 (2): 15–23.

Memel, D. S., J. P. Scott, D. R. McMillan, S. M. Easton, S. M. Donelson, G. Campbell, M. Sheehan, and T. N. Ewing. 2001. "Development and Implementation of an Information Management and Information Technology Strategy for Improving Healthcare Services: A Case Study." *Journal of Healthcare Information Management* 15 (3): 261–85.

Mitchell, E., and F. Sullivan. 2001. "A Descriptive Feast but an Evaluative Famine: Systematic Review of Published Articles on Primary Care Computing during 1980–97." *BMJ* 322 (7281): 279–82.

Morris, A. H. 1999. "Computerized Protocols and Bedside Decision Support." *Critical Care Clinics* 15 (3): 523–45.

Murff, H. J., and J. Kannry. 2001. "Physician Satisfaction with Two Order Entry Systems." *Journal of the American Medical Informatics Association* 8 (5): 499–509.

Noffsinger, R., and S. Chin. 2000. "Improving the Delivery of Care and Reducing Healthcare Costs with the Digitization of Information." *Journal of Healthcare Information Management* 14 (2): 23–30.

Patel, V. L. et al. 2000. "Impact of a Computer-based Patient Record System on Data Collection, Knowledge Organization, and Reasoning." *Journal of the American Medical Informatics Association* 7 (6): 569–85.

Parker, J. L., and P. A. Abbot. 2000. "The New Millennium Brings Nursing Informatics into the OR." *AORN Journal* 72 (6): 1011–17.

Pifer, E. A., S. Smith, and G. W. Keever. 2001. "EMR to the Rescue: An Ambulatory Care Pilot Project Shows that Data Sharing Equals Cost Shaving." *Healthcare Informatics* 18 (2): 111–14.

Prince, T. R. 2000. "Information Technology and Medical Group Management." *Journal of Ambulatory Care Management* 23 (4): 22–30.

Quigley, A. 2000. "Beyond the Double Doors. New Generation Surgical Information Systems." *MD Computing* 17 (5): 29–32.

Reed, G., and E. M. Smith. 2001. "Planning for a Multi-imaging Center Picture Archiving and Communications System." *Journal of Digital Imaging* 14 (2, Supplement 1): 9–11.

Reschneck-Sannes, D. 2000. "Digitial Doctoring." *Healthcare Informatics* 17 (2): 97–98.

Rogers, M. A., D. Small, D. A. Buchan, C. A. Butch, C. M. Stewart, B. E. Krenzer, and H. L. Husovsky. 2001. "Home Monitoring Service Improves Mean Arterial Pressure in Patients with Essential Hypertension. A Randomized Controlled Trial." *Annals of Internal Medicine* 134 (11): 1024–32.

Rogoski, R. R. 2001. "LIS Shake-out." *Health Management Technology* 22 (6): 14–16.

Roine, R., A. Ohinmaa, and D. Hailey. 2001. "Assessing Telemedicine: A Systematic Review of the Literature." *CMAJ* 165 (6): 765–71.

Roughan, J., and E. B. White. 2000. "Making Disease Management Patient- Centric." *Health Management Technology* 21 (6): 46–48.

Ruland, C. M. 2000. "Clinicians' Use of a Palm-top Based System to Elicit Patient Preferences at the Bedside: A Feasible Technique to Improve Patient Outcomes." Proceedings from AMIA Symposium, pp. 739–43.

Selznick, S. H. et al. 2001. "Development and Application of Computer Software for Cell Culture Laboratory Management." *In Vitro Cell Developmental Biology in Animals* 37 (1): 55–61.

Sims, A. J., D. A. Pay, and B. G. Watson. 2000. "An Architecture for the Automatic Acquisition of Vital Signs by Clinical Information Systems." *IEEE Transaction in Information Technology for Biomedicine* 4 (1): 74–75.

Smith, R. S. 2001. "Telemedicine and Trauma Care." *Southern Medical Journal* 94 (8): 825–29.

Staggers, N., C. B. Thompson, and R. Snyder-Halpern. 2001. "History and Trends in Clinical Information Systems in the United States." *Journal of Nursing Scholarship* 33 (1): 75–81.

Stammer, L. 2001. "Dispense Account." *Healthcare Informatics* 18 (3): 45–48, 50.

———. 2001. "Wireless: As Technology Improves, New Applications Take Off." *Healthcare Informatics* 18 (2): 50, 52.

Stamouli, M. A., and J. Mantas. 2001. "Development and Evaluation of a Nursing Service Management and Administration Information System at District Hospital." *Medinfo* 10 (Part 1): 759–63.

Tang, P. C., and C. Y. Young. 2000. "Active Guidelines: Integrating Web-based Guidelines with Computer-based Patient Records." Proceedings from AMIA Symposium, pp. 843–47.

Teich, J. M., P. R. Merchia, J. L. Schmiz, G. J. Kuperman, C. D. Spurr, and D. W. Bates. 2000. "Effects of Computerized Physician Order Entry on Prescribing Practices." *Archives of Internal Medicine* 160 (18): 2741–47.

Tellis, W. M., and K. P. Andriole. 2001. "Finding the Optimal Picture Archiving and Communication System (PACS) Architecture: A Comparison of Three PACS Designs." *Journal of Digital Imaging* 14 (2 Supplement): 72–76.

Travers, D. A., and S. M. Downs. 2000. "Comparing User Acceptance of a Computer System in Two Pediatric Offices: A Qualitative Study." Proceedings from AMIA Symposium, pp. 853–57.

Warren, J. R., J. T. Noone, B. J. Smith, R. Ruffin, P. Frith, B. J. van der Zwaag, G. V. Beliakov, H. K. Frankel, and H. J. McElroy. 2001. "Automated Attention Flags in Chronic Disease Care Planning." *Medical Journal of Australia* 175 (6): 308–12.

Weinstein, A. M. 2001. "The Bandwagon Is Outside Waiting." *Health Management Technology* 22 (5): 50–52.

Whited, J. D. 2001. "Teledermatology: Current Status and Future Directions." *American Journal of Clinics in Dermatology* 2 (2): 59–64.

Winsten, D., J. McMahan, G. Gross, and J. Petrocelly. 2001. "Making it Work: Planning and Executing a Successful LIS Installation." *Clinical Leadership Management Review* 15 (3): 147–52.

MANAGEMENT AND ENTERPRISE SYSTEMS

Most healthcare organizations first entered the automated information-processing field through the development of computer systems that support administrative operations. This chapter discusses applications that support management of administrative functions in the organization. Managed care applications and enterprise systems that facilitate information sharing among components of large organizations and integrated delivery systems are also discussed in this chapter. The application of computers and organized information systems for decision support and strategic management is discussed in Chapter 10.

With the advent in the 1980s of prospective payment systems for Medicare reimbursement followed in the 1990s by expansion of managed care, the need for highly sophisticated administrative and financial information systems has become paramount.

For many years, the healthcare industry lagged behind other businesses in developing effective administrative information systems. Problems have included undercapitalization of the system-development process and management failure to effectively oversee system implementation. The situation has changed substantially in recent years. With heightened competition, increased regulation, and new payment mechanisms affecting the industry, healthcare managers rely heavily on their computer systems to provide information essential to effective competition and survival.

Management/Administrative Applications

In this section, administrative applications are discussed. These applications are categorized as follows:

1. Financial information systems
2. Human resources information systems
3. Resource utilization and scheduling systems
4. Materials management systems
5. Facilities and project management systems
6. Office automation

Financial Information Systems

With increased competition and more governmental regulation, healthcare organizations must have timely and accurate financial information to monitor and guide operational performance. In the face of demands for accountability and cost containment (while still providing high-quality services), managers are acutely aware of the importance of sound financial management in guiding operational performance. Financial information systems support operational activities such as general accounting, patient accounting, payroll, contract management, and investment management. Financial systems also provide information to management for controlling and evaluating organizational performance. Analysis of current and historical information helps in projecting future financial needs of the organization.

Financial information systems require input from transaction-processing systems, external sources, and strategic organizational plans (see Figure 8.1). Transaction-processing systems record the organization's routine activities, collecting information from other administrative subsystems, including payroll, accounts payable, accounts receivable, general ledger, and inventory control. These transactions are the basis for many financial reports required by management. To support effective financial decisions, financial systems also need external information such as government statistics, inflation rates, and information about the marketplace. An organization's strategic plan should contain financial goals and objectives that help provide the framework for preparation of financial reports.

A fully integrated financial information system brings related information together for planning, monitoring, and control. Individual financial subsystems include the following:

• Payroll preparation and accounting, linked to a human resource
  information system

FIGURE 8.1
Financial
Information
System

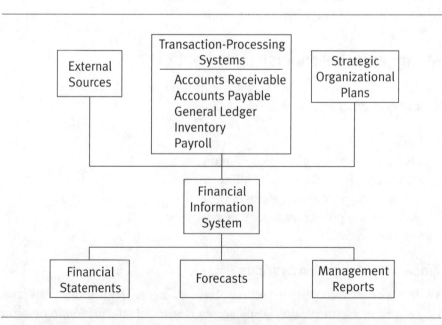

- Processing of accounts payable, linked to purchasing and inventory control systems
- Patient accounting, patient and third-party billing, and accounts receivable processing
- Cost accounting and cost allocation of non-revenue-generating activities and general overhead expense
- General ledger accounting
- Budgeting and budget control
- Internal auditing
- Financial forecasting
- Investment monitoring and analysis
- Financial statement preparation
- Financial reporting for operating supervisors, executive management, board members, external regulators, and third-party financing agencies

The development of a financial information system depends on the existence of a good accounting system. Sophisticated cost accounting is essential in today's environment. An effective cost accounting system enables the financial information system to generate accurate information on resources used to deliver services. In a managed care environment, both providers and managed care organizations need cost information to help negotiate rates and monitor contract performance. Integrated financial reporting based on a solid cost accounting system provides information for product costing, analysis of labor productivity, inventory control, and examination of the productivity of capital.

Increasingly, payment for healthcare is based on either a fixed payment per case (such as Diagnosis Related Groups) or on a fixed payment per person per month (capitation payment systems). For effective management in this environment, a financial information system must have the capability to convert or link cost and net revenue information among multiple units of payment.

Little Company of Mary Health Services (LCM), based in California, operates a network of 12 facilities, including hospitals, clinics, and skilled nursing facilities. The organization faced a problem in the handling of patient accounting and billing for over 80,000 annual registrations across the network. Multiple accounting applications from different vendors were being used. LCM developed a data repository of patient accounting claims information and linked it to an electronic data interchange system accessible to accounting personnel throughout their network. "Easily extractable information helps billers resolve questions more quickly, and promotes faster customer service response to questions about a patient's bill. That reduces the 'hold' time on bills and speeds payment" (Reed 2000).

Steele, Eisert, and Gabow (2001) report on the benefits obtained when Denver Health in Colorado upgraded its financial management information system. Cash collections increased by an average of 14 percent for the first three years of operation of the new system. Dassenko (1997, 36) describes the implementation of an integrated financial application that became necessary when the University of Wisconsin Hospitals and Clinics were separated legally from the State of Wisconsin and the University. A commercial software package was installed that includes human resources, payroll, general ledger, accounts payable, purchasing, materials management, and fixed asset accounting. The system is reported to have reduced paperwork and improved information available to department managers.

A variety of financial software packages are available. Health Management Technology's 2002 Resource Guide lists 103 vendors that offer products in this area.

Human Resources Information Systems

Employees of a healthcare organization constitute its most important resource. Most organizations spend 60 to 70 percent of their operating budgets on employee salaries and benefits. Thus, a good human resources information system (HRIS) is very important to assist management in personnel planning, staffing, and productivity analysis. The functions of a HRIS include

1. maintaining, updating, and retrieving information from a database of employee permanent records;
2. providing automatic position control linked to the budget;
3. producing labor analysis reports for each cost center;
4. producing reports for analyzing personnel problems, such as turnover and absenteeism;
5. maintaining an inventory of special skills and certifications of employees;
6. producing labor cost allocations with linkage to the payroll system;
7. providing information on employee productivity and quality control, assuming that appropriate labor standards have been developed; and
8. comparing compensation and benefit packages to outside industry norms.

An automated database of employee information used in conjunction with a HRIS might include the following components (Austin, Johnson, and Palestrant 1998, 83):

- Personnel information, such as name, address, Social Security number, birthdate, and marital status
- Job-related information, such as job title, department, employment date, date of last promotion, and salary history
- Benefits information, such as medical insurance coverage, life and disability insurance coverage, and pension plan data
- Miscellaneous information, such as special skills, physical limitations, disciplinary actions, awards, and bonuses

The availability of computerized employee record files creates a security issue. Because protecting the employee's right to privacy is essential, organizations need to establish software and hardware security systems and set policies for access and updating of electronic personnel files. (See Chapter 13 for discussion on data security policies.)

In addition to supporting operational work in the human resources department, a well-designed HRIS will produce reports for management planning and control (see Figure 8.2). For example, HRIS management reports can be used to monitor turnover rates, unfilled positions, labor costs, employee productivity, and utilization of benefits. Attitudes of employees and physicians can be monitored through periodic satisfaction surveys.

Some larger hospitals and multi-institutional healthcare organizations have developed automated databases to support recruitment of physicians. Such systems can identify staff needs, plan searches, and schedule interviews with candidates for appointment to the medical staff.

Computer systems are available to maintain current records of physician credentials and practice privileges in the organization. These systems are important for monitoring quality standards and for maintaining documentation required by accreditation surveyors.

Valley Health System of Winchester, Virginia, installed an automated time-and labor-management system to improve human resources management for its 5,000 employees in 12 facilities. Employees at all locations use barcoded badges at one of approximately 65 timekeeper badge readers linked to a central computer system. Data collected by the system are used to analyze and improve staffing patterns and track trends in employee absenteeism. The system also enabled Valley to achieve consistent pay practices across the enterprise (Yerbernetsky and Kizielewic 1999).

Kirby (2001) discusses the decisions to be made in merging two different HRISs when Presbyterian Health Care System merged with Harris

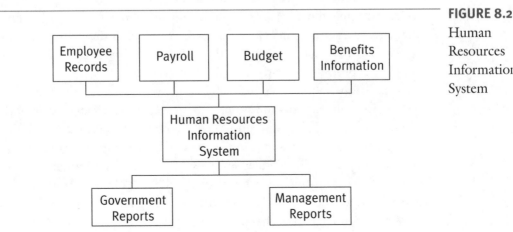

FIGURE 8.2

Human Resources Information System

Methodist Health System in Texas. Maintaining both systems was not practical, and the costs for starting over with a new system were prohibitive. Consequently, the software system used at Presbyterian was upgraded, and the Harris system was merged into it. As a result, the payroll process has been stabilized and a 25 percent reduction in application support costs is anticipated.

A number of HRIS software packages are available. Health Management Technology's 2002 Resource Guide lists 57 vendors that provide human resources and staffing information systems.

Resource Utilization and Scheduling Systems

The need to contain costs is an important reason for every healthcare organization to utilize resources in the most productive way possible. Utilization review is mandated both by regulatory agencies and by insurance companies that provide payment for services rendered. Managers are also charged with the responsibility of ensuring that services are available when needed, and effective scheduling is essential to this end.

In response to the need for efficient resource utilization, healthcare organizations have developed computerized monitoring and scheduling systems. Information systems monitor inpatient occupancy rates, clinic and emergency room activity, and utilization of individual service facilities such as the operating suite. Patient scheduling systems are used for advance booking and scheduling of facilities, both for patient and physician convenience and for efficient allocation of resources, particularly staffing.

Advance bed booking and preadmissions systems are particularly useful in situations where most of the admissions are elective (e.g., a specialized surgical facility). Advance booking also provides time for necessary preadmission certification for Medicare patients and others covered by private insurance that require review and certification of the medical need for the admission. Preadmission information systems can be linked to individual physicians' offices as well. Computer programs can project the average length-of-stay for each elective admission once historical data (including diagnosis, surgical procedure, age, and sex of patient) have been accumulated. After admissions are scheduled and the data entered into the computer's master files, the system keeps track of projected occupancy levels for each day.

Admissions monitoring and scheduling systems improve staffing and work flow in healthcare organizations. These systems can reduce daily fluctuations in a hospital's census and improve employment of flexible staffing systems. Acute general hospitals must maintain an accurate accounting of bed census and occupancy if they are to survive. Census information helps compare projected income against projected budgets. Administrators can also track demands for specific services and adjust staffing levels and scheduling of facilities as demand patterns change.

Computer programs are also available for scheduling operating rooms in hospitals and ambulatory surgery centers. These systems are designed to improve operating room utilization, contain costs, facilitate planning, and aid in the scheduling of specific surgical procedures. St. Luke's Hospital in Bethlehem, Pennsylvania, uses a computerized operating room scheduling system. The system plans for needed supplies and equipment in advance of each procedure and can accommodate physician preferences (Baldwin 2001).

Outpatient clinic appointment and scheduling systems are common in organizations with a large volume of outpatient activity. Brackenridge Hospital in Austin, Texas, operates 30 specialty clinics at sites around the city. Physicians staff the clinics on a rotating basis at intervals from monthly to twice weekly. The hospital recently replaced an in-house clinic scheduling system with Internet-based software (see Chapter 9) that enables staff to schedule appointments online. Preliminary evaluation of the system indicates "that during the first three months of using the new system, with no increase in staff, patient throughput increased 30 percent, cost per transaction decreased more that 30 percent, and patient cancellations fell 12 percent" (Baldwin 2001, 37).

Most resource utilization and scheduling systems in use today operate at the department level. Efforts are underway to develop enterprisewide scheduling systems that meet multiple objectives, including balanced schedules, optimum staffing, and management of resources across the enterprise. "These systems are no longer limited to nursing or surgery departments. Centralized scheduling is becoming the 'one-stop shop' for all appointment and resource scheduling throughout entire healthcare organizations. Surgeons are on-line viewing their upcoming surgery schedule and booking their own cases into pre-defined blocks of time. Even support departments, like dietary and environmental services, are scheduling their employees in the same system once dedicated only to nursing" (Meisel 1999, 19).

Baldwin (2001) lists the following desirable capabilities of an enterprisewide scheduling system:

1. To recognize that certain procedures should be preceded or followed by other procedures
2. To automatically order needed supplies and material
3. To automatically verify insurance status
4. To automatically produce timely patent reminders
5. To suggest how to reassign staff as workloads expand or contract

A large number of scheduling software packages are available to healthcare organizations. Health Management Technology's 2002 Resource Guide lists 113 vendors that offer scheduling systems to the healthcare market.

Materials Management Systems

Computers assist healthcare organizations in more effective management of supplies and materials. These systems include computerized purchasing, electronic data interchange with suppliers, inventory control, use of barcode devices for encoding supplies and materials, and computerized menu planning and food service management.

In a typical materials management system, requisitions for supplies and materials are entered into the computer and matched against budgetary authorization for financial control. Overdrafts on supply accounts are flagged and sent to the appropriate supervisor for follow-up action. Once requisitions are cleared, the computer generates purchase orders. As materials are received, receipt notices are entered into the computer and matched against an open order file. Many automated purchasing systems also include direct linkage to the accounts payable system if system integration has been planned. Some systems also provide the capability for automatic reordering of selected items (see Figure 8.3).

Purchase orders can be transmitted electronically to suppliers. Modern systems of supply chain management link healthcare organizations to vendor information systems using Internet technology. Supply chain applications are designed to reduce processing costs and obtain materials on a "just-in-time" basis, thus reducing the need to carry a large inventory. The savings that result can be significant (Perez 2000; DeJesus 2001; Tabar 2001a). E-procurement applications in healthcare are discussed in more detail in Chapter 9.

Coding standards are an important element of automated purchasing and materials management systems. Standards are needed "to automate, streamline, and track the supply chain end to end" (Marietti 2001). Expanded use of barcodes for all type of medical supplies and pharmaceuticals can be anticipated as purchaser-vendor relationships in healthcare continue to develop. See Chapter 3 for a technical description of barcodes and barcode scanners.

Nalle Clinic in Charlotte, North Carolina, operates 11 satellite clinics throughout its service area. To control procurement costs, the clinic automated its materials management process. The web-based system includes requisitioning, purchasing, receiving, inventory management, task scheduling, and invoice reconciliation. The cost of a purchase order has decreased, and a 75 percent reduction in paperwork has been realized at all levels of the organization (Autry 2000).

St. Luke's Hospital in Cedar Rapids, Iowa, developed a materials management system that includes purchase order generation, bulk inventory management, and linkage to accounts payable for invoice matching and payment. The system was redesigned recently to incorporate automation of inventory distribution and capture of patient charges. One of the major benefits of the system has been a reduction in inventory of over $500,000 per year (*Materials Management in Health Care* 2001).

Computerized menu-planning systems store and analyze data on patients' nutritional and dietary requirements, food items in inventory and their costs, and decision rules on factors other than nutrition and food costs. The systems help plan nutritionally balanced and aesthetically pleasing meals with least-cost menus meeting the constraints imposed by the nutritional model (Sklan and Dariel 1993).

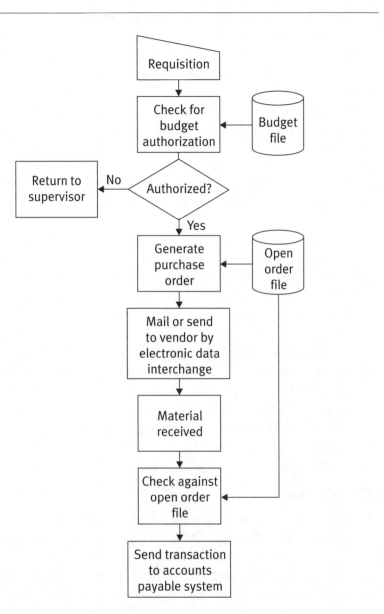

FIGURE 8.3
Materials
Management
System

Health Management Technology's 2002 Resource Guide lists 46 vendors that provide materials management systems and 9 vendors that offer nutrition and menu management systems to the healthcare indurstry.

Facilities and Project Management Systems

Computerized systems can help organizations plan, manage, and maintain physical facilities. Examples include preventive maintenance systems, energy management systems, and project scheduling and control systems (particularly useful in construction and remodeling projects).

Preventive maintenance project management systems help extend the life of equipment and facilities and reduce costly failures. Potential benefits include (1) cost savings through reduced inventory of spare parts for equipment repair, (2) reduced staffing of housekeeping and maintenance department personnel, and (3) improved risk management through better record keeping on equipment maintenance and reduction of safety hazards.

Energy conservation has become an important cost-saving strategy for the healthcare industry as it has for all major industries. Computer packages have been developed to assist in monitoring energy utilization. Actual utilization figures are compared against calculated requirements, and the computer model points out possibilities for reduced consumption.

Healthcare organizations are frequently involved in capital construction and major remodeling projects. Computer systems have been developed to aid in project management. One such system, Program Evaluation and Review Technique (PERT), assists in project scheduling and control (Austin and Boxerman 1995, Chapter 8). System users first construct a network that shows (1) all activities required to complete the project; (2) the relationships of these activities to one another, including those that can be carried out simultaneously and those that must follow a time sequence; and (3) time estimates for completing each activity. The computer responds with a schedule that shows the critical path for project completion. As activities are completed, actual completion times are entered back into the computer system, the program is rerun, and new schedules are prepared for the remaining work. The system is an excellent tool for dynamic scheduling and control of major projects.

A number of project management software packages are available.

Office Automation

Healthcare organizations use computers to carry out office functions such as word processing, electronic mail, project management, meeting scheduling, and maintenance of calendars for management personnel.

Office automation helps to coordinate and manage people and work flow, link organizational units and projects, and coordinate work in the organization across levels and functions.

Managing documents can consume 40 to 50 percent of an office staff's time when all functions are considered—that is, document creation, storage, and retrieval; desktop publishing; and converting documents to other forms. Use of systems for integrated word processing, scheduling, electronic filing of documents, and message/document transmission can dramatically improve efficiency and reduce the costs of office operations.

Office systems can link parts of the organization together by scheduling individuals and groups using electronic calendars and electronic mail (e-mail). E-mail systems link offices and/or individuals together, allowing word-processed documents to be forwarded to others or filed in computer storage for future reference.

A growing number of organizations are expanding the concept of office automation to include groupware. *Groupware* is a broad term that refers to the combination of software and hardware that enables managers to share information in an interactive networked environment. This software/hardware combination facilitates real-time interaction among members of the group to improve problem solving and project management. Groupware activities include

- electronic mail (e-mail),
- teleconferencing,
- interactive two-way compressed video conferencing,
- relational databases (used to search for data and information),
- document editing and management, and
- group calendars and scheduling.

The goal of computer-supported cooperative group work is to change the way people work together. Organizations often move groupware applications that reside on the desktop computer into conference rooms, board rooms, or connected video systems. The goal is to provide environments where people can use their best computerized tools and applications no matter their location.

Managed Care Applications

Managed care is a term describing organizational arrangements by which health plans offer a comprehensive set of services to members of a defined population. Health plan members are offered financial incentives to use physicians and facilities affiliated with the plan. Managed care can assume many different forms. Three of the more common arrangements are health maintenance organizations (HMOs), preferred provider organizations (PPOs), and exclusive provider arrangements (EPAs).

HMOs provide coverage of specified health services to plan members for a fixed premium. Physician services may be provided by employing a group of physicians on a salaried basis or by contracting with an organized physician group.

PPOs are insurance programs in which plan members receive better benefits (usually through reduced deductible and copayment amounts) when they use services offered by a group of preferred providers. Patients can use nonparticipating providers, but at a higher cost. Providers agree to discounted fees for service to receive the preferred provider designation.

EPAs are plans offered by major self-insured employers who contract directly with a group of providers to offer services to their employees. These plans are similar to PPOs except that the middlemen (insurance companies) are eliminated.

Healthcare organizations operating in the managed care environment must have vastly improved financial and clinical information about their operation to monitor the costs and quality of services and negotiate successfully with managed care plans.

Managed Care Information Needs

Four groups need information to function in the managed care environment: purchasers, consumers, providers, and managed care organizations (MCOs) (see Figure 8.4).

Purchasers of care include organizations that provide health insurance benefits to their employees. The federal government is a major purchaser of care for enrollees in the Medicare program. State governments purchase care to serve the Medicaid population in their states. Purchasers of care need information to assess the benefit packages offered by managed care plans and to evaluate the costs and quality of services provided. They also require information on the demographic characteristics and healthcare utilization patterns of their employees or government plan enrollees.

Consumers who are considering enrollment in an HMO, PPO, or other type of health plan need information to evaluate competing alternatives. Large organizations may offer several alternative plans to their employees. Consumers need information on benefits provided by each plan; costs, including monthly premiums, deductible, and copay amounts; quality of services

FIGURE 8.4
Managed Care
Information
Needs

Purchasers	1. Benefits offered by the health plan
	2. Costs of the plan
	3. Quality of services provided
	4. Service utilization history
Consumers	1. Benefits provided by plans available
	2. Costs: monthly premium, deductible, and copay amounts
	3. Quality of services provided
	4. Service convenience
Providers	1. Estimate of costs to provide service under each proposed contract
	2. Monitoring of performance under each contract
	3. Claims submission and reimbursement system
Managed Care Organizations	1. Marketing information
	2. Information for establishing rates and negotiating contracts
	3. Membership records
	4. Monitoring of service utilization
	5. Financial monitoring (costs and revenue)
	6. Other administrative systems for organizational support

available; and convenience of services, including provider location and hours of operation.

Healthcare providers who contract with MCOs need information to estimate the cost of providing services under proposed contracts for contract negotiations, to monitor performance under existing contracts, and to efficiently submit claims for reimbursement. MCOs (including self-insured employer organizations and integrated delivery providers that offer their own health plans) need information for establishing rates (premiums, deductible, and copay amounts); for marketing their plans to purchasers and community organizations; for maintaining health plan membership records; for monitoring utilization of services; and for monitoring costs and revenue generated. In addition, MCOs require administrative information systems of the type described in the preceding section of this chapter to support management of their organizations.

Quality of Care

As mentioned, purchasers and consumers are very interested in the quality and outcomes of care provided by HMOs and other managed care plans. "Report cards" on the costs and quality of healthcare have been developed by individual employers, industry coalitions, and accrediting organizations.

The National Committee on Quality Assurance (NCQA) is a nonprofit, voluntary organization that accredits HMOs and other managed care plans. NCQA has developed the Health Plan Employer Data and Information Set (HEDIS) for use in accreditation of health plans and as a source of information for employers and consumers in making health plan choices. HEDIS evaluates health plan performance in the general areas of access to care, effectiveness of care, patient satisfaction, use of services, cost of care, and health plan stability. Specific measurements include such items as immunization rates, cancer screening rates, inpatient utilization rates, follow-up to hospitalization, prenatal and postpartum care, well-care visits, board certification of physicians, and many others (HEDIS 2002).

Data from managed care information systems are being used to assess quality of care. Unutzer et al. (2000) used data from an HMO information system to examine patterns of care for 1,246 adult patients treated for bipolar disorder. Results indicated that data from the information system were helpful in quality-of-care assessment and suggested opportunities for improving the care of bipolar patients.

Researchers in the department of medicine at Michigan State University used data from an HMO management information system to screen for high-utilizing somatizing patients and target them for treatment (Smith et al. 2001).

Claims Processing and Adjudication

Electronic claims processing systems link providers and managed care plans to handle tasks such as advanced eligibility verification, submission and payment of claims, inquiries on pending claims, and dispute resolution through adjudication.

The Healthcare Financial Management Association released a study that suggests that savings can be achieved by expanded use of electronic claims processing. "Claims inquiry and follow-up transactions are one area where dramatic benefits are possible by applying electronic transaction standards . . . Since most of this work is done through telephone calls, it is by far the most labor-intensive area of patient accounting" (Brutscher 2001).

For providers, electronic claims processing systems speed up eligibility verification and provide ways to check for coding errors before a claim leaves the building. For payers, successful systems can reduce the number of pending items that results from claims that are missing or have errors (Tabar 2001b).

Keener (2001) describes an online service designed to resolve claims disputes between providers and health plans. Both sides submit three offers and counteroffers on a confidential basis. The program compares each set of offers employing predetermined decision rules. If the offers get close enough, a binding settlement results.

The Health Insurance Portability and Accountability Act (HIPAA) mandates electronic transmission of information for processing health insurance claims. HIPAA is described in detail in Chapter 13.

Managed Care Software and Hardware

HMOs and other MCOs use software from a variety of sources. Wholey (2001) studied HMO outsourcing of information system development and operation. Among the findings in the study is that "the greater an HMO's information technology capability and the complexity of information systems supported, the less likely is an HMO to outsource. . . . HMOs less than two years old, for-profit HMOs, local or Blue Cross-affiliated HMOs, and mixed HMOs are more likely to outsource" (Wholey 2001, 229).

An example of a managed care software package is the 3M Clinical Claims Editor, which is " . . . a computerized patient record processing system for insurance companies, managed care companies, claims review companies, and other payers of the provider-submitted patient claims. The functions of the CCE are to assign patient records to Diagnostic Related Groups (DRGs), to evaluate the accuracy and completeness of clinical data, to identify potential coding errors, and to verify provider claims for reimbursement" (3M 2002). Health Management Technology's 2002 Resource Guide lists 113 vendors that provide managed care systems.

Rosen (2000) believes that wireless technology will help improve managed care services by improving medication compliance and lowering utilization expenses incurred from non-compliance-related treatments.

Enterprise Systems

In response to the imperatives of managed care, many hospitals, medical group practices, and other healthcare organizations have come together to form integrated delivery systems (IDSs). An IDS can be defined as an organization that is accountable for the costs and clinical outcomes associated with delivery of a continuum of health services to a defined population. An IDS is a network of hospitals; physicians; and other healthcare providers who furnish comprehensive services to a patient population, in some cases for a fixed annual payment. The components of an IDS may be linked together through a variety of organizational arrangements, ranging from a single organization created through mergers to a federation of semi-autonomous units.

IDSs are tied together by information about the patients being served. Success of an IDS is heavily dependent on the ability to build enterprisewide information systems to provide good clinical, financial, and customer service information to the stakeholders of the organization. Developing such a system often involves the need to integrate diverse information systems developed by individual provider organizations before they were linked together through mergers, acquisitions, or joint ventures.

An enterprisewide system must include an electronic network infrastructure to facilitate sharing of clinical and financial information among members of the IDS—that is, physicians, hospitals, ambulatory care centers, home health agencies, long-term care facilities, and other system components. Increasingly, intrasystem communication is being developed through use of Internet technology (see Chapter 9).

Several questions need to be addressed prior to developing the communications network required for an enterprise system:

1. How many sites must be connected to the network?
2. What kinds of information will be communicated? Will images as well as data be included?
3. What information must be online at all times, and what information can be archived?
4. Who will have access to information on the network?
5. How will information security be maintained? (See Chapter 13.)
6. Will Internet technology be employed in building the network?
7. How will the network be managed?

Wood (2000) states that enterprise data warehousing is one technique for integrating data from across the organization. "A typical warehouse manages financial and clinical data, as well as data brought in from diverse systems. It serves as a strategic complement to operational systems used by caregivers and clerical staff by supplying a separate data store that answers management analysis and reporting needs without impacting information access at the point of care" (Wood 2000, 56). (See Chapter 6 for more detailed discussion of data warehouses.)

Jones et al. (2000) describe the process for developing a set of technology architecture guidelines for information integration within an enterprise. They state that a technology architecture is not a design plan but a set of guidelines that restrain technology choices by components of an organization to achieve integration and cost containment. Technology architecture "requires that certain standards [and] rules are followed once the decision to invest in technology is made. The intent of the architecture is to serve as a road map for consistent systems and technology evaluation, selection, development and implementation" (Jones et al. 2000, 399). System planning and integration are discussed in more detail in Chapter 11.

Oakley (1999) discusses the problems associated with building an enterprise system for an IDS created through merger of multiple hospitals. The costs and technical problems associated with replacing all existing systems from the merged facilities are often overwhelming. One approach is to use software products that sit above existing hospital information systems. Two such products are (1) an enterprise index with information about people (patients, physicians, third-party insurers, etc.) and (2) an enterprisewide scheduling system for use across the IDS.

Health Management Technology's 2002 Resource Guide lists 159 vendors that provide systems integration products.

Summary

Healthcare organizations use computers and information systems to support administrative operations, including financial management, human resources management, resource utilization and scheduling, materials management, facilities and project management, and office automation.

Most healthcare organizations begin using electronic data processing by developing or purchasing financial information systems. Financial data are essential for making least-cost investment decisions; for providing quality services to patients; and for providing management information for planning, controlling, and evaluating operations. Within the healthcare field, financial software is available for payroll, accounts payable, billing and accounts receivable, general ledger accounting, cost accounting, financial reporting, and budgeting and budget control. Various vendors have developed computer models to assist management in financial planning and forecasting.

Employees are the most important resource of healthcare organizations. Human resources data systems can assist in workforce planning and labor analysis. Human resources information systems maintain employee record files, provide position control, produce labor analysis reports, analyze personnel problems (e.g., turnover and absenteeism), maintain inventories of employee skills and certifications, produce labor cost allocations, and provide information on employee productivity.

Increasing pressure for cost containment makes it essential to use resources efficiently. Computerized monitoring and scheduling systems help achieve this goal by allowing advance bed booking and preadmission of inpatients, preparation of bed census and occupancy reports, scheduling of service facilities such as operating suites, and scheduling of patients in outpatient clinics. Efforts are underway to develop enterprisewide resource planning and scheduling systems that meet multiple objectives of balanced schedules, optimum staffing, and cost control.

Computers are used to manage materials and facilities. Administrative systems provide computerized purchasing, inventory control, menu planning and food service management, scheduling and monitoring of preventive maintenance, energy management, and construction-project scheduling and work control.

Office automation has dramatically increased efficiency and reduced costs in the administration of health services. An integrated office automation system includes word processing, e-mail, electronic filing of documents, and scheduling of meetings. Groupware enables managers to share information and solve problems in an interactive networked environment.

Managed care organizations offer a comprehensive set of health services to a defined population, usually for a fixed monthly premium. Healthcare organizations operating in the managed care environment need improved financial and clinical information to monitor the costs and quality of services and negotiate contracts with managed care plans.

Managed care information systems support financial analysis, marketing, membership record keeping, claims processing, utilization monitoring, and quality assessment. Report cards have been developed by purchasers of care to evaluate the costs and quality of care delivered under managed care plans. The National Committee on Quality Assurance accredits HMOs and other managed care plans through a voluntary review process.

Integrated delivery systems are networks of hospitals, physicians, and other healthcare providers who furnish comprehensive health services to a patient population. IDS success is dependent on the development of enterprisewide information systems that provide good clinical, financial, and customer service information to the stakeholders of the organization.

Discussion Questions

8.1 What are some of the more common administrative computer applications?

8.2 Why do most healthcare organizations usually enter the information systems field by first installing financial systems?

8.3 What are the principal purposes achieved by an effective financial management information system? Describe a typical set of healthcare management financial applications.

8.4 How do human resources information systems (HRISs) contribute to effective personnel administration? What are the basic functions of an HRIS?

8.5 How can computers help management achieve more efficient utilization of resources and facilities?

8.6 Briefly describe computer applications available for materials management.

8.7 What are the major objectives of enterprisewide scheduling systems?

8.8 How have financial incentives changed under managed care? What are the implications for information systems?

8.9 Who are the primary users of managed care information systems? What type of information is needed by each group of users?

8.10 What is HEDIS? How is it used in evaluating managed care plans?

8.11 Why is an enterprisewide network important for an integrated delivery system?

8.12 What questions need to be addressed in planning an enterprise network?

Problems

8.1 Contact a local healthcare organization and conduct a survey to determine what financial, human resources, and resource planning and scheduling software applications are currently used. Determine vendor, product name, and date of implementation. Determine expectations for replacing or upgrading the applications.

8.2 The software market for administrative applications is constantly changing. Locate on the Internet four to five vendors for each of the administrative areas discussed in Problem 8.1. For each vendor, describe the following:
- Information contained on the home page
- Length of time vendor has been in operation
- Number of clients vendor has
- If vendor is a single-product vendor or has a wide range of software applications.

Find a recent article in a professional journal that describes use of one of these products. Compare and contrast the article with information you found on the vendor's web site.

8.3 Contact the chief information office of a managed care organization in your area. Discuss what steps his/her organization takes to assess quality of care, including use of HEDIS and accreditation by the National Committee on Quality Assurance (if applicable).

8.4 Assume that you are the project manager for establishing an enterprisewide network for your organization. The organization includes a 550-bed acute care hospital, eight large primary care practices, a 300-bed children's hospital, two long-term care nursing centers, and an outpatient rehabilitation facility. Develop an outline of a project plan for development and implementation of the network. Include descriptions of the key individuals involved, issues to be addressed, and methods for evaluating the success of the project.

References

3M. 2002. [Online information; retrieved 6/30/02]. 3m.com/market/healthcare/his/us/products/cce.

Austin, C. J., and S. B. Boxerman. 1995. *Quantitative Analysis for Health Services Administration*. Chicago: AUPHA/Health Administration Press.

Austin, C. J., J. A. Johnson, and G. D. Palestrant. 1998. "Information Systems for Human Resources Management." In *Essentials of Human Resource Management in Health Services Organizations*, edited by M. D. Fottler, S. R. Hernandez, and C. L. Joiner. Albany, NY: Delmar Publishers.

Autry, R. 2000. "Materials Management: Cutting Time and Expense." *Health Management Technology* 21 (2): 38–39.

Baldwin, F. D. 2001. "Book 'em. Enterprisewide Scheduling Presents Challenges, But CIOs Will Find It Worth the Effort." *Healthcare Informatics* 18 (9): 37–42.

Brutscher, M. A. 2001. "Transaction Standards Can Dramatically Reduce Time Spent on Follow-up Calls." *Healthcare Financial Management* (November 7).

Dassenko, D. 1997. "Restructuring and an Opportunity to Integrate Financial Applications." *Health Management Technology* 14 (3): 36.

DeJesus, E. X. 2001. "Supply Chain Management." *Healthcare Informatics* 18 (2): 74–76.

Health Management Technology. 2002. Resource Guide. [Online information]. www.healthmgttech.com.

HEDIS. 2002. "Summary of Table of Measures, Product Lines and Changes." [Online information on NCQA web site; retrieved 6/30/02]. www.ncqa.org.

Jones, D. T. et al. 2000. "Technology Architecture Guidelines for a Health Care System." Proceedings from AMIA Symposium, pp. 399–402.

Keener, R. E. 2001. "Navigating Managed Care Through Rough Seas." *Health Management Technology* 22 (2): 38–40.

Kirby, M. 2001. "Planning an HR System Merge." *Health Management Technology* 22 (2): 52.

Marietti, C. 2001. "It All Adds Up." *Healthcare Informatics* 18 (11): 6.

Materials Management in Health Care. 2001. "Make it Official: Inventory System Captures It All." *Materials Management in Health Care*.

Meisel, M. 1999. "Resource Management and Scheduling: Managing Basic Costs." *Health Management Technology* 20 (5): 18–20.

Oakley, S. 1999. "Integrated Delivery Systems: How They Improve Quality of Care." *Health Management Technology* 20 (3): 36–41.

Perez, K. 2000. "What .com Means for Materials Management." *Health Management Technology* 21 (2): 39.

Reed, G. 2000. "No More Red Ink with AR Financial Systems." *Health Management Technology* 21 (7): 12–13.

Rosen, J. 2000. "Improve Managed Care Services and the Bottom Line." *Health Management Technology* 21 (11): 54.

Sklan, D., and I. Dariel. 1993. "Diet Planning for Humans Using Mixed-Integer Linear Programming." *British Journal of Nutrition* 70 (1): 27–35.

Smith, R. C., J. C. Gardiner, S. Armatti, M. Johnson, J. S. Lyles, C. W. Given, C. Lein, B. Given, J. Goddeeris, E. Korban, R. Haddad, and M. Kanj. 2001. "Screening for High Utilizing Somatizing Patients Using a Rule Derived from the Management Information System of an HMO: A Preliminary Study." *Medical Care* 39 (9): 968–78.

Steele A., S. Eisert, and P. Gabow. 2001. "Improvements in Billing Processes and Information Systems Increase Cash Collections in a Public Health Care System." *Journal of Health Care Management* 20 (1): 29–36.

Tabar, P. 2001a. "Fixing Healthcare's Supply Chain." *Healthcare Informatics* 18 (10): 16, 18, 20.

———. 2001b. "Electronic Claims: Now What?" *Healthcare Informatics* 18 (7): 19.

Unutzer, J. et al. 2000. "The Use of Administrative Data to Assess Quality of Care for Bipolar Disorder in a Large Staff Model HMO." *General Hospital Psychiatry* 22 (1): 1–10.

Wholey, D. R. 2001. "Determinants of Information Technology Outsourcing Among Health Maintenance Organizations." *Health Care Management Science* 4 (3): 229–39.

Wood, M. T. 2000. "Changing the Rules in Enterprise Data Warehousing." *Health Management Technology* 21 (9): 56, 58.

Yerbernetsky, B., and J. Kizielewic. 1999. "Track Trends in Staffing Enterprise-Wide." *Health Management Technology* 20 (5): 32–33.

Additional Readings

Abbey, D. C. 2001. "Designing and Maintaining an Effective Chargemaster." *Health-care Financial Management* 55 (3): 50–55.

Bazalo, G. R. 2001. "Managed Care Trends in Statin Usage." *Managed Care* 10 (10): 48–50, 53–59.

Curtin, L. 2000. "Staffing and the Quality of Care." *Health Management Technology* 21 (5): 42, 45.

Dexter, F., A. Macario, and R. D. Traub. 2000. "Stastistical Method Using Operating Room Information System Data to Determine Anesthetist Weekend Call Requirements." *AANA Journal* 68 (1): 21–26.

Dexter, F., and R. D. Traub. 2000. "Determining Staffing Requirements for a Second Shift of Anesthetists by Graphical Analysis of Data from Operating Room Information Systems." *AANA Journal* 68 (1): 31–36.

Diers, D., and D. Pelletier. 2001. "Seeding Information Management Capacity to

Support Operation Management in Hospitals." *Australian Health Review* 24 (2): 74–82.

Epstein, R. H., and F. Dexter. 2000. "Economic Analysis of Linking Operating Room Scheduling and Hospital Material Management Information Systems for Just-in-Time Inventory Control." *Anesthesia Analog* 91 (2): 337–43.

Garcia, L. 2000. "Choosing a Staff Scheduling System." *Health Management Technology* 21 (8): 22.

Goldstein, B. 2001. "Appointment Scheduling System: A Vehicle for Increased Productivity." *Journal of the California Dental Association* 29 (3): 231–33.

Goodman, J., and C. H. Nye. 2001. "Successful Medicaid Managed Care Organization: It Is Not an Oxymoron." *Managed Care Quarterly* 9 (2): 5–11.

Jenkins, E. K., and E. Christenson. 2001. "ERP (Enterprise Resource Planning) Systems Can Streamline Healthcare Business Functions." *Healthcare Financial Management* 55 (5): 48–52.

Joch, A. 2000. "Right Place, Right Time." *Healthcare Informatics* 17 (5): 47–50, 52.

McNamara, T. M. 2000. "Health Information Networks: Enabling Care Management in IDSs." *Healthcare Financial Management* 54 (3): 30–32.

Neumann, L., J. Sideras, W. Hern, A. Holloway, J. McGuire, M. Barger, P. DeMuro, and F. Rickabaugh. 2000. "A Look at Healthcare IT from the Financial Suite." *Health Management Technology* 21 (1): 22–25.

Pelton, S. 2001. "Smooth Sailing with Scheduling." *Health Management Technology* 22 (5): 54–55.

Reschneck-Sannes, D. 2000. "Digital Doctoring." *Healthcare Informatics* 17 (2): 97–98.

Rielinger, J. A. 2001. "Preparing for the Inpatient Rehabilitation PPS." *Healthcare Financial Management* 55 (12): 52–55.

Rozich, J. D., and R. K. Resar. 2002. "Using a Unit Assessment Tool to Optimize Patient Flow and Staffing in a Community Hospital." *Joint Committee Journal of Quality Improvement* 28 (1): 31–41.

Ruland, C. M., and I. H. Ravn. 2001. "An Information System to Improve Financial Management, Resource Allocation and Activity Planning: Evaluation Results." *Medinfo* 10 (Part 2): 1203–6.

St. Clair, D. 2000. "The Truth about Managed Care Decisions." *Health Management Technology* 21 (2): 30–31.

Schneider, R. J., S. P. Mandelbaum, K. Graboys, and C. Bailey. 2001. "Process-centered Revenue-cycle Management Optimizes Payment Process." *Healthcare Financial Management* 55 (1): 63–66.

Stammer, L. 2001. "Healthcare from a New Perspective." *Healthcare Informatics* 18 (5): 26–30.

Stead, W. W. 2000. "Integration and Beyond: Linking Information from Disparate Sources and Into Workflow." *Journal of the American Informatics Association* 7 (2): 135–45.

Weil, T. P. 2000. "Management of Integrated Delivery Systems in the Next Decade." *Healthcare Management Review* 25 (3): 9–23.

Wholey, D. R. 2000. "The Diffusion of Information Technology Among Health Maintenance Organizations." *Health Care Management Review* 25 (2): 24–33.

York, G., J. Wortmann, and R. Atanasiu. 2001. "Enterprise-class Digital Imaging and Communications in Medicine (DICOM) Image Infrastructure." *Journal of Digital Imaging* 14 (2, Supplement 1): 63–65.

Zhou, Q. 2001. "A Quality Measurement Framework for Managed Care Organizations." *Journal of Healthcare Quality* 23 (2): 34–39.

E-HEALTH APPLICATIONS

The Internet has had significant impact on the delivery of healthcare and that impact will be even greater in the future. This chapter describes the development of the Internet and the World Wide Web and discusses the evolving field of e-health applications that employ Internet technology. The chapter concludes with management principles for using this technology effectively in healthcare organizations.

Development of the Internet

The Internet is a global network of interconnected computer networks. The origins of the Internet can be traced to research in packet switching and communications carried out by investigators in government, industry, and academia during the 1960s. A group of scientists involved in the development and evolution of the Internet describe it as " . . . at once a world-wide broadcasting capability, a mechanism for information dissemination, and a medium for collaboration and interaction between individuals and their computers without regard for geographic location" (Leiner et al. 2002).

The Internet employs an open architecture. "In this approach, the choice of any individual network technology was not dictated by a particular network architecture but rather could be selected freely by a provider and made to interwork with the other networks through a meta-level 'Internet-working Architecture'" (Leiner et al. 2002).

Created by researchers in Switzerland, the World Wide Web (www) or "Web" is a system for finding and accessing Internet resources. The Web uses browser software technology, such as Netscape and Microsoft Explorer, to enable users to "surf" the Internet using HTML-based hypertext-linked web pages.

Intranets are private computer networks that employ Internet technology for communication within an organization. Fotsch (1997, 26) defines an Intranet as an internal Internet network "that links an organization's communications and information in a way that makes information more accessible and navigation through . . . the organization's computer environment more seamless."

See Chapter 5 for more information on Internet technology.

The Emergence of E-Health

E-health is a term that emerged early in the 21st century to reflect the growing number of applications of Internet technology in the delivery of health services. There is no standard definition of the term. The editor of the *Journal of Medical Internet Research* offers the following definition:

> "E-health is an emerging field in the intersection of medical informatics, public health and business referring to health services and information delivered or enhanced through the Internet and related technologies. In a broader sense, the term characterizes not only a technical development, but also a state-of-mind, a way of thinking, an attitude, and a commitment for networked global thinking, to improve health care locally, regionally, and worldwide by using information and communication technology" (Eysenbach 2001).

Some of the goals of e-health include increased efficiency in healthcare, improved quality of care, increased commitment to evidence-based medicine, empowerment of patients and consumers, and development of new relationships between patients and health professionals (Eysenbach 2001).

Myers et al. (2001) suggest that employers and engaged consumers are forces driving e-health applications. Korpman (2001) discusses the desires of stakeholders. *Patients* want information about their own health. *Providers* want to save time and money and streamline communication with multiple health plans. *Employers* want to be able to analyze health-plans costs and utilization by their employees. *Health plans* want to strengthen relations with members and providers and reduce costs of doing business.

E-health is an emerging industry, and it is still in a developmental stage at this writing. In 1999, the industry generated $6 billion in revenues, a figure predicted to expand to $370 billion by 2004 (Shulman 2001). The downturn in "dot com" businesses in the year 2000 affected the e-health sector as well: "Paralleling the lack of confidence in the mainstream market, e-health companies' rapid fall from grace is highlighted in a report from PricewaterhouseCoopers, New York, of third quarter 2000 venture capital investments. Internet-related investments dropped to 49 percent of the total, down 18 percent from the previous quarter" (Marietti 2001). Nonetheless, there is every indication that the e-health sector will continue to develop, and the Internet will be a major factor in the application of information technology to healthcare.

E-Health Applications

E-health applications cover a wide range of activities in healthcare organizations including many of the systems (clinical, management, strategic decision support) described in chapters 7, 8, and 10. These applications include some that use the public Internet and some that are restricted by use of private Intranets or control of user access through passwords. E-health applications described in this section include e-business, marketing and consumer information, organizational management and communications, and clinical and customer service support. (See Figure 9.1.)

FIGURE 9.1
E-Health
Applications

E-Business Applications	1. E-procurement
	2. Electronic claims processing
	3. Consumer e-business
Marketing and Consumer Information Applications	1. Advertising
	2. Consumer health information
Organizational Management and Communications Applications	1. Distributing organizational information
	2. Education and training
	3. Employee recruiting
	4. Administrative operations
Clinical and Customer Service Applications	1. Patient access to medical information
	2. Patient-physician interaction
	3. Other clinical applications

Health Management Technology's 2002 Resource Guide lists 322 vendors that provide Internet and intranet applications.

E-Business Applications

E-business applications link healthcare organizations with external business partners and vendors. This category of applications also includes Internet web sites used directly by consumers for such things as filling drug prescriptions and purchasing health insurance.

E-Procurement

Internet technology is being used for online order processing between healthcare organizations and suppliers. Vendor web sites provide access to catalogs of supplies and materials and permit online order placement and payment. Successful e-procurement is dependent on linkage with an effective, automated materials management system in the purchasing organization (see Chapter 8).

Standardized identification systems are necessary for effective supply chain management between healthcare organizations and suppliers. "Standards . . . are going to assume great importance in the development of online healthcare procurement. . . . A standard taxonomy of products will make it easier to search and find products" (DeJesus 2001, 76).

Electronic Claims Processing

The Internet is being used by healthcare providers to obtain eligibility information and advanced authorization from insurance companies and health plans for services provided to patients. Internet linkages also are used for insurance claims processing, thereby improving cash flow and accounts receivable.

Well-designed electronic claims processing systems include benefits for both providers and insurers. "For providers, the low-hanging fruit is speeding up eligibility verification and finding ways to correct coding errors before the claim leaves the building. For payors, the key is reducing the biggest claims processing logjam of all— the 'pend' list [list of claims with errors or missing items]" (Tabar 2001a).

Consumer E-Business The Internet is being used by healthcare consumers for direct purchase of items such as prescription drugs and health insurance. Internet pharmacies have become an alternative to mail-order procurement of medicine and drugs for many consumers. For example, the drugstore.com,inc. web site provides services that include drug prices, drug-interaction checking, insurance verification, and maintenance of individual pharmacy records. The eMedAlert™ capability of the web site provides information on product warnings, updates, and recalls (see Figure 9.2).

Barcia (2000, 25) cautions that Internet pharmacies are "semi-automatic at best. Internet pharmacies require that either the patient or physician mail the prescription, or contact must be made with the prescribing physician to obtain a legal prescription. . . . In addition, the patient must fill out a form on the Website to indicate the medication and quantity desired, along with the prescribing physician."

Reuters Medical News (2001) reports that EhealthInsurance, a privately held firm, serves as a go-between with links to 100 health insurers offering 8,000 plans in all 50 states. Individuals and small businesses can access

FIGURE 9.2

Drugstore.com, Inc.

the site to compare rates and benefits and purchase insurance online from the affiliated plans.

Marketing and Consumer Information Applications

Marketing and consumer information applications are designed to provide information to the general public about services available from healthcare organizations and information about health and wellness.

Most healthcare organizations operate web sites that provide detailed organi- *Advertising* zational and service information. These web sites are designed to attract new patients and provide information to existing patients. They typically include information about specific services available, biographical information about affiliated physicians, information about the community, maps to locate organizational units, and much more. They often include general health-related information and information about health education programs offered by the organization. For example, Figure 9.3 is the web site for the Mayo Clinic, which has locations in Arizona, Florida, and Minnesota.

FIGURE 9.3
Mayo Clinic

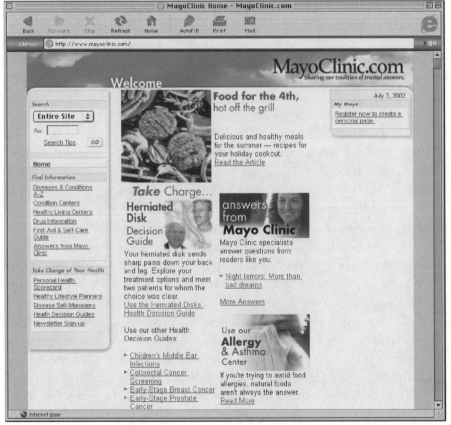

Source: Used with permission from Mayo Clinic.

Managed care organizations and health plans operate web sites that provide information on benefits available and the location of affiliated providers. These sites enable enrollees to review benefits, find a physician or other provider, locate the provider on a map, and perhaps talk to a service representative online through e-mail.

Respondents to the 2002 Annual Leadership Survey conducted by the Healthcare Information and Management Systems Society (HIMSS) listed marketing and promotion as the number one function for their web sites, with 97 percent indicating they use their sites for this purpose (HIMSS 2002).

Consumer Health Information   Healthcare organizations have a responsibility to improve the health of those in communities that they serve. Internet technology is being used extensively for this purpose. Consumer health information web sites are operated by government agencies, private health associations such as the American Heart Association, and by provider organizations. Some of these web sites provide health promotion and wellness information. Others are disease specific. Seventy-one percent of the respondents to the 2002 HIMSS Annual Leadership Survey indicated that their organizations provide consumer health information on their web sites (HIMSS 2002).

One of the most comprehensive consumer health information web sites is healthfinder.gov, operated by the U.S. Department of Health and Human Services (see Figure 9.4). Healthfinder.gov provides information on prevention and wellness, diseases and conditions, alternative medicine, health professionals and facilities and includes medical dictionaries and much more. Extensive links to other web sites are provided as well.

Access to healthcare on the Internet is growing, especially among women, many of whom are the primary healthcare providers and decision makers for their families. DoHealth, a division of The HealthScout Network, launched the Women's Healthcare Advisor. The Advisor provides wellness tools and health management resources to managed care organizations that in turn make them available to women members (Boeke 2000).

Consumers increasingly turn to the Internet to obtain information about their own health. They often use this information when interacting with physicians, and, in some cases, may use the information for self-treatment. Because there are no regulatory controls over the information entered into a web site, concerns have been raised about the quality and accuracy provided through this new medium. The Hi-Ethics consortium is a group of 18 top online health companies. HiEthics has developed an evaluation and monitoring mechanism designed to ensure quality, accuracy, and privacy on health web sites. The eHealth seal of approval program is based on 14 principles, which include standards for privacy, quality of content, and advertising/promotion disclosure (Tabar 2001b).

FIGURE 9.4
Healthfinder.
gov

Source: healthfinder.gov, 2002.

Organizational Management and Communications Applications

Healthcare organizations use the Internet to support operational management and improve internal communications. Most of these applications use Intranets—internal networks that are not available to the general public.

Intranets are used to post and communicate organizational policies, procedures, and announcements to employees. These online documents replace voluminous printed policy and procedure manuals and directories. Savings are realized through easier updating and reduced printing costs. Most healthcare organizations publish internal newsletters to provide information to employees, physicians, and other stakeholders. Intranets are used to publish these newsletters online, reducing costs of printing and distribution.

Distributing Organizational Information

Intranets can also be used to distribute standard forms used within the organization. The system may also be used for downloading standard software applications from a central computer software library.

Education and Training   Intranets can be used to deliver staff educational programs and teleconferences to employees and physicians. Some hospitals and clinics utilize their networks to provide health education programs to patients. Regional and national conferences can be accessed through Internet connections as well.

Townsend (2001, 22) discusses the use of the Internet for participation in staff meetings, continuing medical education programs, and professional conferences: "Since the Internet is virtually everywhere, more people in more locations will be able to take advantage of the new collaborative electronic tools and make more productive use of the workday."

Employee Recruiting   Many healthcare organizations use the Internet to list job announcements, position openings, and employee benefit programs. This listing may take up one section of a general web site used for marketing and promotion, or the information may be posted on a special web site designed for this purpose. In some cases, applicants are able to scan the job list and submit applications by e-mail. For example, Figure 9.5 is the web site of NationJob.com, which healthcare organizations such as Hilton Head Medical Center & Clinics based in South Carolina uses for employee recruiting Eighty-eight percent of the respondents to the 2002 HIMSS Annual Leadership Survey indicated that their organizations use the Internet for employee recruitment (HIMSS 2002).

Administrative Operations   Healthcare organizations use Internet-based applications to support many of the administrative processes described in Chapter 8. White and Terner (2001, 295) describe an Internet application to integrate process automation with communication automation for clinical reference laboratories: "We applied e-automation to create a billing management solution for clinical reference laboratories . . . the result is comprehensive automation of all routine processes driving out errors and costs. . . . The ready access and communication of process details required by e-automation can apply to many other business functions."

Clinical and Customer Service Applications

As mentioned above, the most common healthcare Internet applications relate to marketing and promotion. However, use of web sites for clinical and customer service purposes is on the rise. For example, 20 percent of the respondents to the 2002 HIMSS Annual Leadership survey indicated that their organizations provide patent health-assessment tools on their web sites. Another 29 percent stated that they planned to add patient access to medical records within the next two years.

Patient Access to Medical Information   Some healthcare organizations are building web sites that include personal health records for patients and allow patients to conduct risk assessment of their own health.

Eastern Maine Healthcare has developed a pilot Internet project called MyOnlineHealth. Components of the web-based system include personal

FIGURE 9.5
NationJob.com

Source: Used with permission from NationJob.com.

health records of patients, online messaging and scheduling capabilities, and an online health risk assessment tool (Hagland 2001a). Humana Health Plans in Louisville, Kentucky, operates an e-health system that includes an online personal health record and an electronic mailbox for each member of the plan. The mailbox is used for sending targeted messages such as health tips and reminders for follow-up visits (Hagland 2001a).

Patient-Physician Interaction

The Internet provides a new medium for communication between physicians and their patients. Some physicians have embraced this technology with enthusiasm, but others are skeptical and cautious. A survey conducted in 2000 found that half of the physicians surveyed use the Internet daily in their offices, and interest is growing in the development of practice web sites (Friedewald 2000).

Friedewald believes that the Internet will affect the doctor-patient relationship in two fundamental ways. First, the large amount of health-related information available on the Internet has empowered patients. Physicians are beginning to accept a shared decision-making model with informed consumers. Physicians have an obligation to assist patients who seek outside information, and patients should carefully plan, in advance, the questions they have as a result of surfing the Internet. Second, the Internet reduces the need for face-to-face contact between physicians and patients. Many patients desire e-mail communication with their physicians. Physicians have been slow to accept e-mail because of concerns about privacy protection, time required to respond to voluminous and lengthy questions, and potential liability for answering questions with limited information. However, physicians do use the telephone in communicating with patients, and growing acceptance of e-mail seems inevitable. Automated home monitoring of patients with Internet transmission of data to physician offices also reduces the need for face-to-face contact. "Continuous and remote physical, chemical and biological measurements of blood glucose and drug levels, cardiac function, and even the detection of pathogens are on the horizon" (Friedewald 2000, 80).

Redwood Shores Health Center in California has developed an electronic messaging system between physicians and patients of the clinic. The system uses secure, encrypted communications and allows patients to have access to an electronic medical record: " . . . patients can check their insurance benefits and eligibility, access their personal health records, communicate with their physicians and more online" (Hagland 2001b).

Other Clinical Applications   Many of the clinical applications discussed in Chapter 7 are moving toward the use of web-based systems. Clinical decision-support information available on the Web can provide real-time alerts, warnings, screening capabilities, and access to reference materials to physicians (Portela 2000). PacifiCare managed care organization is working on a web-based disease-management program (Hagland 2001b).

PARTNERS health plan in North Carolina has more than 400,000 members. The plan operates an online communication system with their network of 10,000 providers: "Providers can now look up eligibility and benefits and review and submit claims and referrals on-line; soon they will be able to order and review lab results and perform prescription management" (Riley and Korpman 2001, 37).

SMA Health Plan in Louisiana uses a web-based system to support its utilization-management program. The system employs software from W3Health in a clinical evaluation process: "UM [utilization management] nurses at SMA can access a secure site on the Internet and review the appropriateness of each case they review. UM staff select the level of care criteria, identify the clinical condition for which the patient is hospitalized, review the severity of illness and intensity of service data provided by the attending clinician, and determine an appropriate discharge plan" (Danaher 2000, 43).

Management of Internet Technology

The Internet is a very open communications system. Management policies and controls are needed to ensure that the system is used effectively and not abused. Organizational policies and procedures are needed that cover

- creation of home pages,
- protection of the security of information placed on the Internet,
- legal protection of intellectual property, and
- control of employee use and potential abuse of the system.

Many healthcare organizations are using home pages on the Internet as a marketing tool to make information about programs and services widely available. In some larger organizations, such as university medical centers or complex integrated delivery systems, multiple home pages may be created by individual departments or other organizational units. Central control and policies on home page development are needed. These policies should include items such as

- organizational units authorized to create home pages;
- use of corporate information, logos, etc.;
- responsibilities for maintaining the home page and keeping information current;
- data security policies to be followed (see below);
- graphic design and writing style guidelines to be used; and
- procedures for obtaining central review and approval before the page is posted on the Internet.

Data security policies and procedures are particularly important if Internet technology is to be used for internal communications or sharing of information among organizational units. This is particularly true if clinical or financial information is included. Because the Internet is such an open communications system, extraordinary security features such as encryption of highly sensitive information and creation of "firewalls" to screen information passing through network connections may be necessary.

Some healthcare organizations may be posting copyrighted information and other intellectual property belonging to individuals and/or the organization. This is particularly true of research institutions that post on the Internet publications, data files, and teaching material for use by their colleagues. Organizations and individuals employing the Internet for these purposes should be aware of the rights of authors and copyright owners.

Finally, policies are needed that cover employee use of the Internet to avoid abuses that can easily develop. Of particular concern is potential employee misuse or abuse of e-mail. These policies should cover such items as

- prohibition of use of e-mail for personal communications or those not related to the business of the organization;
- respect of the privacy of e-mail communications of others; and
- prohibition of messages that contain sexually explicit language or language that might be construed as disparagement of others based on race, sex, national origin, religious beliefs, etc.

Employees should be reminded that e-mail differs from telephone conversations in that messages are stored on the network and can be accessed long after a message has been sent.

Employees with web browsers on their computers need to be reminded that Internet access is being provided for business purposes. Internet browsing and surfing can become addictive, and managers should control the amount of time spent by employees who may use the Web for personal reasons or to satisfy idle curiosity about many subjects. Policies are also needed to control which employees are authorized to participate in chat rooms and other information-sharing mechanisms on the Internet.

An important factor to consider when Internet technology is introduced is the impact the technology will have on an organization's culture. Methods of problem solving, sources of information, and power bases may shift with the effective use of the Internet. The management of change is essential when new technologies are introduced.

Information systems planning and management principles are discussed in detail in Part IV of this book. For the most part, these principles apply to e-health applications. Specific management strategies related to implementation of Internet applications include:

1. Ensuring that Internet technologies complement existing information architectures within your organization.
2. Establishing a corporatewide governance group to set policies and guidelines for Internet usage.
3. Appointing a manager to oversee Internet policies in the organization.
4. Developing a network of Internet experts who can support and advise on an enterprisewide information infrastructure.

The implementation of any new technology requires close attention to detail, compatibility of the technology with existing information architecture, compatibility with the corporate culture, and measurement of the benefits and costs of the technology. This requires careful planning and effective management.

Summary

The Internet is a global network of interconnected computer networks. The World Wide Web is a system for finding and accessing Internet resources.

Intranets are private computer networks that employ Internet technology for communication and information sharing within an organization.

E-health is a term that describes the growing number of applications of Internet technology in healthcare. Some of the goals of e-health applications are increased efficiency, improved quality of care, and empowerment of patients and consumers. E-health applications include e-business, marketing and consumer information, organizational management and communications, and clinical and customer support. E-business applications link healthcare organizations with business partners. Examples of these applications include electronic procurement and supply chain management with suppliers, electronic claims processing, and consumer-related e-business such as online pharmacies and health insurance carriers.

Marketing and consumer information applications are designed to promote the organization and provide information to the general public. Provider organization web sites are designed to attract new patients and provide information to existing patients. Managed care organizations operate web sites that provide information on benefits available and the location of providers in their networks. Consumer health information is available on web sites operated by government agencies, private health associations, and provider organizations.

Healthcare organizations use the Internet to support operational management and improve internal communications. Organizational policies and procedures are posted on intranets. Educational programs and conferences are conducted on the Internet. Organizational web sites are used to post job openings and recruit employees and physicians. Many administrative information systems are Internet-based.

Use of web sites for clinical and customer service purposes is increasing. Some web sites include personal health records for patients and enable patients to conduct health risk assessment. Electronic mailboxes are used to send targeted messages and reminders to patients. Interest is growing in the use of e-mail for communication between physicians and patients. Automated home monitoring of patients with transmission of data to physician offices reduces the need for face-to-face contact.

Internet technology must be carefully managed. Policies and procedures are needed to cover creation of home pages, protection of the security of information placed on the Internet or intranet, legal protection of intellectual property, and control of employee use and potential abuse of the system.

Discussion Questions

9.1 Define Internet and intranet. What are the similarities and differences between the Internet and intranets?

9.2 Define e-health. What are some of the general goals of e-health applications in healthcare organizations?

9.3 What are the principal categories of e-health applications?

9.4 Describe some of the e-business applications for healthcare organizations.

9.5 Discuss some of the benefits of electronic claims processing for providers and insurers.

9.6 What information elements would you include in designing a web site for promotion of a healthcare organization?

9.7 How reliable is the consumer health information available on the Internet?

9.8 Describe typical applications of Internet technology for improving management and communications within healthcare organizations.

9.9 Describe typical clinical and customer service applications of the Internet.

9.10 List some of the elements that should be included in organizational policies on Internet use.

9.11 Should organizational culture affect policies for management and control of Internet use in healthcare organizations? Why?

Problems

9.1 Find three web sites for each of the following types of healthcare organizations: individual hospital, HMO or managed care organization, medical group practice or clinic, integrated multihospital system. For each web site describe the following:
  • The content and scope of the web site
  • The types of applications used and the business strategies these applications support
  • Links to other web sites, if any, and the purpose of those links
  • Your assessment of the quality of information found at each site

9.2 Find a consumer health information web site operated by each of the following types of organizations: government agency, private health association, provider organization. Contrast the information found and the approach followed by each of these organizations in building their web sites.

9.3 Interview the chief information officer of a hospital or medical center in your community. Prepare an interview report that includes a summary of how the Internet is being used and the policies that have been developed to guide Internet application development and use.

References

Barcia, S. M. 2000. "Internet Pharmacies: All Hype With No Help?" *Health Management Technology* 21 (4): 24–25.

Boeke, A. 2000. "Women and E-Health." *Health Management Technology* 21 (12): 48.

Danaher, K. 2000. "Using the Internet to Improve Daily Operations." *Health Management Technology* 21 (2): 43.

DeJesus, E. X. 2001. "Supply Chain Management." *Healthcare Informatics* 17 (2): 74–78.

Eysenbach, G. 2001. "What Is E-Health?" *Journal of Medical Internet Research* 3 (2): e20.

Fotsch, E. 1997. "Net Worth of the Internet, Intranets and Extranets." *Health Care Financial Management* 51 (3): 26, 29.

Friedewald, V. E. 2000. "The Internet Influence on the Doctor-Patient Relationship." *Health Management Technology* 21 (11): 79–80.

Hagland, M. 2001a. "Finding the *e* in Healthcare." *Healthcare Informatics* 18 (11): 29–32, 34.

———. 2001b. "When the Medium Is the Message." *Healthcare Informatics* 18 (3): 26, 28, 30.

Health Management Technology. 2002. Resource Guide. [Online information]. www. healthmgt.tech.com.

Healthcare Information and Management Systems Society. 2002. *Thirteenth Annual Leadership Survey.* Chicago: HIMSS.

Korpman, R. A. 2001. "Managed Care and e-Health." *Health Management Technology* 22 (2): 12–14.

Leiner, B. M., V. G. Cerf, D. D. Clark, R. E. Kahn, L. Kleinrock, D. C. Lynch, J. Postel, L. G. Roberts, and S. Wolff. 2002. "A Brief History of the Internet." [Online article; retrieved 6/30/02]. www.isoc.org/internet/history/brief.shtml.

Marietti, C. 2001. "Cold Wind Blowing." *Healthcare Informatics* 18 (3): 8.

Meyers, J., D. Van Brunt, K. Patrick, and A. Greene. 2001. "Personalizing Medicine on the Web." *Health Forum Journal* 45 (1): 22–26.

Portela, A. 2000. "Clinical Decision Support via the Internet." *Health Management Technology* 21 (2): 43.

Reuters Medical News. 2001. "EHealth Insurance Booms During Nation's Bust." *Reuters Health* (December 26).

Riley, T., and R. A. Korpman. 2001. "Beyond Connectivity: What the Success of One Health Plan's e-Solution Means For the Future of the Healthcare Industry." *Journal of Healthcare Information Management* 5 (1): 37–49.

Shulman, S. 2001. "Look Before You Leap." *Healthcare Informatics* 18 (6): 93–95.

Tabar, P. 2001a. "Electronic Claims: Now What?" *Healthcare Informatics* 18 (7): 19.

———. 2001b. "Health Web Site Watchdog Program." *Healthcare Informatics* 18 (2): 16.

Townsend, T. 2001. "Collaboration, Internet Style." *Health Management Technology* 22 (10): 22–24.

White, L., and C. Terner. 2001. "E-health, Phase Two: The Imperative to Integrate Process Automation with Communication Automation for Large Clinical Reference Laboratories." *Journal of Healthcare Information Management* 15 (3): 295–305.

Additional Readings

An increasing number of Internet journals are becoming available to administrators and clinicians in the healthcare field. See, for example, *technologyinpractice.com—*

an online journal with articles and news about information technology in medical practice.

Ball, M. J., and J. Lillis. 2001. "E-Health: Transforming the Physician/Patient Relationship." *International Journal of Medical Informatics* 61 (1): 1–10.

Coile, R. C. 2001. "Physician Executives Straddle the Digitial Divide." *Physician Executive* 27 (2): 12–19.

Combs, J. L. 2000. "Technology: Exploring the Realm of E-health." *Trustee* 53 (3): 26–28.

De Angelo, M. 2000. "Internet Solution Provides Important Component in Reducing Medical Errors." *Health Management Technology* 21 (2): 20–21.

Glaser, J. P. 2000. "Management Response to the E-health Revolution." *Frontiers of Health Services Management* 17 (1): 45–48.

Goldsmith, J. 2000. "The Internet and Managed Care: A New Wave of Innovation." *Health Affairs* 19 (6): 42–56.

Goldstein, D. E., and C. L. Toth. 2001. "MedDigital Trends and Tactics to Lead into the Future." *Physician Executive* 27 (2): 20–28.

Lutz, S. 2000. "E-Business Means Survival for Health Care Organizations in 2010." *Managed Care Quarterly* 8 (3): 1–8.

Parente, S. T. 2000. "Beyond the Hype: A Taxonomy of E-Health Business Models." *Health Affairs* 19 (6): 89–102.

Perez, K. 2000. "What .com Means for Materials Management." *Health Management Technology* 21 (2): 39.

Tabar, P. 2001. "The e-Business of Privacy." *Healthcare Informatics* 18 (3): 22, 24, 26.

———. 2001. "Fixing Healthcare's Supply Chain." *Healthcare Informatics* 18 (10): 16–20.

Terry, N. P. 2000. "Rating the Raters: Legal Exposure of Trustmark Authorities in the Context of Consumer Health Informatics." *Journal of Medical Internet Research* 2 (3): E18.

STRATEGIC DECISION-SUPPORT APPLICATIONS

The information systems applications discussed thus far are designed to support and enhance the delivery of care; support routine, day-to-day administrative operations; and improve patient access to health information and provider organizations. Although these systems provide many benefits to nurses, physicians, ancillary personnel, first-line managers, and patients, they tend to have little direct impact on the functions of senior managers. In fact, most senior healthcare managers have historically viewed information systems (IS) as operational tools with no particular relevance to their senior management role.

One possible explanation for this perception of IS is the tendency of senior managers to dismiss the role of data in the managerial decision-making process. Senior managers often view decision making as an art, based on such qualitative features as experience, judgment, insight, astuteness, and political savvy. Certainly these are all important components of the decision-making process. However, the increasing complexity created by managed care, patient demands, fixed revenues, and new approaches for delivering care requires managers to employ more sophisticated decision-making techniques, including systems specifically designed to support the decision-making process.

This chapter is designed to provide the senior manager with an understanding of these *decision-support systems*—"computer-based technology that aims to get the right knowledge in the right form to the right persons at the right time so they can better make decisions and make better decisions" (Holsapple and Joshi 2001, 40). Although the applications presented in previous chapters are typically used by a diverse group of clinicians, support staff, departmental managers, and patients, senior managers are the targeted users of the systems described in this chapter.

The Concept of Decision Support

Before the details of decision-support systems are considered, understanding the concept of *decision support* first is important. Stated simply, decision support can be viewed as an *approach* to problem solving that is based on the use of data. Many strategies might be considered for the actual *implementation* of this approach, ranging from a totally manual strategy to one that is totally automated. For example, consider the executive director of a multispecialty group practice faced with the decision of whether to sign a contract with a particular managed care plan. The contract provides for the group's physicians to be paid a fixed amount per month per patient to provide care to the plan's patient population.

The group's executive director can certainly make this decision based on intuition, the desire to generate additional revenue for the group, and/or a personal relationship established with the managed care plan. A better approach, however, is to obtain appropriate *data*, including the time availability of the group's physicians, the demographics of the patients belonging to the managed care plan, the healthcare services utilization patterns of these patients, and the costs incurred by the plan in providing various types of healthcare services. A *summarization* of this data provides a better understanding of the plan's patient population as well as the costs incurred by the group in providing care.

Using this understanding of the data, the executive director can then create a *model* that facilitates the computation of profitability as a function of variables such as payment mechanism, patient demographics, utilization patterns, method of delivering care, etc. By choosing reasonable values for these variables, the executive director can *examine* the expected consequences of signing the contract and thus come to an appropriate decision. In some cases the decision might involve choosing from among several alternative contract arrangements rather than the present simpler choice between accepting or rejecting a single contract. The steps followed by the executive director in deciding whether to sign the contract can be summarized in the flowchart shown in Figure 10.1. (See, for example, Austin and Boxerman 1995, Chapter 1 for a more complete discussion of managerial problem solving and decision making in healthcare organizations.)

Today's senior managers are typically faced with decisions that must be made within relatively short time frames and that require the analysis of large volumes of data. A manual approach to decision support is therefore impractical. Even with the use of spreadsheet or statistical software, the aggregation, management, analysis, and reporting of the data present a challenge to the timely completion of the decision-making process. It is no longer viable for senior managers to continue their past practice of requesting their data processing departments (perhaps renamed *information services*) to generate special reports to provide the data needed for making pressing decisions. Frequently, the turnaround time for producing these custom reports has extended beyond the decision's deadline date.

It is theoretically possible for the decision maker to create a custom computer-based solution each time a particular model and its data are defined. However, the decision maker would very likely prefer to have available an information system that provides ease of interaction, supports data retrieval and display, employs appropriate modeling, and reports results clearly and concisely. These features are offered by a decision-support system (DSS) and are summarized in Figure 10.2.

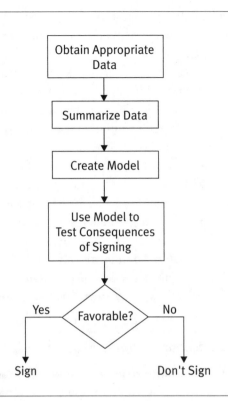

FIGURE 10.1
Steps for
Deciding
Whether to
Sign a Contract

- Interacting with the system is easy
- Retrieving and displaying data is supported
- Modeling capability is built in
- Reporting of results is clear and concise

FIGURE 10.2
Desirable
Attributes of
a Decision-
Support
System

An Overview of Decision-Support Systems

The field of DSSs has its roots in two main research areas: (1) theoretical studies of organizational decision making during the late 1950s and early 1960s and (2) technical developments during the 1960s. Since the early 1970s, DSS technology and applications have evolved significantly, offering improvements in both the efficiency as well as the effectiveness of the decision-making process (Shim et al. 2002).

Within healthcare, the concept of management DSSs began in response to the impending prospective payment system for Medicare patients and the related need for case-mix analysis. Beginning in the late 1970s and early 1980s, a parallel development in management decision modeling was initiated that combined industrial productivity systems engineering with units of hospital production (patient charges and procedures). These systems merged medical records data, patient billing data, utilization statistics, and human resources information to provide management with a basic decision-support model (Raco, Shapleigh, and Cook 1989).

The importance of these systems in today's healthcare environment has in no way diminished. A DSS is "invaluable for an organization to incorporate business intelligence. For health care organizations, using clinical, financial, and operational information in an integrated decision support data base to provide immediate access to health care practitioners and management is becoming crucial" (Shams and Farishta 2001, 26). Senior managers can use this technology to examine specific performance indicators and analyze their organization along clinical, operational, and strategic lines. As described in Chapter 7 clinicians are increasingly making use of this technology as well, perhaps even more than are senior healthcare managers.

A DSS can be characterized in terms of the components that comprise the system as well as the functions that the system performs for the user. Each of these two perspectives is presented below, followed by a review of the characteristics of useful management information.

Components of a Decision-Support System

An effective DSS must be more than a communication and data processing system; it must contain modules that combine to produce the desirable attributes highlighted in Figure 10.2. A conceptual model of the components comprising such a DSS is shown in Figure 10.3, and each component is discussed briefly in the following paragraphs.

User Interface   The user interface allows the senior manager to communicate easily with the DSS. Whether communication with the system uses a menu format or free-text input, the key objective is to ensure that the input process is as simple and intuitive as possible. The same issues associated with accessing databases (see the discussion of data manipulation languages in Chapter 6) are also applicable to the design of the user interface for a DSS.

Model   The system typically contains a model manager, which is software designed
Manager   to coordinate the creation, storage, and retrieval of the models that comprise the model library. Depending on the nature of the request made by the user of the DSS, a linkage to the appropriate model would be made so that the desired analysis can be obtained.

Model Library   An important component of a DSS is its model library, which consists of an array of analytical capabilities, including statistical, graphical, financial, and "what-if" models.

• Statistical models support such functions as summarizing data, testing hypotheses, performing forecasting, and constructing control charts.

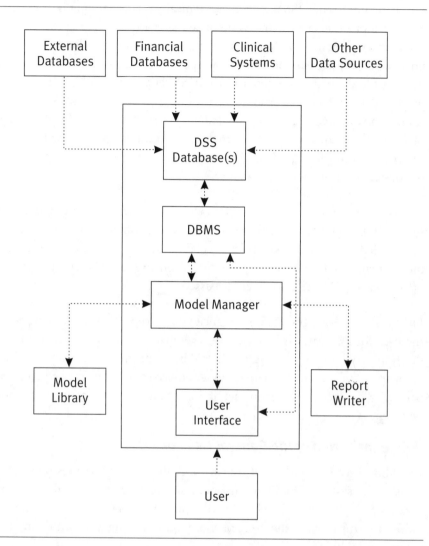

FIGURE 10.3
Conceptual Model of a Decision-Support System

- Graphical models facilitate the construction of graphical displays of data in a variety of formats, including scatter diagrams, pie charts, bar graphs, and multidimensional plots.
- Financial models provide the basis for performing break-even analysis, examining cash flows, and computing the internal rate of return associated with investments.
- "What-if" models allow users to determine how variations in one or more variables impact the value of an outcome of interest.

Depending on the type of decision being made, any of the models comprising the fields of operations research or management science might be utilized by the DSS. This use of modeling is in fact a major strength of DSSs.

Database   Fundamental to the DSS is a database, typically relational, that is designed for easy retrieval of needed data. As discussed later in this chapter, this database draws its contents from a number of sources, including a clinical repository, financial databases, data obtained from special studies, and external databases. Among the elements contained in the DSS database are (1) units of service produced, (2) resources consumed in producing those services, (3) data for assessing the quality of services provided, and (4) indicators of the effectiveness of services provided in meeting perceived community health needs. Keeping the contents of the DSS databases current often requires a staff person with the designation of database manager.

Database-
Management   Access to the databases in the DSS is facilitated by the database-management system (DBMS). For a specific decision-making problem, the DBMS retrieves
System   the needed data and makes them available directly to the user and/or the model manager for use in a specific decision model. The components and operation of a DBMS have been discussed in Chapter 6.

Report Writer   Finally, the value of the DSS is enhanced by its report writer, which provides the user with a clear, easily understood report containing the solution to the decision problem. Depending on the application, this report might provide a comparison of several alternatives under consideration, the consequences of a particular decision, or a recommendation of an optimum action that should be taken.

A Categorization of the General Uses of a DSS

In addition to the components of the DSS, interest also focuses on the functions of the system. The DSS must be designed to perform well in the organizational environment in which it will operate. Alter (1976) has categorized DSSs in terms of what the users of the systems actually do with them. These categories include

- systems in which the users retrieve isolated data items,
- systems used as a mechanism for ad hoc analysis of data files,
- systems that provide prespecified aggregations of data in the form of standard reports,
- systems that assist in estimating the consequences of proposed decisions,
- systems that propose decisions to management, and
- systems that make decisions according to predetermined decision algorithms.

Although proposed more than 25 years ago, Alter's categorization of these systems suggests an interesting paradigm for understanding the breadth of DSS capabilities. Figure 10.4 summarizes Alter's six categories and indicates for each category the type of contemporary DSS required. For example, the retrieval of isolated data items can be accomplished with any system having a database manager and direct-query capabilities. Similarly, to perform ad hoc analyses of a single data file one can use any of the many available generic statistical packages. Tables based on prespecified aggregations of data comprised the standard reports that were the mainstay of managerial applications run on mainframe computers for many years. Today, colorful graphs and charts supplement tabular output in the executive information systems gaining increasing use. These systems are discussed in more detail later in this chapter.

The last three categories proposed by Alter define today's traditional applications of a DSS. To estimate the consequences of a proposed decision, the manager can use a DSS with a "what-if" modeling capability. The addition of optimization modeling to the system supports the search for optimal decisions that can then be offered as a proposed solution. Finally, unlike the uses described thus far, where the DSS serves as a supplement to the decision maker, the last use involves systems that can actually make independent decisions. Such systems, often called expert systems, consist of a DSS that utilizes the science of artificial intelligence. More details of these systems are provided later in this chapter.

Shim et al. (2002) describe advances in DSS tools that facilitate uses beyond those suggested by Alter's categorization. The first tool, the *data warehouse*, provides "a solution for integrating data from diverse operational databases to support management decision-making" (Shim et al. 2002). It is subject oriented and contains a large amount of data. Many issues must be addressed in implementing a data warehouse, including data ownership, data integrity, and data reliability. Breen and Rodrigues (2001) offer a case study describing how a healthcare facility dealt with the challenges of such an implementation.

Alter's Categorization of Use	Type of System
Retrieve isolated data items	Simple database management system with query capability
Perform ad hoc analysis of a data file	Generic statistical package
Generate aggregation of data in a standard report	DSS with report generator; executive information system
Estimate consequences of a proposed decision	DSS with "what-if" modeling capability
Propose decisions to management	DSS with optimization modeling capability
Make decisions according to predetermined algorithms	Expert system; DSS with artificial intelligence

FIGURE 10.4
DSS Systems Corresponding to Alter's Categorization of Uses

Analysis of these data is facilitated by using a second tool, *online analytical processing* (OLAP). OLAP is "software for manipulating multidimensional data from a variety of sources that has been stored in a data warehouse. The software can create various views and representations of the data" (Power 1999). One application of OLAP is the extraction of data from an electronic patient record. Ebidia et al. (1999) describe the steps of such an implementation, including the creation of the analytical data warehouse that is accessible for analysis.

Web-based decision-support tools constitute a third tool. These systems facilitate making information for decision making available to managers in geographically distributed locations. "Using Web-based DSS, organizations can provide DSS capability to managers over a proprietary intranet, to customers and suppliers over an extranet, or to any stakeholder over the global Internet" (Shim et al. 2002). Breen and Rodrigues (2001) describe the value of coordinating the roll-out of their data warehouse with the launching of a new intranet in their facility. The authors suggest that "the data are of little value if you can't get to them, and the intranet is our method for accessing them" (Breen and Rodrigues 2001, 95).

Finally, cooperative work is facilitated through the use of a fourth tool—*group decision-support systems* (GDSS). A GDSS is "an interactive, computer-based system that facilitates solution of unstructured problems by a set of decision-makers working together as a group. It aids groups, especially groups of managers, in analyzing problem situations and in performing group decision making tasks" (Power 1999). Lam and Schaubroeck (2000) describe a study that compared GDSS with face-to-face group discussion regarding information exchange and decision quality. Participants given conflicting information tended to share more of their unique data and engage in more critical argumentation when using GDSS than when meeting face to face.

The Characteristics of Useful Management Information

The characteristics of useful management information were discussed in Chapter 2 and summarized in Figure 2.9. Because management information lies at the heart of DSSs, summarizing these characteristics again is useful. To be useful, management information must be

- *Information, not raw data,* intelligently processed in accordance with predesigned plans;
- *Relevant* to the purposes for which it is to be used;
- *Sensitive* enough to provide discrimination and meaningful comparisons for operating managers;
- *Unbiased* so as not to meet self-fulfilling management prophecies;
- *Comprehensive* so that all important elements of a system are visible to those charged with decision-making responsibility;
- *Timely* so as to be available in advance of the time when decisions or actions are required;

- *Action oriented* so as to facilitate the decision process rather than just present passive facts about current operations;
- *Uniform* so as to allow comparisons over time, both internally (against previous performance) and externally (against the experience of other institutions);
- *Performance targeted* so as to allow comparison with predetermined goals and objectives; and
- *Cost effective* so that the anticipated benefits obtained from having the information available exceed the costs of collecting and processing that information.

Information Needs for Decision Support

The overviews of decision support and DSSs have emphasized the important role of information. The characteristics of useful management information were summarized in the previous section. Two logical questions naturally arise from these discussions: What specific categories of information does the decision maker need? Where does the decision maker obtain this necessary information? This section addresses these two questions.

Categories of Information

Few would disagree that a variety of decision-support information is needed in the modern healthcare organization. In some cases, however, defining the exact items that should be maintained in the databases of a given organization is difficult. Shams and Farishta (2001) suggest that healthcare data can be classified into four categories: "[1] patient-centric data, which is related directly to patients; [2] aggregate data, which is based on performance and utilization/resource management data; [3] transformed-based data for planning, clinical, and management decision support; and [4] comparative data, incorporating health services research, outcomes measurement, and epidemiology" (26).

In November 2000, surveyors interviewed 30 healthcare provider organizations "to better understand how to turn clinical data into useful information in acute healthcare settings" and to explore "reasons for data warehouse successes and failures. . . . Most of those interviewed could not describe their organizations' goals for aggregate use of information" (Warner 2001, 30). Nevertheless, persons familiar with the healthcare industry realize that some basic categories of data or information needs exist. Examples of such categories are discussed below.

Information to Support Strategic Planning The organization's strategic information needs are dictated by contextual variables such as size, competitive environment, and structure, and they are dependent on the organization's strategic orientation. Porter's competitive analysis model, described by Austin, Trimm, and Sobczak (1995), offers a framework for understanding this relationship between strategic orientation and information requirements. The Porter model suggests that the strategy employed by the organization to compete in the marketplace—cost leadership, differentiation, or niche-focused strategy—will dictate how the IS must be tailored. The strategies and associated information needs are tabulated in Figure 10.5.

All three strategies require continuous monitoring of market share. However, organizations following a cost-leadership strategy must continuously monitor costs of services and productivity in reference to competitors. Those employing differentiation (provision of products or services that are different from those of the competition) will need to monitor measures of patient satisfaction, quality, and changes in the demographic characteristics of the marketplace. Product-line-management information will be essential for those organizations choosing to employ a niche-focused strategy.

Information to Support the Marketing Function   Austin, Trimm, and Sobczak (1995) describe how the Miles and Snow typology can provide a conceptual basis for identifying information helpful in supporting marketing efforts. The application of this model is summarized in Figure 10.6. According to this framework, healthcare organizations can be classified into one of the following categories:

1. *Prospectors:* those that continuously and aggressively pursue new markets
2. *Defenders:* those that try to be very good at what they do and follow a "stick to the knitting" approach to maintaining market share
3. *Analyzers:* those that do not rush into new markets and services but continuously track and analyze trends, technology, and consumer demand
4. *Reactors:* those that are undirected and respond to forces after changes in the marketplace have occurred

With regard to information needs, all of the strategic orientations require historical data on service utilization along with demographic projections to support forecasting demand for services. Also important is an understanding of the social and cultural determinants of service utilization

FIGURE 10.5
Porter's Strategies for Competing in the Marketplace and Associated Information Needs

Strategy	Information Needs
Cost Leadership	• Market share • Cost of services • Productivity relative to competitors
Differentiation	• Market share • Patient satisfaction • Quality • Changes in demographics characteristics of the marketplace
Niche Focused	• Market share • Product-line management information

Strategic Orientation	Information Needs
Prospectors	• Demographic changes • Market share • Product-line performance
Defenders	• Productivity • Costs • Quality factors
Analyzers	• Demographic changes • Market characteristics • Competitor performance
Reactors	• Information needs vary, depending on perceived threats and opportunities

FIGURE 10.6
Miles and Snow's Strategic Orientations to Marketing and Associated Information Needs

along with demographic indicators to help predict how these factors may change. Prospectors must continuously monitor market share, demographic changes, and product-line performance. Defenders will focus on productivity, costs, and quality factors. Analyzers need to track changes in demography, market characteristics, and competitor performance. The information needs of reactors will vary depending on perceived threats and opportunities that arise.

Information to Assist in Resource Allocation

To remain competitive and survive under the cost pressures associated with managed care, healthcare managers must be very efficient in their allocation and utilization of resources. When healthcare organizations were compensated on a "cost-plus" basis, wasteful utilization of resources was a tolerable, if not optimal, strategy. Today, however, providers typically receive a fixed payment so that the wise allocation of resources is quite important. The availability of accurate and timely information to assist in the resource-allocation process is a definite asset to the manager. Important items of information include cost estimates of personnel, materials, equipment, and other capital requirements for each program or major service line offered by the provider. In many cases, these data become the parameters in an optimization model such as linear programming, which allows the manager to solve for the "optimal" mix of programs that should comprise the organization's product lines. (See, for example, Austin and Boxerman 1995, Chapter 5.)

Information to Support Enhancement of Productivity and Operating Efficiency

Once the "optimum mix" of programs and services to be offered by the healthcare organization has been identified, the pressures of managed care make it incumbent that each program comprising this mix be operated in a productive and efficient manner. A number of improvement techniques have been successfully used by healthcare organizations, including benchmarking (Karpiel 2000) and reengineering (Walston, Kimberly, and Burns 2001). Common to these and other techniques for improving processes and systems is the important role of data in providing a basis for identifying the changes to be made and guiding the design and implementation of the new system (Benson 1996).

Harrison (1995, 245) emphasizes the difference between *process* benchmarking, which seeks to understand "how processes work differently from one organization to the next," and *outcome* benchmarking whose focus is on a "comparison of metrics from one organization to another." The power of process benchmarking as a process-improvement tool depends on the availability of data collected along process lines rather than the more traditional cost-center orientation. Specific data needs are cost data, defined as "operating cost per unit of throughput (e.g., cost per admission, cost per radiology procedure, etc.)"; process quality indicators such as "waiting times in the Admitting office, denied claims due to inadequate data capture, subsequent transfers because of off-unit admissions . . ."; and cycle times or throughput times at the process and subprocess levels (Harrison 1995, 248).

Benchmarking is not without its challenges. "Healthcare facilities have difficulty standardizing their data elements across different internal computer systems. . . . With this in mind, try to imagine what would happen if a multitude of healthcare facilities were to combine their patient information in a data warehouse. Would there be any standardization of data elements?" (Dols 2001, 184). The use of industry standards has helped somewhat to address this challenge, and the mandates of the Health Insurance Portability and Accountability Act (HIPAA) should provide additional standardization.

Information to Support Outcomes Assessment

Healthcare organizations must evaluate their performance on a continuous basis, both to improve the quality of services delivered and to meet the scrutiny of a variety of external constituents, including regulatory agencies, managed care organizations, business coalitions, and patients. In fact Kachnowski (1997, 27) suggests that "the future success of the provider organization relies on a system that probably costs less than any other system in [the provider's] budget, and consists of about one-to-two percent of [the provider's] total IS expenditures: the outcomes system."

The literature tends to indicate general categories, rather than specific items, of information needed for outcomes assessment. Aller and Rosenstein (1996, 22) suggest that payers, researchers, managed care officials, providers, and patients each have different outcomes information interests. These are summarized in Figure 10.7. As a result, the authors suggest the need for systems capable "of measuring indicators that span the gamut of health care activities to reflect outcomes related to cost, utilization, quality and patient satisfaction."

The use of outcomes measurements is no longer an optional activity for healthcare organizations. In February 1997, the Joint Commission on Accreditation of Healthcare Organizations (JCAHO) announced the ORYX® initiative, which integrates outcomes and other performance-measurement data into the accreditation process. It is intended to be a flexible and affordable

FIGURE 10.7

Categories of Outcomes Measurement Interests by Constituent Group

Constituent Group	Information Interests
Payers	• Overall costs of care • Information to identify cost-effective providers
Researchers	• Large epidemiological studies • Information to assess impact of care on health status of populations
Managed Care Officials	• Resource consumption assessments • Evaluation of cost efficiencies of care
Providers	• Evaluations of impact of care • Assessments of quality of care
Patients	• Functional benefits resulting from an intervention • Perceptual benefits resulting from an intervention

Source: Adapted from "Outcomes Measurement: Collecting Data for Payors, Providers and Patients," by K. Aller and A. Rosenstein. 1996. *InfoCare* (September–October): 22.

approach for supporting quality-improvement efforts in JCAHO-accredited organizations and for increasing the value of accreditation. The ORYX initiative allows JCAHO to review data trends and patterns and to work with organizations as they use data to improve patient care.

The ORYX initiative has clear implications for the IS in healthcare organizations because data must be collected on selected measures and submitted to their performance-measurement system(s) provided by a vendor that has been approved by JCAHO. The data are transmitted periodically to JCAHO who analyzes them using control and comparison charts to identify performance trends and patterns. During an accreditation site visit, the identified trends and patterns help the surveyors assess how well the healthcare organization uses selected core measure sets in their performance-improvement activities. By the end of June 2002, hospitals were to have chosen their measure sets based on the healthcare services they provide. Data collection was to have begun July 2002, and the first quarterly data report was due to JCAHO during January 2003 (JCAHO 2002).

Sources of Information

Three basic sources are available for obtaining the information needed for decision support in healthcare settings: internal transaction processing systems, specially constructed databases, and external data sources.

A number of internal transaction processing systems, described in previous chapters, are used in conjunction with the day-to-day delivery of healthcare. In addition to serving an important operational function, these systems contain information that has a great deal of value on an aggregate basis. For example, the admitting system stores a number of important sociodemographic

Internal Transaction Processing Systems

variables on each patient. When accumulated in a data repository, these data provide an excellent overview of the sociodemographics of the patients served by the healthcare organization.

Transaction processing systems also store valuable clinical information that indicates volumes of service provided as well as the results of laboratory tests or radiological procedures performed. Bear in mind that these transaction systems were initially installed to facilitate communication of test orders and results as well as to support the billing function. Only recently have senior managers begun to realize the importance of aggregating clinical information for decision-support purposes. Therefore, special attention must be given to the process of ensuring this aggregation so that the information is not lost when the patient is discharged.

If the DSSs interacted directly with the databases of the transaction processing systems, serious degradation in the transaction processing performance would occur. For that reason, either a copy or a subset of the transaction processing data is brought into the DSS database to support the DSS function.

Specially Constructed Databases   A number of items of information about the healthcare organization are needed for decision support, but they may not be collected by the internal transaction processing systems. Examples include patient satisfaction data, waiting times associated with various patient-flow processes, and times spent by nursing personnel in various categories of caregiving. A variety of data-gathering methodologies are required to obtain this needed information, including questionnaires and work sampling. The information gathered must then be stored in a database accessible to the DSS.

Similarly, many physicians and clinical departments, particularly in academic medical centers, will build and maintain dedicated databases. These systems store specific clinical information for a research study, maintain data to satisfy a physician's interest in various aspects of his or her practice, or support other uniquely defined departmental efforts. These systems are often a valuable source of information for a DSS.

External Data Sources   A number of decision-support applications will require information about the world outside of the healthcare organization. This information includes community demographic data, information on market share, age-specific national utilization data, information on physicians in the area, etc. Such information is available from a variety of sources, which are summarized in Figure 10.8.

The data obtained from sources such as those summarized in Figure 10.8 are frequently "raw data" requiring some degree of manipulation, or processing, to be useful for decision support. A number of commercial vendors offer databases containing a variety of information that has already been aggregated and edited so that it is ready for use by healthcare organizations. The manager evaluating the purchase of one of these commercial data products must compare the cost of the product with the cost of performing comparable

FIGURE 10.8
Some Sources
of "External"
Healthcare
Data

- Agency for Healthcare Research and Quality
- American Association of Health Plans
- American Hospital Association
- American Medical Association
- Bureau of Labor Statistics
- Census Bureau
- Center for Disease Control
- Centers for Medicare and Medicaid Services
- Health Insurance Association of America
- National Center for Health Statistics
- State Hospital Association Data Sets

analyses in-house. This evaluation process is one part of the larger question regarding how the entire DSS will be acquired, a question discussed in the next section.

Approaches to Acquiring and Implementing Decision-Support Systems

Once the healthcare manager has decided that decision-support capability is needed, a DSS must be acquired and implemented. Note that a DSS is software, so the options for obtaining any software capability also apply to the acquisition of a DSS. However, even though specialized software-generation tools are available to support in-house development, most healthcare organizations will choose to purchase their DSS capability. Health Management Technology's 2001 Resource Guide lists 62 vendors in its category labeled "Decision Support, Financial."

Two alternatives are available to the healthcare manager seeking to purchase a DSS. One option is to choose one of the many turnkey packages available for use in the healthcare industry. The term "turnkey" refers to the fact that these systems are delivered essentially ready for use, with little need to define the nature of the queries or reports that the users will desire. A number of vendors offer turnkey DSSs for a wide range of applications. Some vendors offer products in several categories, others have only a single product, while others offer a decision-support component to one of their transaction systems.

Healthcare organizations might find that a turnkey system fails to answer their information questions. They then need to consider a more sophisticated package that allows them to tailor the system to their specific needs. Although this tailoring process does not require programming expertise, it does require the "input" of people familiar with the business and clinical processes of the organization. For those healthcare organizations willing to expend the effort, the results are often well worth the effort.

Whether the DSS is purchased as a turnkey system or is tailored to the organization's specific needs, the system has no value without the availability of appropriate data. The data to support the DSS should not be stored as part of the organization's operational systems, but they should be stored in a separate database (or databases). The database(s) can range in size from a small departmental *data mart* to a large enterprisewide *data warehouse*. In most cases it will be the responsibility of the healthcare organization to copy data from internal or external sources into the database(s). This often is not an insignificant task. Furthermore, depending on how rapidly the source data change, daily, weekly, or monthly updates of the database(s) must be made if the DSS is to remain a timely source of information for the decision maker.

Healthcare managers planning for a new DSS must also bear in mind that the system will require attention beyond its initial installation. Some larger healthcare organizations employ a database administrator in the IS department who has responsibility for maintenance and oversight of databases and database-management systems.

The implementation of the DSS requires no less attention than the acquisition. Callan (2000, 86–87) suggests several issues that need to be addressed prior to implementation, including senior management's commitment to information as a key strategic objective, identification by senior management of performance measures and key critical success indicators, and transformation and cleansing of raw data prior to their storage in the database(s) of the DSS. With regard to the actual implementation, Callan (2000, 88–89) suggests establishing common nomenclature and data standards across the healthcare organization; adding appropriate infrastructure, such as a data warehouse, to support the implementation of the DSS; and implementing the DSS in stages beginning with delivering available information to users.

Decision-Support Applications

Management databases and related DSSs have been applied to a variety of problems facing healthcare managers and their organizations. Benefits reported from the use of these systems include "improved access to and awareness of revenue performance," "empowerment of end-users to generate their own reports," "ability to maintain historical data," and the determination of "true costs and profit potential of various types of cases . . ." (Evans 1997a, 37–38). Representative applications are reviewed in the following sections.

Financial Modeling Applications

A California insurance company uses a simplified version of a DSS to manage fixed-income portfolios worth $370 million and to analyze 36 different types of fixed-income securities and derivatives for risk and return (Sodhi 1996). Prior to implementing the DSS, the company accomplished these tasks with a spreadsheet, commercial software having a significant annual license fee, and manual methods. The new system was custom developed by a management science Ph.D. student using object-oriented programming, which facilitated the integration of mathematical models, database entities, and a user interface.

The DSS is used to perform a variety of tasks, including

- making trades,
- analyzing individual securities and portfolios,
- performing "what-if" analyses to determine the effect of potential trades on portfolios,
- performing structured query language (SQL)-based ad hoc queries for accounting-related issues,
- generating a variety of reports for the corporate board, and
- generating monthly reports for the accounting department.

The portfolio manager has expressed extreme satisfaction with the system, indicating that the program "has and should continue to be an invaluable tool in increasing portfolio returns" (Sodhi 1996, 33).

A Cleveland, Ohio, inpatient rehabilitation facility was worried about the effects of the inpatient rehabilitation prospective payment system on its continued financial success. To evaluate this impact they created a database, containing combined financial and clinical data, from which costs could be estimated by cost center and revenues could be estimated for each case-mix group (CMG)—the inpatient rehabilitation equivalent of diagnosis-related groups. Components included in the database were patient-level financial, clinical, and demographic data; a table of the facility's cost centers with cost-to-charge ratios listed by department; patient assessment data; and ICD-9 diagnosis codes.

The facility was able to anticipate the impact of the new prospective payment system on its revenue stream, to generate reports listing costs per discharge and per day for each CMG, and to allow physicians to compare their utilization patterns with the facility average for a given CMG. Plans called for incorporating a custom costing system, which the facility was developing, that would replace the Medicare cost-to-charge ratios to estimate costs (Rielinger 2001).

Planning and Marketing Applications

Healthcare managers have begun to catch up with users in other industries in applying geographic information systems (GISs) and mapping software to a variety of planning and marketing studies. "The term 'geographic information system' is often used, appropriately, as an umbrella term for a system designed to process any type of information that traditionally would have been recorded on maps" (Mallach 1994, 428). By using a GIS and mapping software, healthcare managers and planners are able to gain a better understanding of their customers and potential customers as well as their competitors.

Evans (1997b) describes several applications of GIS and mapping software. A New York managed care organization uses this software to determine if its members are able to access physicians and other healthcare providers within a reasonable amount of time. Prior to having the software, the organization used tabular charts or a blank zip-code map on which it manually filled in the information. Similarly, a large Wisconsin insurer describes its mapping software as "a great tool for demonstrating how easy employee groups can access [their] provider groups" (Evans 1997b, 60). Finally, a New York-based home health care provider employs a mapping-based program to find the best routes for its drivers and professional field staff. The software helps the company assign new patients "to the appropriate nurse or aide in the correct sequence" (Evans 1997b, 60).

Silver Cross Hospital and Medical Centers in Joliet, Illinois, is using its web site as a tool for obtaining information about its patients and prospective patients to build a relationship marketing database. This database will help the hospital to identify healthcare needs of consumers in Joliet as well as the broader geographic region surrounding the city. Their effort is part of a growing planning and marketing strategy in the healthcare industry called customer relationship management (CRM). A CRM plan is designed to help a hospital discover consumers' needs and to identify marketplace gaps that might exist (Rees 2000).

Resource Allocation Applications

Among the areas of application of DSSs to resource allocation processes in healthcare organizations are the following:

- *Labor planning*, including analysis of staffing patterns, determination of optimal staffing levels, and projection of future staffing needs
- *Supplies and facilities planning*, including minimization of costs, consolidation of vendors/sources, and standardization of products/break supplies
- *Equipment-utilization control*, including monitoring of equipment purchases, reviewing maintenance and lost charges, and determining future purchases

McClean and Millard (1995) describe a decision-support tool that improves the efficiency of bed management and thus facilitates the more effective use of resources. Input to the system comes from data downloaded from the patient administrative system. A query-by-example function enables the decision maker to separate data into meaningful subgroups, and a "what-if" capability allows proposed changes to the system to be assessed prior to their implementation.

Ruland (2001) describes the development of a DSS called CLASSICA that helps nurse managers in financial management, resource allocation, activity planning, and quality control. Nurse managers were active participants in the development of the system, helping to define information needs, data input, and output and interface requirements. A major goal of the system was to improve the nurse managers' competence in financial management and decision making.

Applications for Improving Operations

With cost control an imperative to survival in an era of managed care, health-care organizations are constantly looking for ways to improve the operation of the systems and processes within their organization. In many cases, the techniques that are available to accomplish these improvements use relatively straightforward models. The key is the presence of a DSS in which the data needed to apply the model are available, and a user-friendly interface enables managers with little technical background to use the system.

Mayo Clinic in Jacksonville, Florida, uses a DSS for their operating rooms that is "designed to help caregivers determine the total costs of inpatient and outpatient surgical cases while improving financial and clinical efficiency" (Siwicki 1995, 33). The system developer claims that although "most information systems for operating rooms are designed solely for scheduling or anesthesia recordkeeping, . . . [this system] encompasses every aspect of the surgical process, from scheduling and anesthesia to interoperative procedures and recovery" (Siwicki 1995, 33). A variety of reports regarding costs, equipment and facility utilization, and volumes can be generated. But of particular importance is the ability to manipulate the data once they are stored in the relational database of the system.

Stewart and Lockamy (2001) suggest that healthcare organizations can improve their competitiveness through the implementation of performance-measurement systems. The authors' model of such a system "views direct patient care, indirect patient care, and administration as the three primary, aggregate functions of a healthcare organization that need to be linked" (Stewart and Lockamy 2001, 49). Data are collected from each of these three functions to facilitate investigating three key aspects of performance: "*Effectiveness*—Is the organization doing the right things? *Efficiency*—Is the organization doing the right things with the minimum expenditure of resources? *Quality*—Is the organization exceeding the expectations of payers, patients, and internal customers?" (Stewart and Lockamy 2001, 50).

In closing, one point bears repeating. Although the systems described make data accessible and provide the modeling capability to allow alternatives to be evaluated, the user makes the final decision. Systems that go beyond data aggregation and modeling are discussed in the next section.

Expert Systems

The DSS applications discussed thus far represent the administrative analog to the passive clinical DSSs introduced in Chapter 7. These systems are able to collect, organize, and communicate data to the user. This section looks at a special type of administrative DSS, known as an *expert system*, which is the counterpart of the active clinical DSS. "Expert systems are man-machine systems with specialized problem-solving expertise. The 'expertise' consists of knowledge about a particular domain, understanding of problems within that domain, and 'skill' at solving some of these problems" (Power 1999).

Recall the three components of expert systems introduced in Chapter 7: (1) a *general knowledge base* (also known as a *rule base*), which contains the expertise of the system; (2) a *database*, which the knowledge base is matched against; and (3) a *rule-based inference engine*, which generates conclusions for consideration by the decision maker. Mallach (1994) suggests two additional components that might comprise the expert system: (1) a *user interface* that facilitates interaction between the system and the user and (2) *workspace*, where the system stores the facts about a situation. A possible conceptual model of an expert system composed of these components is shown in Figure 10.9.

The field of expert systems is part of a larger discipline, known as artificial intelligence, which attempts to simulate human problem-solving techniques in a computer environment. Although artificial intelligence programs date back to the 1950s, applications in healthcare first appeared in the 1970s. These early applications, developed at academic medical centers, typically had a clinical orientation, and several representative applications were described in Chapter 7. But expert systems can be beneficial to managers as well, particularly for recurring, tactical, structured types of problems. Representative applications are described below.

A Connecticut-based insurance company makes use of artificial intelligence to "find fraud and abuse in claims" (Siwicki 1996, 50). The system, which is capable of looking at vast amounts of data in a matter of minutes, identifies suspicious claims by looking for "subtle changes in behavior patterns" in a provider compared to his or her peer group. "By itself, a fraudulent claim might look normal. But when it's instantly compared with millions of other claims, . . . that normal-looking claim can be viewed in a new light"

FIGURE 10.9

Conceptual Model of an Expert System

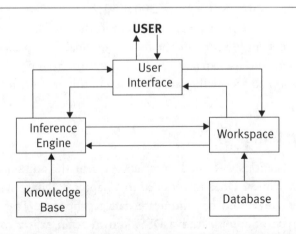

Source: Adapted from *Understanding Decision Support Systems and Expert Systems*, p. 461, by E. G. Mallach. 1994. Burr Ridge, IL: Irwin.

(Siwicki 1996, 50). Whereas considerable time was required to search for needed data when an allegation of fraud arose, the expert system has greatly reduced the time required to generate fraud and abuse reports and has made possible analyses of the behavior of providers.

The value of expert systems in fighting fraud has been emphasized more recently by Garcia (2002) who indicates that "fraudulent healthcare claims cost America's insurance industry more than $90 billion annually, according to the U.S. General Accounting Office" (32). Garcia (2002) credits software programs, which make "warehousing of data convenient while providing built-in tools to aid investigators in quickly evaluating the stored information," with helping to identify claims where questionable transactions are evident (34).

DeJesus (2000) describes several healthcare applications of expert systems. One system developed by a Connecticut company helps the user determine the correct ICD-9 code for a diagnosis by answering questions about details of the diagnosis. The system uses a "*decision tree* structure: each answer takes the user along a different branch, and a complete set of answers leads to a single leaf, a correct ICD-9 code" (DeJesus 2000, 55).

An alternative to the decision tree approach is the use of a *natural language*-based expert system. Rather than have users respond to specific questions, such a system would "take input from ordinary language, such as spoken or text descriptions of the diagnosis, then process that natural language to determine the correct code. The natural language approach saves time and effort by using existing text descriptions" (DeJesus 2000, 56).

Adoption of decision-support technology by healthcare managers (and clinicians, for that matter) has proceeded somewhat slowly. This very likely parallels the historical reluctance of managers to use data and quantitative modeling as part of their decision-making process. Perhaps, as Essex (2000, 74) suggests it reflects a "strong reluctance to relieve human experts of any decisions for which the legal system holds them ultimately responsible." Nevertheless, executives are becoming increasingly aware of their need to monitor the key indicators or critical success factors that indicate the financial and operational "health" of their organization. Managers can monitor these indicators using printed reports, or they can access the information electronically using one of the information systems described in the next section.

Executive Information Systems

An executive information system (EIS) is "an information system which draws from multiple applications and multiple data sources, both internal and external to an organization, to provide executives and other decision makers with the necessary information to monitor and analyze the performance of the organization" (van den Hoven 1996, 49). Healthcare managers are typically interested in a variety of measures indicating their organization's financial performance, clinical outcomes, human resources utilization, access and continuity, and customer satisfaction. The EIS—a specialized database-management system capable of query and data retrieval, graphic display, and report generation—can display values for all of these measures, or the manager might specify that only the values that have fallen "out of range" should be provided.

EISs are only as good as the information that is loaded into them. Development of a system requires that the healthcare organization has accurate clinical and business information that can be quickly downloaded to a data warehouse, where the information is consolidated into predefined formats and made accessible to the manager user. Utilization, in turn, depends a great deal on the design of the EIS.

The system must provide relevant and desired information in a simple, user-friendly manner, allowing managers to view their data in pictorial form or with tabular displays. A layered information format within the EIS facilitates probing for more detailed information about a particular measure, and an ongoing design issue is how deeply managers really want to delve into their data.

In fact, Poon and Wagner (2001) report on research showing that "although EIS and their successors are supposedly specifically tailored to top executives' information needs, few executives made significant direct use of them" (393). The authors go on to indicate that the "majority of executives did not rate EIS benefits very highly, . . . that implementation success cannot be taken for granted, and that even successful implementations might not be used as intended" (Poon and Wagner 2001, 393–394). As a matter of fact, the authors suggest that factors influencing the success or failure of general information systems might not apply to EISs.

Poon and Wagner (2001) suggest ten "critical success factors (CSFs)" that need to be met to ensure success of an EIS.

1. The EIS needs a committed and informed manager sponsor sufficiently committed to the EIS to invest time and effort.
2. The EIS needs an operating sponsor to manage the details of implementation.
3. An IS staff sufficiently knowledgeable to support the EIS must be assigned.
4. Appropriate hardware and software must be in place.
5. The EIS must have access to reliable internal and external data.
6. The EIS must be clearly linked to business objectives and provide added value.
7. Provision must be made to address the political resistance to an EIS system from groups who would prefer to keep their own data collection techniques.
8. The organization must be prepared for system evolution and demands by peers or subordinates for access to a similar system.

9. The EIS development methodology should be evolutionary, with the use of prototyping as new systems are introduced.
10. Managers' information needs must be defined early in the system development.

Concluding Comments

The development of DSSs requires an appropriate level of systems analysis and skilled system designers. Management's information needs and related information requirements must be fully understood and analyzed before a software system is installed. The systems analyst's responsibility is to pose appropriate questions, and the manager's responsibility is to provide answers prior to any system design or implementation.

Performance failures are most likely to occur when the development process lies at either extreme of the design spectrum. An overly simplistic design results in a system able to merely collect and aggregate data rather than to serve as a DSS. DSSs do not spring automatically from existing IS activities. Rather, they must be planned in advance according to a model or format specified by the managers who will use them. Information systems designed to produce periodic operating statistics for hospitals often simply aggregate data rather than break them down into meaningful categories, resulting in organizations that are "data rich and information poor."

At the other extreme, design teams often focus too much effort on developing overly sophisticated computing technology. These systems might have clever menus, sound effects, and "eye-catching" visuals, but they have limited ability to interface with operational information systems and to provide the manager with needed information. In some cases, the system developers feel it is necessary to include these "special features" to capture the manager's attention and interest.

These pitfalls can be minimized when the development process has the involvement and *sincere* interest of top management. Senior managers must look on the installation of a DSS in their organization as one of *their* strategic projects, rather than a necessary activity to be delegated to the IS staff.

Even when the managers have been a part of the development of a DSS, they have frequently been critical of the system's inability to account for many "intangible" components of the problem. In truth, the conceptual model depicted in Figure 10.3 represents what has been termed a "conventional DSS view of decision making, which scarcely considers anything but the technical perspective" (Courtney 2001, 30). Future systems will need to incorporate "unbounded systems thinking (UST)" taking into account not only "technical perspectives, . . . but also broad organizational and personal perspectives, and ethical and aesthetic issues, as well" (Courtney 2001, 18). At the heart of this newly configured DSS will be a new component—a *mental model*. This mental model will determine what is examined and what perspectives are developed, and it should allow the "nonquantifiable components" of a decision-making problem to be more easily incorporated into the solution. Perhaps this paradigm will facilitate increased use of DSSs by healthcare managers.

Summary

Decision-support systems (DSSs) enable senior managers to adopt an approach to problem solving that is based on the use of data. These data serve as input to a model from which alternatives can be generated and a proposed solution can be identified. Although this problem-solving approach could be implemented manually, a DSS has several favorable attributes, including ease of interaction, ability to retrieve needed data, ability to appropriately summarize data, built-in modeling capability, and a report writer.

DSSs can be characterized in terms of the components that comprise the system as well as the functions that the system performs. The six components of a DSS are: (1) a user interface, which allows easy communication with the system; (2) a model manager, which coordinates the creation, storage, and retrieval of the models used by the system; (3) the model library, which contains statistical, graphical, financial, and "what-if" models; (4) a database(s) containing data copied or extracted from sources such as the organization's transaction processing systems as well as external databases; (5) a database-management system, which retrieves the needed data; and (6) a report writer, which generates clear, easily understood reports.

DSSs can also be characterized in terms of the functions they perform: retrieve isolated data items, ad hoc analysis of data files, provide standard reports, assist in estimating the consequences of proposed decisions, propose decisions to management, and make decisions according to predetermined decision algorithms.

Management information needs in the modern healthcare organization include information to support strategic planning, the marketing function, resource allocation, enhancement of productivity and operating efficiency, and outcomes assessment. To be useful, the information must be relevant, sensitive, unbiased, comprehensive, timely, action oriented, uniform, performance targeted, and cost effective. A management database should include information on (1) units of service produced, (2) resources consumed in producing those services, (3) the quality of services rendered, and (4) indicators of effectiveness in meeting perceived community health needs.

The information needed for decision support in healthcare settings can be obtained from three basic sources: (1) internal transaction processing systems, which include a variety of financial, operational, and clinical measures; (2) specially constructed databases containing data obtained in special studies, attitudinal surveys, etc.; and (3) external data sources, including demographic, marketshare, utilization, and physician data.

A DSS today is typically purchased rather than developed in-house. Two alternatives are available for purchasing a DSS. One is to purchase a "turnkey" package that requires minimum preparation for use. If a "turnkey" system fails to meet the organization's needs, a more sophisticated package that can be tailored to those needs would be chosen. In either case, the system has no value without the availability of appropriate data. The data to support the DSS should be stored in a separate data mart, or data warehouse. Keeping this mart or warehouse current is often a full-time job performed by a database administrator.

Among the many applications of DSSs are (1) financial modeling, including analysis of investments and budgeting; (2) planning and marketing, including geographic information systems, mapping, and customer relationship management; (3) resource allocation, including labor, supplies, and facilities planning; and (4) operations improvement, including scheduling and performance-measurement systems.

A system that goes beyond the data storage, retrieval, modeling, and reporting capabilities of a DSS is known as an *expert system*. This system attempts to simulate human problem-solving techniques in a computer environment. An expert system consists of a *knowledge base* containing the system expertise, a *database* that the knowledge base is matched against, an *inference engine* that generates suggested conclusions, a *user interface* that links the user to the system, and *workspace* that serves as a "scratch pad."

Executive information systems (EISs) are sophisticated database-management systems with data retrieval, graphics, and report generator capabilities. The EIS requires that the organization have accurate internal and external information available to download into the system. EIS software products are available from several vendors or, occasionally, are developed in-house.

Information systems (IS) development in healthcare organizations has tended to focus primarily on applications that support day-to-day operations. Healthcare managers must begin to use IS *strategically* for survival and growth in the future. This requires that IS planning be guided by the strategic directions of the organization. The implementation of DSSs is one step in this reorientation.

Discussion Questions

10.1 Define the term decision support.
10.2 Discuss the factors that make having a DSS particularly important for today's healthcare managers.
10.3 Name and describe the six components that comprise a DSS.
10.4 According to Steven Alter, the uses to which DSSs are put fall into what six categories?
10.5 Give a brief definition of the following terms:

a. data warehouse

b. OLAP

c. web-based decision-support tools

d. Group decision-support systems

10.6 What are some of the characteristics of useful management information? How difficult do you believe it would be to build these characteristics into the design of a DSS?

10.7 What categories of information should be included in a management database?

10.8 Describe the three strategic orientations suggested by Michael Porter and the information needs associated with each of these orientations.

10.9 What is the relationship between information collected to assist resource allocation and optimization models like linear programming?

10.10 Explain the difference between process benchmarking and outcome benchmarking. What are the implications of this difference on information needs?

10.11 Briefly describe the information interests in outcomes measurements among the various healthcare constituent groups.

10.12 Describe the implications of ORYX on the information systems function.

10.13 Name and describe the sources of information for decision support.

10.14 Discuss the two ways of acquiring a DSS.

10.15 Provide a brief overview of applications that have been made of DSSs in healthcare.

10.16 Name and describe the components of an expert system. How does an expert system differ from a traditional DSS?

10.17 What is an executive information system? Describe how it differs from a DSS.

10.18 Describe the importance of senior manager participation in the process of developing an executive information system.

Problems

10.1 Assume you are the chief executive officer of a health system consisting of a corporate office, a 600-bed teaching hospital, a 400-bed community general hospital, and a 325-bed community general hospital. You plan to appoint a special task force to develop a DSS for your health system.

a. What do you suggest should be the composition of this task force?

b. Develop an outline of the talk you will give at the opening meeting of this task force. Your focus should be the charge that you will give to this task force as they begin carrying out this project.

10.2 Conduct an audit of the DSS of a healthcare organization in your locale. Determine the extent to which good management information is available for the following:

a. financial modeling, including budgeting and investment analysis;
b. marketing analysis, including overview of present patient population as well as a competitor analysis;
c. productivity analysis;
d. analysis of patient flow through a department, including waiting times and scheduling; and
e. measurement of outcomes.

10.3 Use either the organization contacted in Problem 10.2 or another healthcare organization to determine whether their DSS was purchased as a "turnkey" system or was tailored to their specific needs. In particular, determine the issues that were considered as part of their decision. Finally, determine the support staff required to maintain their DSS, including the updating of their data mart and/or warehouse.

10.4 Obtain information from vendors of three executive information system software packages. Compare and contrast the features of each of these packages. (The Internet serves as a good source for part of this information.)

10.5 Arrange an interview with a senior healthcare manager.
a. Determine how well this manager is able to articulate his/her data needs to support the decision-making function. In particular, discuss a recent decision-making exercise the manager was engaged in and define the specific data that the manager used in reaching the final decision.
b. Determine how well the manager's data needs are being met by his/her organization.
c. Determine whether the manager makes use of an executive information system.

References

Aller, K., and A. Rosenstein. 1996. "Outcomes Measurement: Collecting Data for Payors, Providers and Patients." *InfoCare* (September-October): 22–24.

Alter, S. L. 1976. "How Effective Managers Use Information Systems." *Harvard Business Review* 54 (November-December): 97–104.

Austin, C. J., and S. B. Boxerman. 1995. *Quantitative Analysis for Health Services Administration*. Chicago: AUPHA/Health Administration Press.

Austin, C. J., J. M. Trimm, and P. M. Sobczak. 1995. "Information Systems and Strategic Management." *Health Care Management Review* 20 (3): 26–33.

Benson, H. R. 1996. "Benchmarking in Healthcare: Evaluating Data and Transforming It into Action." *Radiology Management* 18 (1): 40–46.

Breen, C., and L. M. Rodrigues. 2001. "Implementing a Data Warehouse at Inglis Innovative Services." *Journal of Healthcare Information Management* 15 (2): 87–97.

Callan, K. 2000. "Preparing for a Decision Support System." *Topics in Health Information Management* 21 (1): 84–90.

Courtney, J. F. 2001. "Decision Making and Knowledge Management in Inquiring

Organizations: Toward a New Decision-Making Paradigm for DSS." *Decision Support Systems* 31 (1): 17–38.

DeJesus, E. X. 2000. "Achieving Expert Ease." *Healthcare Informatics* 17 (1): 55–56, 58, 60–61.

Dols, V. 2001. "Challenges Faced by E-Healthcare Comparative Data Warehouses." *Journal of Healthcare Information Management* 15 (2): 183–88.

Ebidia, A. et al. 1999. "Getting Data Out of the Electronic Patient Record: Critical Steps in Building a Data Warehouse for Decision Support." Proceedings from AMIA Annual Symposium, pp. 745–49.

Essex, D. 2000. "Long-Awaited Technology Eases into Healthcare, May Stimulate e-Business." *Healthcare Informatics* 17 (2): 74, 76.

Evans, J. 1997a. "The Virtual Focus Group: Decision Support Systems." *Health Management Technology* 18 (6): 36–38, 52.

———. 1997b. "The Lay of the Land: GIS and Mapping Software." *Health Management Technology* 18 (5): 58, 60.

Garcia, J. L. 2002. "Using Technology to Fight Fraud." *Health Management Technology* 23 (1): 32, 34.

Harrison, M. 1995. "Process Benchmarking in Health Care." In *Proceedings of the 1995 Annual HIMSS Conference,* Volume 3, pp. 241–52. San Antonio, TX: Healthcare Information and Management Systems Society.

Health Management Technology. 2001. Resource Guide. [Online information; retrieved 2/7/02]. www.healthmgttech.com.

Holsapple, C. W., and K. D. Joshi. 2001. "Organizational Knowledge Resources." *Decision Support Systems* 31 (1): 39–54.

Joint Commission on Accreditation of Healthcare Organizations. 2002. "Oryx/ Performance Measurement." [Online information; retrieved 6/30/02]. http://www.jcaho.org/oryx_frm.html.

Kachnowski, S. 1997. "Outcomes Management: A System Long Overdue." *Healthcare Informatics* 14 (1): 27–29, 32–33.

Karpiel, M. S. 2000. "Benchmarking Facilitates Process Improvement in the Emergency Department." *Healthcare Financial Management* 54 (5): 54–59.

Lam, S. S., and J. Schaubroeck. 2000. "Improving Group Decisions by Better Pooling Information: A Comparative Advantage of Group Decision Support Systems." *Journal of Applied Psychology* 85 (4): 565–73.

Mallach, E. G. 1994. *Understanding Decision Support Systems and Expert Systems.* Burr Ridge, IL: Irwin.

McClean, S., and P. H. Millard. 1995. "A Decision Support System for Bed-Occupancy Management and Planning Hospitals." *IMA Journal of Mathematics Applied in Medicine and Biology* 12 (3–4): 249–57.

Poon, P., and C. Wagner. 2001. "Critical Success Factors Revisited: Success and Failure Cases of Information Systems for Senior Executives." *Decision Support Systems* 30 (4): 393–418.

Power, D. J. 1999. "Decision Support Systems Glossary." [Online article; retrieved 6/30/02]. http://DSSResources.COM/glossary/.

Raco, R., C. Shapleigh, and D. Cook. 1989. "Decision Support in the 1990s: The Future Is Now." *Computers in Healthcare* 10 (12): 26–29.

Rees, T. 2000. "Illinois Hospital Using Web to Build Database for Relationship Marketing." *Profiles in Healthcare Marketing* 16 (4): 1, 3, 4–9.

Rielinger, J. A. 2001. "Preparing for the Impatient Rehabilitation PPS." *Healthcare Financial Management* 55 (12): 52–55.

Ruland, C. M. 2001. "Developing a Decision Support System to Meet Nurse Managers' Information Needs for Effective Resource Management." *Computers in Nursing* 19 (5): 187–193.

Shams, K., and M. Farishta. 2001. "Data Warehousing: Toward Knowledge Management." *Topics in Health Information Management* 21 (3): 24–32.

Shim, J. P. et al. 2002. "Past, Present, and Future of Decision Support Technology." *Decision Support Systems* (in press).

Siwicki, B. 1995. "Slicing Costs in the OR." *Health Data Management* 3 (9): 33–34.

———. 1996. "Artificial Intelligence." *Health Data Management* 4 (4): 46–48, 50–53.

Sodhi, M. 1996. "Development of a DSS for Fixed-Income Securities Using OOP." *Interfaces* 26 (2): 22–33.

Stewart, L. J., and A. Lockamy, III. 2001. "Improving Competitiveness Through Performance-Measurement Systems." *Healthcare Financial Management* 55 (12): 46–50.

van den Hoven, J. 1996. "Executive Support Systems and Decision Making." *Journal of Systems Management* 47 (2): 48–55.

Walston, S. L., J. R. Kimberly, and L. R. Burns. 2001. "Institutional and Economic Influences on the Adoption and Extensiveness of Managerial Innovation in Hospitals: The Case of Reengineering." *Medical Care Research & Review* 58 (2): 194–228; discussion 229–33.

Warner, H., Jr. 2001. "Mining the Gems: Strategies to Help CIOs Effectively Use Clinical Databases While Avoiding the Data Warehouse Money Pit." *Health Management Technology* 18 (10): 30–32.

Additional Readings

Abidi, S. S. 2001. "Knowledge Management in Healthcare: Towards 'Knowledge-Driven' Decision-Support Services." *International Journal of Medical Informatics* 63 (1–2): 5–18.

Backiel, R. B., II. 2001. "Successful Database Benchmarking: What Do We Need?" *Journal of Healthcare Information Management* 15 (2): 177–82.

Bhatt, G. D., and J. Zaveri. 2002. "The Enabling Role of Decision Support Systems in Organizational Learning." *Decision Support Systems* 32 (3): 297–309.

Coddington, D. C. 2002. "Leading IDSs Heed the Call to Invest in IT." *Healthcare Financial Management* 56 (2): 36–40.

DeGruy, K. B. 2000. "Healthcare Applications of Knowledge Discovery in Databases." *Journal of Healthcare Information Management* 14 (2): 59–69.

Diers, D., C. Torre, Jr., D. M. Heard, J. Bozzo, and W. O'Brien. 2000. "Bringing Decision Support to Nurse Managers." *Computers in Nursing* 18 (3): 137–144, 146.

Dutta, A., and S. Heda. 2000. "Information Systems Architecture to Support Managed Care Business Processes." *Decision Support Systems* 30 (2): 217–225.

Einbinder, J. S., K. W. Scully, R. D. Pates, J. R. Schubart, and R. E. Reynolds. 2001. "Case Study: A Data Warehouse for an Academic Medical Center." *Journal of Healthcare Information Management* 15 (2): 165–75.

Elliott, J. 1996. "Making the Executive Decision." *Healthcare Informatics* 13 (7): 33–34, 36, 38.

Garvin, D. A. 1993. "Building a Learning Organization." *Harvard Business Review* (July-August): 78–91.

Goel, V., J. Moehr, and G. Browman. 1998. "The Role of Group Support Technology in Developing the HEALNet Research Agenda." *International Journal of Medical Informatics* 51 (2–3): 215–19.

Hristovski, D., M. Rogac, and M. Markota. 2000. "Using Data Warehousing and OLAP in Public Health Care." Proceedings from AMIA Annual Symposium, pp. 369–73.

Kelly, B. 2001. "Stacking the Shelves With Data." *Health Data Management* 9 (2): 122, 124,126.

Kolar, H. R. 2001. "Caring for Healthcare." *Health Management Technology* 22 (4): 46–47.

Laureto-Ward, R. A. 1996. "Searching for the Perfect EIS." *Healthcare Informatics* 13 (7): 74.

Marietti, C. 2000. "Diamond Mining." *Healthcare Informatics* 22 (7): 47–48, 50, 52.

Orefice, J. J. 2001. "Moving to the Next Level." *Health Management Technology* 22 (7): 46–47.

Pedersen, M. K., and M. H. Larsen. 2001. "Distributed Knowledge Management Based on Product State Models: The Case of Decision Support in Health Care Administration." *Decision Support Systems* 31 (1): 139–58.

Porter, M. E. 1985. *Competitive Advantage*. New York: Free Press.

———. 1980. *Competitive Strategy: Techniques for Analyzing Industries and Competitors*. New York: Free Press.

Prince, L. H., and A. Carroll-Barefield. 2000. "Management Implications of the Health Insurance Portability and Accountability Act." *Health Care Manager* 19 (1): 44–49.

Rao, S. K. 2000. "Marketing Decision Support Systems for Strategy Building." *Marketing Health Services* 20 (2): 14–18.

Rivers, J. A., and P. A. Rivers. 2000. "The ABCs for Deciding on a Decision Support System in the Health Care Industry." *Journal of Health & Human Services Administration* 22 (3): 346–53.

Simpson, R. L. 2000. "Minding the Store: How IT Impacts Outcomes Measurement." *Nursing Administration Quarterly* 24 (2): 87–90.

Stearns, F. E., and J. Mazie. 1996. "Using PC-Based Decision-Support Technology to Improve Efficiency." *Healthcare Financial Management* 50 (11): 39–41.

Valusek, J. R. 2002. "Decision Support: A Paradigm Addition for Patient Safety." *Journal of Healthcare Information Management* 16 (1): 34–39.

Wood, M. T. 2000. "Changing the Rules in Enterprise Data Warehousing." *Health Management Technology* 21 (9): 56–58.

Planning and Project Management

11

STRATEGIC INFORMATION SYSTEMS PLANNING

Strategic information systems (IS) planning is the process of identifying and assigning priorities to the applications of information technology that will assist an organization in executing its business plans and achieving its strategic goals and objectives. With healthcare organizations growing in size and complexity and information technology becoming increasingly sophisticated, the need for careful system planning is paramount. Managers must take responsibility for an orderly planning process to ensure that information technology is used to support the strategic priorities of the organization.

In recent years, IS priorities have changed to focus on integration of systems across multiple facilities, automation of patient records, and improved decision support for clinicians and managers. Achieving these complex objectives requires a careful planning process to develop a flexible information architecture that facilitates data exchange and provides user access to information remotely from all locations.

Historically, information systems in some healthcare organizations evolved in a piecemeal fashion rather than resulted from a carefully controlled planning process. Specific requirements for capturing data, storing them, and retrieving them when needed developed on an ad hoc basis as new programs and services were added. As a result, the same data were captured repetitively, files were duplicated needlessly, and information was not always available when needed. If an IS planning process is not in place, priorities for development of individual computer applications often are established by the exigencies of the moment.

Gabler (2001) points out that governing boards and senior managers of healthcare organizations are increasingly concerned about the business value of investments in information technology and want assurances that information systems will deliver strategic benefits to the enterprise. Strategic IS planning has assumed higher priority as a result. In 1996, 35 percent of the respondents to the Healthcare Information and Management Systems Society Annual Leadership survey indicated that their organizations did not have a strategic IS plan (HIMSS 1996). In January 2002, only 8 percent of the responding organizations indicated that they did not have such a plan in place (HIMSS 2002).

This chapter presents an overview of the process of IS planning in healthcare organizations. Topics covered include the purposes of planning, the importance of system integration, organizing a planning effort, the elements of a strategic IS plan, and the development of enterprisewide standards and policies.

Purposes of Strategic Information Systems Planning

Strategic IS planning serves multiple purposes in the healthcare organization. The most important of these are listed in Figure 11.1 and discussed briefly below.

Strategic Alignment with Organizational Goals and Objectives

Information systems should support the strategic goals, objectives, and priorities of the organization they serve. As healthcare organizations become more sophisticated in IS planning and management, they use information more effectively in strategic positioning within the environment in which they operate (Austin, Trimm, and Sobczak 1995, 27).

Historically, hospitals and other healthcare organizations have employed information technology to support day-to-day operations. Increasingly, healthcare managers are recognizing the role of information systems in increasing market share, supporting quality assessment and improvement, and adding value to the organization. To accomplish these strategic objectives, the IS plan must be closely aligned with the strategic plans of the organization. Because these objectives change over time, the information technology plan should be reviewed frequently to ensure it remains in alignment with current organizational strategy.

Turisco (2000) calls for value management in justifying information technology investments: "There is a growing demand for ensuring that healthcare [information technology] IT investment practices and processes not only justify the large cash outlays, but track and realize the value. . . . Values can only be realized through measurable business changes supported by the business units."

Definition of Information Requirements and Priorities

Given limited resources and pressures for cost containment, healthcare organizations must make choices and set priorities for their information systems. Consequently, the IS plan should identify the major types of information required to support strategic objectives and establish priorities for installation

FIGURE 11.1
Purposes of
Strategic
Information
Systems
Planning

- To align information systems goals with strategic goals and objectives of the organization
- To define specific information requirements and priorities
- To define the information technology infrastructure of the organization
- To develop a budget for resource allocation

of specific computer applications for the time period covered by the plan (normally about five years).

Definition of the Information Technology Infrastructure

The third essential purpose of strategic IS planning is more technical in nature. To meet strategic objectives and develop high-priority applications, the health-care organization must develop blueprints for its information technology infrastructure. This involves decisions about hardware configuration (architecture), network communications, degree of centralization or decentralization of computing facilities, and types of computer software required to support the network.

The 2002 HIMSS Annual Leadership Survey (HIMSS 2002) identified the following information technology infrastructure priorities:

- high-speed networks,
- intranets (internal communications using Internet technology),
- client-server systems, and
- wireless information appliances.

Budgeting and Resource Allocation

The final purpose of strategic IS planning is to provide data to estimate the resources required to meet the objectives and priorities established through the planning process. Planning will provide the basis for development of operating and capital budgets for information technology in the organization.

The Importance of System Integration

System integration is one of the most important objectives of strategic IS planning. Healthcare organizations are highly interconnected enterprises. Units of the organization must be able to communicate with one another and share information. Clinicians need information that is generated by several different departments. Mixing of clinical and financial information is essential for effective management and strategic decision support.

Healthcare organizations also need to be connected externally to a variety of organizations, including business partners and other providers in an integrated delivery network, to mention only two.

Oas (2001) states that system integration has been slow in coming to healthcare. Information systems developed in the 1980s focused on billing and business office functions. Most of these systems contained limited clinical information. In the 1990s, emphasis shifted to automation of clinical processes and provision of access to clinical data to individuals across the enterprise. Seamless integration and information sharing is essential in today's environment.

Achieving system integration requires careful front-end planning prior to the selection and acquisition of computer hardware and software. Some of the technical aspects of data and software integration were discussed in Part II of this book. The planning processes described in the remainder of this chapter are essential to help ensure that systems are connected for information sharing across the organization.

Organizing the Planning Effort

The development of information systems in a modern healthcare organization is a complex task involving major capital expenditures and significant manpower commitments if the systems are to function properly. Development of an overall master plan for IS development is an essential first step in the process. To exclude this critical planning activity would be analogous to beginning a major construction project without functional specifications for the new building. Yet, many organizations have moved directly into the acquisition of computer systems without any kind of master plan.

The chief executive officer (CEO) should take direct responsibility for organizing the planning effort. An IS steering committee should be formed with representatives from major elements of the organization, including the medical staff, nursing staff, financial management, human resources management, planning and marketing, facilities management, clinical support services, and information technology staff. The committee should be directed by a senior manager, preferably the chief information officer (CIO) if such a position has been established. Strategic information planning is primarily a managerial function, not a technical one. A suggested organizational chart for the planning effort is shown in Figure 11.2. Steering committee members should serve as chairs for the subcommittees; additional personnel from the organization and technical consultants can be appointed members of specific subcommittees as needed.

Consideration also should be given to use of outside consultants if additional technical expertise is needed. However, consultants should be chosen carefully. They should possess technical knowledge of systems analysis and computer systems and should be well informed about healthcare organizations. Consultants must be independent practitioners not associated with any equipment manufacturer or firm that sells software. Finally, consultants should be familiar with the latest technological developments but are able to resist the temptation to push for applications that are too close to the leading edge.

Lohman (1996) suggests that the following factors be considered in selecting an IS consultant:

1. *Independence and objectivity:* The consultant should exclusively focus on the interests of the client.
2. *Healthcare expertise:* The consultant should have an understanding of healthcare business and clinical issues.

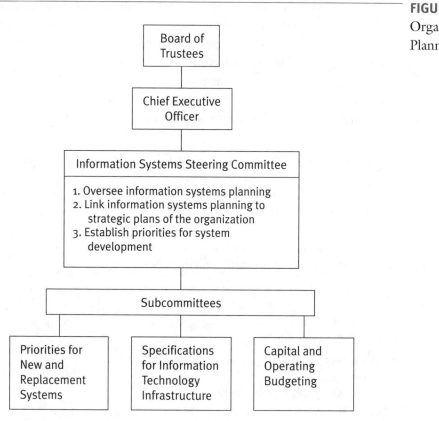

FIGURE 11.2

Organizing the
Planning Effort

3. *Resources:* The consultant should have sufficient breadth and depth of resources to complete the assignment without "on-the-job training."
4. *Effective personality:* The consultant should have an appropriate mix of character traits and skills.

Consultants should be used as sources of technical information and as facilitators of the planning process. They should not be employed to do the planning; this must be the responsibility of knowledgeable managers and users of information within the organization itself. Before using a consultant's "off-the-shelf" planning product, ensure that the planning methodology is compatible with the organization's culture and strategic priorities.

The CEO should ensure that staff members participating on the steering committee are provided sufficient released time from their normal duties so that they can participate fully in the planning efforts. Released time estimates should be drawn up in advance, and formal written notification of this should be provided to all involved. The administration and board of trustees should be prepared to spend a significant amount of the institution's manpower resources on carrying out this important task.

As stated above, the organization's CIO should chair the steering committee, if the CIO position has been established. Reporting directly to the CEO or COO, the CIO serves two important functions: (1) assisting the senior management team and governing board in using information to support strategic planning and management and (2) providing management oversight and coordination of information systems and telecommunications throughout the organization. The CIO's role is further discussed in Chapter 14.

Elements of a Strategic Information Systems Plan

Figure 11.3 lists the major elements that should be included in the strategic IS plan. These are also discussed in the following section.

FIGURE 11.3
Elements of the
Information
Systems
Strategic Plan

1. Statement of corporate/institutional goals and objectives

2. Statement of information systems goals and objectives
   a. Management information needs
   b. Critical success factors
   c. Information priorities

3. Priorities for the applications portfolio
   a. Clinical
   b. Management/Administrative
   c. Electronic networking and e-health
   d. Strategic decision support

4. Specification of overall systems architecture and infrastructure
   a. Level of distribution
   b. Network architecture
   c. Data location (central data warehouse to total data distribution)
   d. Integration via Internet (Webgration)
   e. Database security and control requirements

5. Software development plan
   a. Commercial packages
   b. In-house development
   c. Contract software development
   d. Application services providers
   e. Combinations of the above

6. Information systems management and staffing plan
   a. Central information systems staffing and control
   b. Limited central staffing in support of department-level information systems
      staff
   c. Outsourcing
   d. Combinations of the above

7. Statement of resource requirements
   a. Capital budget (hardware, software, network communication equipment)
   b. Operating budget (personnel, supplies, consultants, training, etc.)

Corporate Goals and Objectives

The plan should begin with a review and concise statement of major organizational goals and objectives for the planning period (usually two to five years). IS goals and objectives should be aligned with the strategic objectives of the organization. For example, if continuous quality improvement is a major priority, then this goal should be reflected in the priorities for IS development, paying particular attention to medical records; clinical protocols; incident reporting; and measures of patient, physician, and employee satisfaction. If diversification and expansion of the market service base are strategic objectives, then information systems should focus on utilization analysis and forecasting, analysis of changes in the demographic profile of the service market, and analysis of resource requirements for new service development. If an urban medical center has placed priority on expansion of ambulatory care services, but IS priorities continue to focus on inpatient services, then the organization has a serious problem of goal displacement.

In a classic *Harvard Business Review* article, Rockart (1979) proposed that critical success factors be used in defining information requirements and IS goals during the planning process. Top management needs to define these requirements but often have difficulty describing their needs for management information. By specifying those critical areas where things must go right for the organization to flourish, managers assist the IS planning team in determining information requirements and setting priorities for system development.

Information System Goals and Objectives

IS objectives should be as specific as possible and should flow from a review of strategic priorities and an analysis of deficiencies and gaps in current information processes. Avoid general statements of objectives such as "information systems for Metropolitan Health System should be designed to improve the quality of care and increase the efficiency of system operations." Such statements are self-evident and nonfunctional as far as planning is concerned. Rather, a detailed list of objectives should be established that will provide specific targets against which future progress can be measured and systems can be evaluated. Examples of specific objectives might include the following:

1. Information systems for the health plan should be designed such that all records from the master patient index file are available online to all physicians in the plan.
2. Information systems for the clinic should be designed such that all diagnostic test results are available online within two hours after the tests have been completed.
3. Information systems should be designed so that information on inpatient and outpatient activity by major diagnostic categories is reported to corporate management on a monthly basis, with reports indicating the health system's share of the total services provided in the market area.

4. Disease-management protocols for the ten highest volume chronic conditions should be available online and should be used to provide automatic reminders to all physicians practicing in the hospital.

Applications Priority List

Healthcare organizations will not be able to acquire all the systems they need in any given year. The statements of corporate and IS objectives will aid the steering committee in preparing a priority list of individual computer applications to be acquired. The applications priority list, in turn, will be essential in planning how limited resources can be used to have the greatest impact on strategic priorities.

The applications list should consider the needs of all major functional areas of the healthcare organization for clinical, management/administrative, e-health, and strategic decision-support systems. Both new and replacement systems should be considered, and the need for major changes to existing systems should be reviewed as well. Applications should be rank ordered in the recommended sequence for implementation, and items on the applications priority list should be linked to specific organizational strategies. If an IS steering committee determines that financial control is the most pressing organizational problem, the development of a new financial information system might assume highest priority.

Many healthcare organizations have initiated programs of business process reengineering to achieve operational efficiency through dramatic improvement in core processes used in the organization. Many of these reengineering projects involve development of new information systems, and these should be considered by the IS steering committee in developing the applications priority list.

After these steps have been completed, the steering committee should report preliminary results back to the CEO and board of trustees. The statement of objectives and priority lists should be carefully reviewed and modified as necessary.

Systems Architecture and Infrastructure

Specification of overall systems architecture is a critical task in the planning process. The plan must specify an overall system architecture and infrastructure to include

1. the degree to which computing will be centralized or decentralized throughout the organization;
2. the network architecture that specifies how computers and workstations will be linked together through communication lines and network servers;
3. the manner in which data will be stored and distributed throughout the organization, including database security and control requirements; and

4. the manner by which individual applications will be linked so that they can exchange information.

Options for information exchange include a multivendor ("best of breed") approach with interfaces developed to link the various applications; a single-vendor approach in which applications are already integrated in the vendor's package; and use of Internet technology to link applications, sometimes referred to as "Webgration" (Oas 2001).

Opinions differ about the degree to which computing should be centralized or decentralized in healthcare organizations. Proponents of centralization argue that this approach facilitates system integration and provides better control over the costs of hardware and software. Central control may reduce unnecessary duplication of data entry and storage. In addition, technical staff expertise can be maximized by concentrating IS professionals in one central unit.

Proponents of decentralization argue that this approach places control of IS back where it belongs—in the hands of users. Decentralization fosters innovation in system design and develops increased user interest and support. Local flexibility is maintained, and the frustrations of lengthy programming and processing backlogs at a central facility are avoided.

Chapter 5 includes a detailed description of alternative network architecture configurations, including

1. central mainframe architecture,
2. client/server architecture,
3. file/server architecture, and
4. distributed processing architecture.

Data distribution plans will help determine which type of network architecture should be employed by the healthcare organization. Alternatives range from creation of large, centralized (enterprisewide) "data warehouses" to complete distribution of data in which each organizational unit on the network maintains its own database.

Many healthcare organizations, particularly integrated delivery systems (IDSs), are moving toward a combination of approaches to data distribution. For example, the IDS might develop a centralized data warehouse containing a master patient index and computerized records for all patients in the system. Individual organizational units (hospitals, ambulatory care centers, etc.) might maintain their own data files for patient appointments, employee records, inventory control, budgeting, and financial management. The telecommunications network supporting the system will be designed to facilitate electronic exchange of information so that patient records are accessible at all treatment sites and financial information can be transmitted to corporate offices on a periodic basis. In addition to network architecture, the plan should specify how the infrastructure will support related activities such as audio, video, and wireless communications; document imaging; and radiographic imaging.

Regardless of the approach followed for data distribution and system integration, data standards will be required. This topic is discussed in detail later in this chapter. Data security and protection of information confidentiality is the subject of Chapter 13.

The subcommittee that reviews systems architecture (see Figure 11.2) must include competent technical staff and/or consultants working closely with representatives of management, the medical staff, and other major system users.

Software Development Plan

The IS plan should also specify procedures for software development. In the early days of healthcare computing (1960s to 1980s), most hospitals and other healthcare organizations employed a staff of computer analysts and programmers to develop computer applications in-house. Today, most healthcare organizations rely primarily on software packages purchased from commercial vendors. A wide array of software products are available; see, for example, the annual Resource Guide published by *Health Management Technology* magazine, which is available online at www. healthmgttech.com.

Use of Applications Service Providers (ASP) is another alternative for software acquisition that is growing in popularity among healthcare organizations. An ASP is an organization that contracts with a healthcare provider to access and use applications on an off-site server on a subscription basis (Monohan 2001). Many large healthcare organizations and IDSs will use combinations of these software development options. Commercial software may be combined with tailor-made programs developed by in-house staff, particularly programs that support database management and electronic communications across the network. ASPs may be used for selected applications by smaller units affiliated with the enterprise. Software evaluation and selection procedures are described in more detail in Chapter 12.

Information Systems Management and Staffing Plan

The IS plan should also specify the IS management structure for the organization. Most healthcare organizations still employ an in-house staff for system operation and management, even if all or most software is purchased from commercial vendors or leased from ASPs.

Decisions must be made on the extent to which IS technical staff will be centralized or distributed among the major user departments of the organization. An increasing number of organizations are *outsourcing* all or some of their information-processing functions to contractors who provide on-site system implementation and management services.

Centralized staffing offers the advantages of economies of scale and reduction in the number of technical personnel to be employed. Decentralized staffing brings systems management closer to the user and offers the potential for increased support and user involvement in system development and operation.

Outsourcing of IS functions allows the healthcare organization to get out of the information technology business through contracting with experts in the field. However, the costs of outsourcing may be high and may tend to generate too much distance between users and technical systems specialists. A more detailed discussion of information resource management issues is found in Chapter 14.

Statement of Resource Requirements

The final element of the IS plan specifies resources required to carry it out. A capital budget should include five- to ten-year projections for the cost of computer hardware, network and telecommunications equipment, and software. The operating budget includes costs for personnel, supplies and materials, consultants, training programs, and other recurring expenses. Both budgets should be updated annually, and the timing for their preparation should be coordinated with the overall organizational budget cycle.

Although the information technology budgets for healthcare organizations lag behind those of other information-intensive industries, the 2002 HIMSS Annual Leadership Survey reports that budgets are increasing in an attempt to keep pace with developing technology. Eighty-three percent of the survey respondents indicated that their budgets would increase in the current year (HIMSS 2002).

Review and Approval of the Information Systems Plan

The IS plan should specify an overall schedule and set of target dates for implementation. Although cost estimates and target dates will be preliminary at this point, they will assist management and board members in evaluating the magnitude of organizational commitments required to implement the recommended set of alternatives.

After the IS steering committee has approved the plan, it should be presented to executive management and the governing board for review and approval prior to implementation. The written plan should be submitted to management in advance of a formal presentation and discussion session.

As with any plan, the strategic IS plan must be a dynamic instrument that is reviewed periodically and updated. At least once a year, the steering committee should review progress in meeting the original criteria set forth in the plan, and the plan should be changed as necessary.

End-User Computing

A problem that many healthcare organizations face is what to do about dissatisfaction among organizational units whose information systems needs are not identified as priorities in the strategic IS plan. End-user computing strategies offer one potential solution to this problem.

Many employees have become quite sophisticated in computer use. Powerful personal computer systems with user-friendly software and user-oriented programming tools have helped to facilitate end-user computing that does not require the services or resources of the central IS department.

End-user computing most often involves use of departmental software packages purchased from vendors (e.g., laboratory, pharmacy, radiology systems). Contracting directly with an ASP offers another alternative. In some cases, computer-literate users may write programs to meet specialized needs in their departments. An example would be creation and maintenance of a database of companies who provide medical supplies for an outpatient clinic in a large medical center, where the clinic used database software to create and maintain the list of suppliers.

End-user computing offers the potential to expand the base of IS development and overcome problems of low priority assigned to certain applications that are viewed as important to units within the organization. However, end-user computing must be approached cautiously. Most activities in healthcare organizations are interrelated, and computer applications must be able to exchange information for efficient operations. If a departmental system can stand alone, management might authorize acquisition, provided that department funds are available and the system is developed in accordance with the strategic IS plan and enterprisewide standards and policies. However, if the system will need to exchange information with other units of the organization, central control and planning is needed before the end-user department should be authorized to acquire the system. *Data compatibility*—use of common codes and data definitions for electronic information exchange across the organization—should be mandatory (see the following section).

Enterprisewide Standards and Policies

To implement the strategic IS plan, the IS steering committee should oversee the development of a set of enterprisewide policies that govern the design, acquisition, and operation of information systems throughout the organization. Important policies needed by every organization include data security policies; data definition standards; policies governing the acquisition of hardware, software, and telecommunications network equipment; and policies on use of the Internet. Information-security policies are the subject of Chapter 13, and Internet policies were discussed in Chapter 9.

Data Standardization

As discussed previously, system integration is an important element of strategic IS planning in healthcare organizations. Most computer applications must include the ability to share information with other systems. For example, a laboratory-results-reporting system must be able to transfer information for storage in the computerized medical records system operated by the organization.

Electronic data exchange cannot occur without some level of standardization of data structures used in computer applications. For this reason, healthcare organizations should consider developing a data dictionary that specifies the format of each data element and the coding system (if any) associated with that element. For example, the data element "Date of Birth" might be defined as follows in the organization's data dictionary:

Date of birth: Eight digit numeric field with 3 sub-fields:

Month—two digits ranging from 01 to 12
Day—two digits ranging from 01 to 31
Year—four digits ranging from 1850 to 2050

Notice that the range of the sub-field for year in this example is designed to accommodate historical records of patient with birth dates back to the mid-19th century and accommodate future records through the mid-21st century.

In addition to data compatibility among information systems within the organization, there is a growing need to facilitate extraorganizational exchange of information among health systems, insurance companies, medical supply and equipment vendors, etc. A number of projects have been initiated to develop voluntary, industrywide standards for electronic data interchange in the healthcare field. Examples of these projects include the following:

1. *The American National Standards Institute (ANSI) X.12 Group* (working on specifications for transactions involving the processing of health insurance claims)
2. *Health Industry Bar Code Supplier Labeling Standard (HIBC)* (common coding of supplies, materials, and equipment)
3. *Health Level-Seven (HL7) Standard for Healthcare Electronic Data Transmission* (Version 3)
4. *MEDIX* (the Institute of Electrical and Electronics Engineers Committee for Medical Data Interchange)

The HL7 project was initiated in 1987. It is a voluntary effort of healthcare providers, hardware and software vendors, payers, consultants, government groups, and professional organizations with the goal of developing a cost-effective approach to system connectivity. Version 3 of HL7 embodies a new approach that includes messaging, component specifications, structured document architecture, and more. "When the [Version 3] project is complete, HL7 will provide a critical, sorely needed contribution to healthcare information technology—a set of coherent standards for messages, component interfaces and documents that is firmly anchored in precise standards" (Beeler 2001, 104).

In addition to these *voluntary* efforts at industrywide data standardization, the Health Insurance Portability and Accountability Act (HIPAA) establishes *mandatory* electronic data standards and standard transaction formats for claims processing. Providers will be required to follow these standards to receive reimbursement from Medicare, Medicaid, and other health insurers. HIPAA is discussed in detail in Chapter 13.

As part of the strategic IS planning process, the IS steering committee should study requirements for data interchange including HIPAA mandates and should develop a policy on data standardization for the organization. For example, many hospitals and IDSs are specifying that all software purchased from vendors must meet an industry standard protocol such as HL7.

Hardware and Software Standards

A number of technical policies related to information systems need to be developed by healthcare organizations. Most of these are highly technical and should be developed by the CIO or director of information systems. However, the IS steering committee should oversee the development of a broad set of policies related to the acquisition of computer hardware, software, and networks communications equipment for the organization.

The committee must determine whether or not the organization will require central review and approval of all computer hardware and software purchases. As the costs of personal computers and related software packages have come down, they are often within the budgetary authority of individual organizational units. However, some compelling reasons exist for requiring central review and approval, regardless of costs. These reasons include the following:

1. Central review will help ensure compatibility with enterprisewide data standards such as HL7 (see above).
2. Central review of personal computer purchases can ensure that data terminals and workstations use a common operating system such as Windows.
3. Central review and purchasing of generalized software provides cost advantages through the acquisition of site licenses for multiple users of common packages (word processing, spreadsheets, database-management systems, etc.).
4. Central review will ensure that hardware and software will be of a type that can receive technical support and maintenance from the IS staff.
5. Central review can help prevent illegal use of unlicensed software within the organization.

The IS steering committee should also approve the network communications plan for the enterprise. A variety of network configurations are possible, and the network plan must be compatible with the overall IS development plan for the organization.

Strategic Information Systems Planning for Integrated Delivery Systems

IDSs must consider the need for integration of information systems across institutions as well as within individual organizational units. Such integration is particularly critical in vertically integrated organizations where patients may progress and seek treatment at various organizational components, including clinics, surgicenters, acute care hospitals, substance abuse centers, and skilled nursing home facilities. Information systems must be patient centered to aggregate data from the various medical care units and track patients throughout the system. At the same time, corporate system management must recognize that different types of facilities within the organization (hospitals, ambulatory care centers and clinics, nursing homes, home health agencies) have their own distinct information requirements. Corporate policy must provide mechanisms for specialized information systems to meet the needs of individual units in the system.

Information systems for an IDS must also be able to provide comparative financial data for management to efficiently allocate resources to individual units. Such a capability is especially critical when healthcare costs are paid on a capitation basis. Corporate management will need to carefully monitor how patient care dollars are being spent across system units for actuarial risk analysis. The IDS also will have special information needs for market research and analysis of competitor services. Physician performance in various components of the system must be monitored as well.

At the technical level, information systems for an IDS may require standardization of coding and data definition for all organizational units— for example, a common chart of accounts for financial reporting. If such an approach is not possible, then complex data conversion tables will be required to facilitate electronic data exchange. To serve corporate management information needs and operational support requirements of each medical care unit, IDSs need to strike a balance between centralized data management and local control of data processing.

In recent years, hospitals have merged to form corporate systems, medical centers have acquired community hospitals and brought them into their organizations, and some corporate systems have sold or divested some of their existing facilities. These mergers and changes in ownership can create special problems with respect to information systems at the individual facilities.

If the corporate system has highly centralized information processing through a corporate data center and a new facility is acquired, special planning will be required to bring the new unit into the central system while allowing it to continue to use its current hardware and software to support ongoing operations. If computing within the corporate system is decentralized at the facility level, the newly acquired facility may not have compatible hardware and/or software with other units of the enterprise. Conversion programs may be required to convert data from these legacy systems to meet corporate reporting requirements. Unique information-processing problems usually result from these mergers, acquisitions, and joint ventures. Management at both the corporate and institutional levels must be prepared to address these problems as the plans for organizational change are developed.

Many health systems are developing data warehouses to serve the needs of facilities within their systems. Breen and Rodrigues (2001) present a case study on development of a data warehouse. "Successful implementation of a data warehouse involves a corporate treasure hunt—identifying and cataloging data. It involves data ownership, data integrity, and business process analysis to determine what the data are, who owns them, how reliable they are, and how they are processed" (87).

Rush Presbyterian-St. Luke's Medical Center in Chicago implemented a clinical data repository that collects and consolidates information from departmental systems throughout the organization. Data is filtered through a data dictionary, which standardizes information on an enterprisewide basis. As a result, clinical data is available from a single source (Oas 2001).

Summary

Information systems (IS) development in healthcare organizations should begin with development of a master plan that is linked to the strategic plan of the organization. The plan should include (1) a statement of IS goals and objectives aligned with organizational goals and priorities; (2) a list of priorities for the computer applications portfolio (clinical, management/administrative, electronic networking and e-health, and strategic decision support); (3) specification of overall system architecture and infrastructure; (4) a software development plan; (5) an information resources management plan; (6) a statement of resource requirements, including projected capital and operating budgets; and (7) schedules and target dates for implementation of various elements of the plan.

The planning process should be guided by an enterprisewide IS steering committee with membership from senior management, medical staff, nursing staff, financial management, human resources management, planning and marketing, facilities management, and clinical support services. The chief information officer should chair the committee if the healthcare organization has established such a position.

System integration—that is, the ability of information systems to communicate with one another and share information—is essential. Integration can be achieved through a number of alternative information network architecture configurations, including a central mainframe approach, client/server architecture, file/server architecture, and distributed processing.

End-user computing can supplement central planning to facilitate development of systems for users whose applications are not high on the priority list. However, caution must be exercised to ensure that user-developed computer applications meet requirements of data compatibility with other information systems with which they will exchange information.

The planning process should include development of major institutional policies related to information systems. The IS steering committee should oversee policies related to data security, privacy, and confidentiality; data standardization; acquisition of hardware, software, and telecommunications network equipment throughout the enterprise; and policies on use of the Internet.

IS planning within IDSs must strike a balance between the need for central data management and data processing requirements of individual organizational units. Health systems created through mergers, acquisitions, and joint ventures must deal with the problem of major investments already made in "legacy" systems in individual organizations with the need to exchange clinical and financial information across the system through a carefully planned telecommunications network.

Discussion Questions

11.1 Why is planning important in the development of healthcare information systems?

11.2 Describe a typical organizational structure for oversight of information systems planning in a vertically integrated health delivery system.

11.3 Describe the elements of a master plan for information systems development.

11.4 What is meant by the term information systems integration? Why is it an important element of strategic information systems planning?

11.5 Describe some of the alternatives available to healthcare organizations for system design and software development.

11.6 Discuss some of the special information planning requirements and problems of integrated delivery systems created through mergers and acquisitions.

11.7 What are application service providers? Do you expect their use to increase?

11.8 What are data warehouses? How are they used to achieve system integration?

Problems

11.1 Assume that you are the president of a healthcare corporation consisting of a medical group practice, 200-bed acute care hospital, day surgery center, and 75-bed skilled care nursing home. Develop an outline of an organizational plan for an information systems steering committee for the corporation.

11.2 Conduct an interview with the CIO of a healthcare organization in your community regarding information systems planning practices in the organization. Obtain a copy of the strategic IS plan if possible. Prepare a summary of your interview and a critique of the planning process being followed.

11.3 Search the literature and find three articles that describe the development of data warehouses in healthcare organizations. Prepare a summary and critique of the information contained in the articles.

References

Austin, C. J., J. M. Trimm, and P. M. Sobczak. 1995. "Information Systems and Strategic Management." *Health Care Management Review* 20 (3): 26–33.

Beeler, G. W. 2001. "The Crucial Role of Standards." *Healthcare Informatics* 18 (2): 98–100, 102, 104.

Breen, C., and L. M. Rodrigues. 2001. "Implementing a Data Warehouse at Inglis Innovative Services." *Journal of Healthcare Information Management* 15 (2): 87–97.

Gabler, J. M. 2001. "Linking Business Values to IT Investments." *Health Management Technology* 22 (2): 8, 10.

Healthcare Information and Management Systems Society and Hewlett Packard Co. 1996. *Seventh Annual Leadership Survey.* Chicago: HIMSS.

———. 2002. *Thirteenth Annual Leadership Survey.* Chicago: HIMSS.

Lohman, P. 1996. "Measure Consultant's Objectivity and Character Before Contracting." *Health Management Technology* (July): 31.

Monohan, T. 2001 "And an ASP Is . . . ?" *Healthcare Informatics* 18 (2): 54–56.

Oas, B. 2001. "Integration: Organizations Streamline the Business of Healthcare by Joining Disparate Systems." *Healthcare Informatics* 18 (2): 58, 60.

Rockart, J. F. 1979. "Chief Executives Define Their Own Data Needs." *Harvard Business Review* 57 (2): 81–84.

Turisco, F. 2000. "How to Justify the Investment: Principles for Effective IT Value Management." *Health Management Technology* 21 (3): 12–13.

Additional Readings

Burrows, S. C., K. M. Moore, and H. L. Lemkau. 2001. "Creating a Web-accessible, Point-of-care, Team-based Information System (PoinTIS): The Librarian as Publisher." *Bulletin of the Medical Library Association* 89 (2): 154–64.

Cerchiara, K. M. 2000. "Show Me the Money: The Tough ROI Assessment." *Health Management Technology* 21 (7): 14.

Clark, R. C., and M. L. DeMarco. 2001. "Development of an Information Management System Using a Strategic Planning Process." *Topics in Health Information Management* 22 (2): 44–51.

Covvey, H. D. 2001. "A Framework for Best Practices in the Deployment of Departmental Information Systems." Proceedings from AMIA Symposium, pp. 677–81.

DeFauw, T. D., and D. L'Heureux. 1995. "How to Strategically Align Information Resources with the Goals of an Integrated Delivery System." *Healthcare Information Management* 9 (4): 3–10.

Health Management Technology. 2001. "Integration Inspiration." *Health Management Technology* 22 (12): 40–41.

Martin, J. B., A. S. Wilkins, and S. K. Stawski. 1998. "The Component Alignment Model: A New Approach to Health Care Information Technology Strategic Planning." *Topics in Health Information Management* 19 (1): 1–10.

Memel, D. S. et al. 2001. "Development and Implementation of an Information Management and Information Technology Strategy for Improving Healthcare Services: a Case Study." *Journal of Healthcare Information Management* 15 (3): 261–85.

Orens, J. 1996. "Strategic I/T Planning: A Four-Pronged Approach." *Health Management Technology* (March): 62–64.

Ortiz, A. O., and M. P. Luyckx. 2002. "Preparing a Business Justification for Going Electronic." *Radiology Management* 24 (1): 14–21.

Winsten, D., J. McMahan, G. Gross, and J. Petrocelly. 2001. "Making It Work: Planning and Executing a Successful LIS Installation." *Clinical Leadership Management Review* 15 (3): 147–52.

Winter, A. F. et al. 2001. "Strategic Information Management Plans: The Basis for Systematic Information Management in Hospitals." *International Journal of Medical Information* 64 (2–3): 99–109.

APPLICATION DEVELOPMENT AND PROJECT MANAGEMENT

The information system (IS) plan establishes overall parameters for the development of information systems in healthcare organizations, including specification of general system architecture and priorities for the development of specific computer applications (see Chapter 11). This chapter discusses project organization and management for development of individual computer applications, from initial systems analysis through operation and maintenance after implementation.

Good project management is essential for successful IS implementation. Healthcare managers must ensure that well-established project-management procedures are followed and that a user-driven focus is followed in the system development and implementation process. O'Neill (2001) stresses the importance of project management to maximize the effectiveness of existing resources by directing them to mission-critical IS projects.

Project Organization

Major IS projects should be carried out by an interdisciplinary team of user department personnel, management representatives, and information analysts (see Figure 12.1). If the system to be developed includes clinical components, a representative(s) from the medical staff should be involved as well. A senior systems analyst from the IS department should serve as the project leader. This individual should not be a narrow specialist in computer technology but should have technical knowledge along with experience and understanding of the healthcare organization and its operations.

At least one representative from each department using information from or generating data for the system should be assigned to serve on the project team. Departmental representatives should be key staff members who understand departmental procedures and policies in their totality rather than individuals who are specialists in only one phase of departmental activity. Departmental representatives play a key role in liaison with employees in their departments, and they must be well accepted by their colleagues to lend credibility to the changes that will be necessary when the new system is implemented. Physician involvement is essential, particularly if the information system includes processing of clinical information.

FIGURE 12.1
Information
Systems Project
Organization

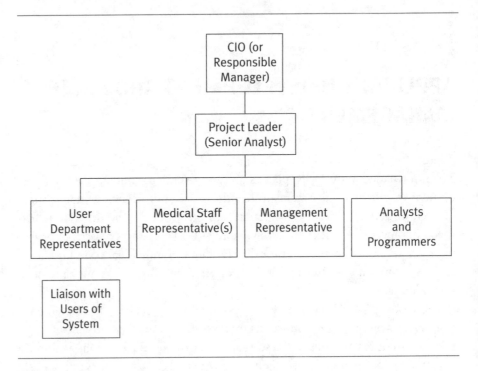

Every major project team should include a representative of central administration who can interpret organizational policy and serve as a liaison with the CEO or COO as the new system develops.

Technical personnel (systems analysts and programmers) are assigned to each project as needed. Technical personnel requirements will be higher for systems to be developed in-house and lower when packaged software or applications service providers are to be used. Actual staffing requirements will depend on who will have responsibility for installing the system and how much work will be required by in-house staff for building interfaces to other applications.

If a systems development project is to be carried out under contract, the contract specifications should call for a similar form of project organization. The contractor will provide the project leader and technical staff, but operating and clinical personnel should be involved in the same way as they would be for an in-house development effort. If this user involvement is not included, the result often is a system that is technically correct but out of touch with the realities of a particular organization, its culture, and environment. Early involvement of users in a contractor-developed system will aid immeasurably in system operation and maintenance after the new system is working and contractor personnel have departed.

Lauer, Joshi, and Browdy (2000) stress the importance of user acceptance to system success. Technical problems can be overcome with added resources, but there is no easy solution to end-user resistance. Lauer and colleagues (2000) have developed an Equity Implementation Model (EIM), which "provides an understanding of issues useful in determining users' acceptance of or resistance to a new system, technology, work practice, or other change in the work environment" (92). Information obtained from the model can be invaluable during system development. "User stress can be reduced by improved [user friendly] design. . . . Employee training and communication initiatives can explain the rationale for system design choices, improve user understanding, and alter the perceptions of users about system-related stresses and benefits" (Lauer, Joshi, and Browdy 2000, 101).

Once the project team has been organized, agreement should be reached on a regular schedule of periodic meetings to assess progress and to report on various phases of the project. Estimates should be made of the time requirements for each team member, and these should be formalized in writing with approval obtained from the appropriate department manager and from top management. Formalizing a time commitment for each member of the team will help ensure availability of key personnel when they are needed, particularly when other demands for their time compete with the system project, as inevitably they will. The best insurance against a poorly developed information system is the active and enthusiastic involvement of user personnel at all stages of the project.

Project teams should report to the CIO or other manager with responsibility for oversight of information systems in the organization. Further discussion of information systems staffing and the role of the CIO is found in Chapter 14.

The System Development Life Cycle

The process of IS development (often referred to as the life cycle for a system) involves seven major activities (see Figure 12.2). As discussed below, many alternative approaches to system design and development exist. The general principles embodied in the system development life cycle are applicable regardless of the alternatives selected for software acquisition and system implementation. Taking shortcuts or skipping steps in the life cycle process inevitably results in problems once systems are operational.

1. *Systems analysis*—the essential first step in any application development—is the activity in which current information practices are reviewed and functional system requirements are established. It is the process of collecting, organizing, and evaluating facts about IS requirements and the environment in which the system will operate.
2. Systems analysis serves as the basis for *selection of a design approach* for the proposed new information system. Alternative approaches available include use of predesigned or "packaged" software purchased from commercial vendors, design and programming of the system by in-house staff, use

1. Analyze functional requirements (systems analysis)
2. Select design approach
3. Specify system requirements (system design)
4. Acquire or construct system
5. Install system (implementation)
6. Operate and maintain system
7. Evaluate and improve system

of contractual services for design and programming, leasing of online software from an applications service provider (ASP), and combinations of the above alternatives. Most healthcare organizations are choosing to use predesigned or packaged software systems if a suitable package is available that meets organizational requirements as determined through systems analysis. Some in-house programming may still be required to modify the software packages or to build linkages with other systems.

3. *System design* is the process of converting functional IS requirements into a set of specifications for an application. If the system is to be implemented by in-house computer programming, detailed design specifications are required. If commercial software or software from an applications service provider is to be used, a more general set of functional requirements should be developed to support the software selection process. For large and complex applications, this might involve the development of a request for proposals to potential vendors.

4. *System acquisition or construction* involves evaluation, selection, and purchase or lease of commercial software and/or writing of computer programs by in-house staff. In some cases, specification of new hardware to add to or replace existing equipment may be necessary. In addition, this step includes reengineering of processes and development of organizational policies and procedures associated with the new system.

5. *System implementation* includes ordering of new equipment (if needed), preparing space, training personnel to use the system, building databases, converting data files, and system testing prior to operation. The importance of careful system testing cannot be overemphasized. Many catastrophes in healthcare IS projects could have been avoided if adequate testing had been carried out prior to putting systems into operation.

6. *Operation and maintenance* is the next step in the cycle. System maintenance is particularly important. Some organizations seem to believe that automated information systems, once operational, require no further attention. Nothing is further from the truth. No matter how good the system testing, operational systems are subject to occasional breakdowns, and trained personnel must be available to make quick corrections.

7. Healthcare organizations are dynamic, and the requirements placed on information systems are subject to frequent change. All information

systems should be *evaluated periodically*, with changes made to improve the effectiveness and efficiency of each system. Each major system should be formally evaluated to see if goals have been achieved and functional requirements met within reasonable costs. Post-implementation evaluation and quality improvement may result in the need to repeat some of the steps in the life cycle to make modifications to the system.

Each of these seven steps in the system development life cycle are described in more detail in the following sections.

Life Cycle Step 1: Systems Analysis

Systems analysis is the process of collecting, organizing, and evaluating data about IS requirements and the environment in which the system will operate. It is an essential first step (see Figure 12.2) in the development of any health-care information system. Guided by the principles and priorities set forth in the master plan for IS development, systems planners should conduct a careful study of functional requirements in advance of the design stage of a project. Technically trained staff (systems analysts and management engineers) and personnel who will be using the information system must join in this effort. Systems analysis will pay dividends whether or not any automated information system is the result.

Note that this definition of requirements determined by systems analysis is necessary even if vendor-produced or ASP software will be used. Functional requirements will be needed to evaluate the vendor software and select the package that best meets organizational needs.

Systems analysis should provide answers to a series of questions regarding the proposed new system:

- What are the weaknesses of the present system?
- What are its strengths?
- Why is a new system needed?
- What specific kinds of information should the system generate?
- When does this information need to be available?
- Who will use it? In what ways will it be used?
- Where does the needed data originate?

Answering questions such as these is the basic task of systems analysis.

Note that the question, "How will the new system provide the requisite information?" is not included here. This is the basic task of the design phase of the project. The details of how IS requirements are to be met should not constrain a systems project too early. Rather, requirements should be stated and ways should be found to meet these requirements. More problems in healthcare information systems have resulted from inadequate analysis and

FIGURE 12.3

Information

Systems

Analysis

1. Study existing systems
2. Define end-user requirements
3. Identify alternatives
4. Evaluate alternatives
5. Prepare report
6. Obtain management review and approval

lack of specification of system requirements than from shortage of available information technology.

Figure 12.3 shows the steps to be carried out in conducting an IS analysis. These steps are discussed below.

1. *Study existing system.* If the proposed information system is to replace an existing one, regardless of whether information is obtained manually or through machine processing, then the first step of systems analysis should be a complete study of existing procedures, their strengths and weaknesses. The information obtained serves as a basis for the establishment of realistic requirements for the proposed new information system.

2. *Define end-user requirements.* Future business needs and end-user requirements should be defined in detail. The project team may find that major reengineering of existing work processes is required rather than simple refinement of current procedures.

3. *Identify alternatives.* The project team should look for cost-effective alternatives in deciding how far to go in attempting to meet all user-defined requirements for the proposed system. Reynolds (1995, 376) suggests that system requirements be divided into three categories: high, medium, and low priority. He recommends that at least three alternative approaches be considered:

   a. the *"do-everything alternative,"* which meets or exceeds all user requirements regardless of priority assigned to them;

   b. the *"lots of features alternative,"* which includes all high-priority requirements, most medium-priority requirements, and many low-priority requirements; and

   c. the *"low-cost alternative,"* which meets most high-priority requirements, a few medium-priority requirements, and almost none of the low-priority items.

4. *Evaluate alternatives.* The choice among these alternatives will be dependent on the priority assigned to the proposed information system in meeting business objectives tempered by the resources available for system acquisition and implementation. The alternative of doing nothing should always be considered. If the project team fails to identify high-priority

requirements and benefits from the new system, it may be appropriate to invest scarce resources in other areas of the organization where the payoffs would be higher.

5. *Prepare the systems analysis report.* Careful documentation of the systems analysis is essential, both for management review and to serve as the basis for preparation of system design specifications. The report should include:

   a. the purpose and scope of the project, the user departments involved, and procedures followed in the study;

   b. the objectives to be served by the information system being considered; and

   c. the major findings of the study including strengths and weaknesses of the present system, user requirements for the proposed new system, and justification for proceeding to the next step, if this is the recommendation.

6. *Obtain management review and approval.* The systems analysis report should be reviewed by senior management as well as middle-level management from all user departments involved in the proposed new system. Signatures of approval should be obtained before proceeding to the next step.

Systems Analysis Tools

A number of tools are available to assist in the process of systems analysis (see Figure 12.4). This section includes a brief description of some of these tools.

Data Collection
1. Interviews
2. Questionnaires
3. Observation
   a. Work sampling
   b. Continuous monitoring

Data Organization
1. Summary tables and statistics
2. Interview summaries
3. Flowcharts
4. Narrative reports to accompany data tables and flowcharts

Data Analysis
1. Workload
2. Output utilization
3. Input and data collection
4. Coding systems
5. Database analysis
6. Procedures and information flow
7. Cost analysis

FIGURE 12.4
Tools of Systems Analysis

Data Collection
Tools

Data on system requirements can be collected through a variety of mechanisms. Key personnel in the operating departments involved in the information system should be interviewed as one means of documenting present procedures and obtaining input on new system characteristics that are desirable. Interviews should be carefully planned, and a structured interview guide should be prepared in advance to facilitate the interview and to ensure that key points are covered. An example of an interview guide to be used in obtaining information from the director of the clinical laboratory in an integrated delivery system is shown in Figure 12.5. Following a structured format, data are obtained on departmental organization, staffing, workload, facilities, current procedures, information flows, problems, and unmet information requirements.

Data can also be obtained through the use of questionnaires. Time and resources permitting, however, a face-to-face interview is preferable because it permits elaboration and dialog not possible with a questionnaire. Questionnaires can be particularly useful in obtaining a representative sample of data from a larger group—for example, patient opinions on an existing service or proposed new procedure.

Interviews and questionnaire development require special skills that are developed through education and experience. Systems analysts should be trained in these techniques and be familiar with the extensive literature available on this subject.

In questionnaire development, decisions must be made between the use of open-ended and closed-ended questions. Responses to open-ended questions provide more freedom to the respondents, but they may provide answers that are not relevant to the intent of the question. Open-ended questions require interpretation by the analyst and coding before the results can be analyzed. Closed-ended questions, on the other hand, facilitate uniformity and ease of analysis. However, too much structuring can potentially result in omission of issues that might be considered important by those completing the questionnaire. (See Figure 12.6 for suggested guidelines to be followed in developing questionnaires.) This is only a brief introduction to the important topic of survey research and collecting information through interviews and questionnaires. Readers interested in more detail should consult specialized reference material on this subject.

In addition to using interviews and questionnaires, those involved on the project team, particularly the project leader and other members of the technical staff, should observe operations in the departments to be involved in the information system. Observation will supplement information obtained through interviews and often will point the need for system characteristics that did not surface during conversations with user personnel. Of particular importance, systems analysts should pay close attention to environmental factors while observing departmental operations. Physical facilities, leadership styles of supervisors, degree of formality or informality in

FIGURE 12.5

Interview
Guide: Director
of Clinical
Laboratory

Background Information
1. Describe goals and objectives of laboratory. Is a copy of the goals statement available?
2. How is the laboratory organized? Is a chart available?
3. What are current staffing levels (numbers of personnel by job category and levels of training)? Are position descriptions available?
4. What are current lab workloads? What is the volume of work by type of tests? What is the percentage of stat orders? Is a statistical summary available?
5. What kinds of equipment and other specialized facilities are used? Are there any urgent needs for new equipment at present?
6. Describe relationships with other units of the health system: (a) frequent interaction (e.g., daily) and (b) less-frequent interaction.

Departmental Procedures
1. How are specimens obtained from patients?
2. How are stat orders handled?
3. What degree of automation is used in testing?
4. How are test results transmitted back to the patient's chart?
5. How are charges transmitted to the business office?
6. What kinds of quality control procedures are used?
7. Is a procedures manual available?

Information Flows
1. What reports are generated in the lab?
2. What other kinds of information are produced? telephone communications? verbal reports?
3. What kind of input information do you receive from other departments? Are sample forms available?
4. What kind of data-coding systems are used? Are code lists available?
5. What master files do you maintain in the lab?

Assessment and Problems
1. What are your major problems in lab operations? What are some of your less serious problems?
2. Are there any specific problems in information flow?
3. What are the major gaps and inefficiencies in your lab information system? Are error rates too high? Are input forms or reports consistently late?
4. How could a new or revised information system serve you better? What would you like to see in such a system?
5. Are there other comments or suggestions?

departmental procedures, and other elements of the day-to-day working environment can have a tremendous impact on how a system will function in a given organization.

Observation may be continuous over a fixed period of time, or work sampling techniques may be employed. Work sampling is based on statistical sampling theory: "Work measurement . . . involves the measurement of tasks or component parts of a job. The number of times each task is performed

FIGURE 12.6

Guidelines for
Questionnaire
Development

1. Respondents must be competent to answer the questions included on the survey instrument.
2. Questions should be relevant to the topics under study.
3. Each question should deal with only one issue.
4. Questions should be clear and unambiguous.
5. Questions should be kept as short as possible.
6. Response categories to closed-ended questions should be exhaustive and mutually exclusive.
7. Negative questions and biased items or terms should be avoided.
8. The questionnaire format should be spread out and uncluttered.
9. The order of questions is important and can affect the answer given.
10. A questionnaire should include a concise introduction explaining its purpose and should contain clear instructions for completion.

Source: Adapted from *The Practice of Social Research,* 4th edition, by E. Babbie. 1986. Belmont, CA: Wadsworth Publishing Company.

is tabulated and a time standard for the job is determined. This is later converted to human labor requirements, once all activities are applied to a time standard and the total time required to perform the job is calculated" (HIMSS 1995, 11.)

Notes should be taken throughout the data collection process, and other written documentation should be obtained, including sample reports, completed forms, procedural manuals, and organizational charts.

Data Organization Tools

The collected data should be analyzed according to standard formats, and summary tables should be prepared. In addition to tabular and graphic organization of data, interview reports and observations of department operations should be written in concise narrative format.

One of the most useful tools in systems analysis is the flowchart. Flowcharts provide a concise, logical, and standardized mechanism for depicting and analyzing current information flows. They help to pinpoint errors, inconsistencies, and inefficiencies in information flows and are very helpful in estimating the effects of changes on current operations. Flow charts illustrate relationships among various organizational functions as far as information interchange is concerned. This is a critical element of IS analysis because the identification of interfaces among functions is most important when attempting to achieve systems integration.

Figure 12.7 is an example of a system flowchart produced as part of a systems analysis of the clinical laboratory of a 273-bed general medical and surgical facility. The flowchart indicates the process followed in ordering lab tests, obtaining specimens, conducting the tests, and reporting results. (Order entry and results reporting is a high-priority application in many healthcare organizations today.) The flow of information throughout this process is shown in a concise and logical format through the chart.

Several problems were identified as a result of the analysis. These included breakdowns in communication between ward and lab personnel, lost charges for tests performed, problems with the pneumatic tube system used to transmit information, and the need for more preadmission testing. With the aid of the flowchart and other tools of systems analysis, immediate solutions to each of these problems could be recommended to management. In addition, the flowcharts and other analyses served as the basis for an automated information-processing system in the laboratory.

After data have been collected and organized into tables, graphs, flow charts, **Analysis Tools** and narrative summaries, analysis and evaluation can begin. The analysis should include a complete examination of all aspects of the present system and documentation of new system requirements. The following elements should be included.

1. *Workload.* Are loads evenly distributed across workstations, or are there bottlenecks at critical points in the process? How are workloads distributed over time, and why are they so distributed? Are there peak load periods and slack periods? How does information aid or impede the work of the departments involved in the system? How could a revised information system facilitate workload?

2. *Output Utilization.* How are output data screens and reports actually used? Are there some that really are not used at all? Are the costs of generating a particular system output worth the benefits received from having it? What are the deficiencies in current output? What new or revised data screens and reports should be included in the new system?

3. *Input and Data Collection.* What are the current problems in data collection? Are forms efficiently designed? Are data unnecessarily copied from document to document, increasing the possibility of errors in transcription? What are the error rates on data entry? Are the same data captured repetitively by various organizational units? How can data collection be improved? What new kinds of data are needed to meet system requirements? What data elements currently collected can be eliminated?

4. *Coding.* What codes and coding systems are presently used? Are they consistent throughout the organization? Are codes designed simply to identify data elements, or do they also categorize? Are checking systems built into coding structures? Are codes flexibly designed and expandable to handle an increased volume of transactions? Are the codes consistent with those used by other organizations for comparative purposes? Are the codes consistent with external reporting needs? What kinds of coding systems are needed to design the new information system?

5. *Databases.* Are data elements duplicated in databases throughout the organization? Is such duplication necessary? Can needed information be

FIGURE 12.7

System Flowchart: Ordering Tests, Obtaining Specimens, and Testing and Reporting

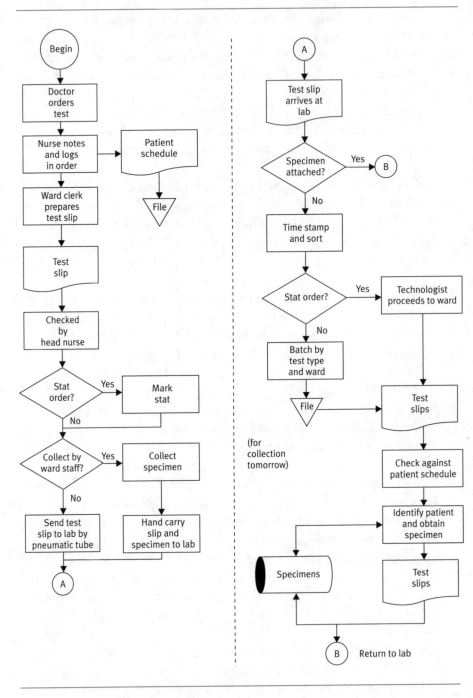

Continued

FIGURE 12.7
Continued

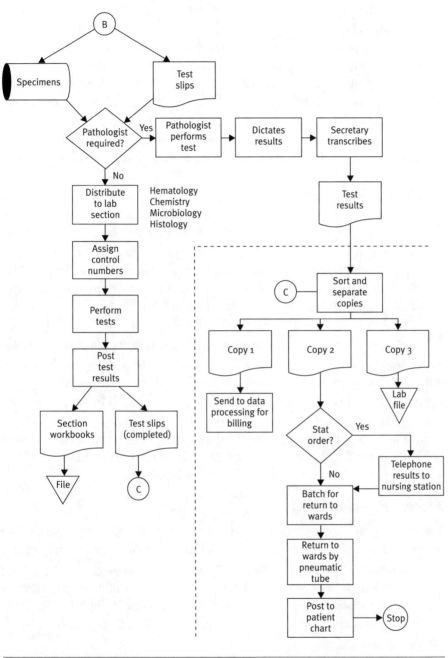

obtained easily from existing databases maintained by other organizations in the health system? Is database content updated according to a periodic schedule? Have databases become cluttered with out-of-date material? Is content properly indexed and accessible for retrieval of needed information? What data are being retained needlessly? How can databases be improved? What new databases are needed for the new system?

6. *Procedures and Information Flow.* How efficient are current operating procedures? What improvements are needed? Does information flow smoothly and on a timely basis? How can information flow be handled more expeditiously so that information truly supports operations and management decisions?

7. *Cost Analysis.* What are the current costs of processing information in the area under study? Are these costs reasonable or higher than expected? The cost analysis should be a complete study of all costs incurred in collecting, storing, processing, retrieving, and utilizing information under procedures presently employed. Cost data gathered at this phase of a system project provide important benchmark information for later comparison with costs of the proposed new system.

The systems analysis process itself has been aided by automation. Computer-aided systems engineering (CASE) is a technology that provides a set of software tools for use in the process of systems analysis, design, and implementation. CASE tools are designed to increase productivity in the system analysis process, provide a vehicle for communication between analysts and users on the project team, provide a set of standards for the design requirements, and simplify system documentation (Lee 1996). Some software vendors use CASE technology for development of packaged applications.

Process Reengineering

Many healthcare organizations have used information technology as a tool for automating existing processes. Currently, increased emphasis is being placed on reengineering processes rather than simply mechanizing existing procedures. Project teams involved in systems analysis of healthcare information systems are well advised to follow principles of process reengineering rather than simply looking for ways to automate existing activities in the organization.

Process reengineering involves analysis and redesign of everything associated with a business process to achieve performance improvement. "Everything is challenged: work flow, job definitions, management procedures, control processes, organizational structures, and even corporate values and culture . . . Every company operates according to a great many rules—most of them undocumented, many of them decades old, and some of them no longer valid. Reengineering requires finding and vigorously challenging the rules blocking major business process changes (Reynolds 1995, p. 11).

Jerva (2001) discusses the benefits of business process redesign (BPR) in IS development projects. Process redesign is underutilized in application development by many organizations. However, " . . . BPR is absolutely necessary in forging a synergy between organizational structure, people, technology and tasks" (30).

Benefits of Systems Analysis

Systems analysis offers many benefits, whether or not a new information system is developed. Systems analysis requires careful self-examination of current procedures. Any such analysis, properly performed, will result in procedural changes and methods improvement that in themselves should be worth the cost of the analysis. Systems analysis will also result in the development of standards for both procedure and performance. In most healthcare organizations, such standards are needed badly to improve management control and accountability of operations. The analysis also provides documentation of existing procedures and information flow that many organizations do not compile in a systematic manner. Finally, systems analysis permits decisions about information systems to be based on objective data and careful examination of requirements rather than intuition. As such, it provides a strong foundation on which a new information system can rest.

Systems analysis is a critical first step in the IS development process that should not be bypassed or shortcut even when predesigned application software will be used for implementation of the new system.

Life Cycle Step 2: Selection of a Design Approach

Functional requirements determined through systems analysis are used by the project team in selecting an approach to systems design (see Figure 12.2). Alternative approaches include

1. use of predesigned (packaged) systems,
2. use of ASPs,
3. in-house design,
4. use of contractual services (outsourcing), and
5. combinations of the above.

Most healthcare organizations will use a commercial package or online (ASP) software system if one is available that meets organizational needs as specified in the statement of functional requirements. Use of a predesigned software system will eliminate most of the costs of the in-house design effort, particularly if no modifications of the standardized system are required. However, in some situations, the packaged system must be modified to meet specific institutional needs and organizational idiosyncrasies. Before making a decision to employ a predesigned system, the project team should carefully review the costs and benefits of this approach. Savings in computer-programming costs will be offset to some degree by the purchase price or lease cost of the packaged system plus the additional costs required to modify it, if any.

Some larger organization may choose to develop an in-house information system tailored to the organization's specific requirements. The system is designed in detail and computer programs are written using functional requirements as specified during the systems analysis phase of the project.

Some healthcare organizations choose to outsource design and development of information systems through contractual services. For large and complex systems, this may involve a competitive bidding process in response to a request for proposals developed in accordance with functional requirements from the systems analysis. When outsourcing is used, healthcare organizations should have clear specifications for the work with performance requirements enumerated in a written contract.

The sections that follow present more detailed information on evaluating, selecting, and contracting for packaged software and contractor services.

Life Cycle Step 3: System Design Specifications

System design is the process of converting IS requirements into a set of specifications for the application. Detailed design specifications are needed for applications to be developed through in-house programming. More general specifications can be used for evaluating commercial software or online software from ASPs.

The project team organization described earlier should be continued during the design phase of a project. However, emphasis will shift to the more technical tasks requiring the skills of trained systems analysts or management engineers. Additional technical personnel may be needed at this point for systems to be developed in-house. System users should continue to serve as a sounding board for the technical design characteristics developed by the analysts working on the project.

Design Specifications for In-House Projects

For systems to be developed in-house, the results of the design phase should be a formal, detailed set of system specifications. The content of specifications for an in-house development effort is shown in Figure 12.8.

The first step in the process is definition of system objectives. What are the specific goals the organization expects to achieve through the design of the new information system? Objectives should be as specific as possible and should be measurable later when the system is operational.

Output specifications, the second step, should flow readily from a specific statement of system objectives. Reporting requirements will be specified by departmental representatives on the project team working with the systems

FIGURE 12.8
System Design
Specifications

1. Statement of System Objectives

2. Output Specifications
   a. Data screens
      • Purpose
      • Content
      • Format
   b. Printed reports
      • Purpose
      • Content
      • Format
      • Distribution and reporting schedule
      • Estimated volume

3. Input Specifications
   a. Sources of data
   b. Forms
   c. Procedures for converting to machine-readable form
   d. Coding systems
   e. Schedule and estimated volumes

4. Database Specifications
   a. Content and format
   b. Estimated volumes and file sizes
   c. Updating and purging schedules
   d. Security procedures

5. Procedures and Data Flow
   a. Flowcharts
   b. Narrative
   c. Computer program specifications (if in-house development is planned)

6. Cost-Benefit Estimates
   a. System development costs
   b. Operating costs
   c. Maintenance costs

7. Management Approvals (Signatures)

analysts. Each data screen and report to be produced by the system should be specified in detail. The specific content and format should be specified, and sample displays should be drawn up by the systems analysts.

Input specifications, the third step, are derived from system objectives and output formats. Specific input data requirements are derived from the content of output reports and from data retrieval specifications. For each set of input data to be processed by the system, the source of the data must be specified and forms or other means of capturing the data must be designed. As a general rule, it is desirable to capture data as close to the original source as possible and it is also wise to minimize transcription of data before entry into the computer for processing. Direct input of data through terminals or capture of data in a machine-readable format, if possible, is highly desirable.

Input specification also includes development of codes and coding systems. Codes should be simple and easy to use. They should be flexible and easy to expand as the volume of transactions increases.

The fourth step in system specifications is database design. Each database must be specified in detail, including content and format, estimated volume of transactions, and average size. The system design should also include a procedure and schedule for periodic updating and purging of content in the database. The latter is often neglected, and the resultant system must cope with cluttered amounts of outdated information. Database security procedures are another essential element of design specifications. Protection of the patient's right to privacy must be paramount in the construction of medical record databases, and safeguards should be built into the initial design to ensure that records are accessible only to authorized employees.

Inputs, outputs, and databases are system components that must be related to one another through the specification of procedures and data flow, the fifth step. Flowcharts, similar to those used in systems analysis, are the basic tools employed in specifying information flow in the new system. In addition, narrative descriptions and elaboration of procedures, revised policies, and new organizational structures should be detailed in this section of the specifications. Also included should be written specifications for computer programs to be developed by in-house staff.

The sixth step in the development of system specifications should be a thorough estimate of the costs and benefits of the proposed new system. Three kinds of costs should be estimated: system development costs, operating costs, and maintenance costs. Development costs include the remaining costs of design and implementation, including computer programming, training of personnel, procedures writing, system testing, conversion of data files, and other similar tasks. Operational costs include labor, materials, and a prorated share of computer time used for the new system. Maintenance costs are often overlooked. These are the personnel costs incurred in keeping qualified systems analysts and programmers available to make necessary changes in the system after it goes into operation and to evaluate it periodically for improvements.

These costs must be matched against the anticipated benefits of the system—tangible benefits, which can be translated into dollar savings for the organization, and intangible benefits, which cannot be measured directly in financial terms but which are expected to improve the effectiveness of service delivery.

Once the cost-benefit analysis has been completed, system planners should again critically evaluate whether or not to proceed with implementation of the system. A system that looked attractive after an initial systems analysis can be found to be prohibitively expensive or not feasible after a detailed design is completed. In such a situation, the project team and management personnel must be bold enough not to proceed with implementation. A decision to proceed because a major investment has been made in the design phase is foolish; unfortunately many healthcare organizations have implemented computer systems when the results of a design effort dictated against such action.

The final step is obtaining management approvals. The specifications should be submitted for formal review to the manager of each department and service unit involved and also to administration. Meetings should be scheduled to elaborate on the specifications, answer questions about them, and discuss possible problems with the system design. Once necessary changes have been made, signatures of approval should be required.

Specifications for IS Acquired from Vendors or Contractors

Before considering the use of any application software package or contract service, healthcare organizations should develop a statement of functional requirements for the system to be acquired. A detailed list of functions and features should be prepared with requirements categorized into two groups—those that are *mandatory* and those that are *desirable*. If the software is to be used on an existing computer configuration, then hardware and operating system software compatibility requirements should be stated. Most applications will need to be linked to other operational systems requiring the specification of necessary system interfaces. For example, a proposed new system for scheduling patient appointments in an ambulatory care center might require linkage to the medical records and patient accounting systems already in place. In this case, the clinic must decide whether to require the new system vendor to supply the interface, contract with the vendors of the existing systems to build interfaces, or do the work in-house.

Life Cycle Step 4: System Acquistion or Construction

If the system is to be developed in-house, computer programmers will need to write and test the new software. The sections that follow describe the processes to be followed in system acquisition through purchase of commercial software, use of ASPs, or outsourcing.

Evaluation of Application Software

For major software acquisitions that involve multiple applications, consideration should be given to a formal bidding procedure through use of a request for proposals (RFP) or a request for information (RFI). Guidelines for the development and use of RFPs and RFIs are included later in this chapter.

Information on application software in the healthcare field can be obtained from a variety of sources (see Figure 12.9). Guidebooks and directories

FIGURE 12.9

Sources of
Information on
Vendors and
Software

1. Directories and guidebooks
2. Exhibits at professional association meetings
3. Internet home pages on the World Wide Web
4. Direct contact with other users
5. Hardware- and software-user groups
6. Consulting firms

provide general information about software products and their use in health-care organizations. For example, *Health Management Technology* and *Health-care Informatics* publish annual directory issues and include the same information on their web sites (healthmgttech.com and healthcare-informatics.com). Vendors display their products at major professional meetings such as the annual meetings of the Healthcare Information and Management Systems Society, the American Medical Informatics Association, the American Health Information Association, the American Hospital Association, and the Medical Group Management Association, to name just a few.

Most software vendors maintain web pages on the Internet, and general information on their products can be obtained through Internet searches. Information can be obtained directly from other healthcare organizations or from user groups that have been formed to share information about experiences with particular hardware and software products. Consulting firms can provide information on available products, but care should be exercised in selecting a consultant to ensure the firm has no business ties to any particular vendor. Use of consulting services is discussed in more detail later in this chapter.

Figure 12.10 lists some of the most important factors to consider in evaluating packaged application software for a healthcare facility.

FIGURE 12.10

Packaged
Software
Evaluation
Criteria

1. Congruence with organizational requirements
2. Level of satisfaction of other users
3. Compatibility with existing hardware and software
4. Ability to interface/integrate with other applications
5. Support available
   a. Training
   b. Documentation
   c. Maintenance
6. Costs
   a. Software lease or purchase
   b. Additional hardware (if any)
   c. Implementation
   d. Operational maintenance and upgrades
7. Financial stability of vendor

Using the statement of functional requirements as a base for comparison, an analysis of how well each package under consideration meets organizational requirements is essential. If a given software package does not exactly match stated requirements, to what extent is the organization willing and able to adjust operations to meet the general specifications of the software?

Consideration should also be given to the experiences of others who have used a particular packaged software system. Careful checking is essential and should be carried out independently from the vendor. Ask the vendor to supply a list of organizations that have purchased the software, then make direct contact with a selection of these facilities through telephone interviews or site visits.

Determination of compatibility of the proposed application package with existing hardware and software must be part of the evaluation process. If hardware modifications or a complete new configuration are required, what are the costs involved (purchase and maintenance)?

Consideration must also be given to building system interfaces to other applications. Will this be done in-house, or will the vendor be responsible for them? What are the costs involved. If the healthcare organization follows an industry standard for data such as HL7 (see Chapter 11), is the vendor's software package compatible with this standard?

Support services available from the vendor are very important. These include education and training programs for users and technical personnel involved in operating the system. What training is provided, and what are the costs? Software updates and maintenance are important factors to consider in evaluating application packages. Will the vendor provide periodic updates to incorporate changes suggested by users or those required by changing regulations? How often will updates be offered, and what will they cost? If the healthcare organization wishes to provide its own maintenance and make modifications as necessary, will the vendor offer contractual permission to do so and provide the source code for use by in-house programmers? In such circumstances, good documentation of the computer programs is essential if changes are to be made by in-house programmers.

Cost analysis is an important element in software evaluation. Costs fall into four categories:

1. The purchase or lease cost of the software itself
2. The cost of additional hardware if any is required
3. The cost to implement the software, including building of interfaces to other systems and personnel training
4. Costs of software maintenance and updates once the package is operational

All four elements of cost must be carefully estimated in comparing vendor products. The software package with the lowest purchase cost may not have the lowest overall cost when these other elements are considered.

The financial stability of the vendor must be considered as well. The application software industry is volatile with frequent changes in vendors as a result of mergers, acquisitions, and business failures. Carefully review the financial history of each company under consideration. How long have they been in business? Do the company's financial statements and ratings appear stable?

Leasing Software from Applications Service Providers

As discussed in Chapter 11, an ASP is an organization that contracts with a healthcare provider to access and use applications obtained from an off-site server on a subscription basis (Monohan 2001). These Internet-based products offer an alternative to purchased software or in-house development. They are used by a number of healthcare providers, particularly smaller organizations. Both administrative and clinical applications are available from ASPs.

Potential benefits from use of ASPs include avoidance of large capital outlays for software, more predictable IS operating costs, lower costs for staff and training, subscriber fees commensurate with usage, and reduced time to get new systems operational. Potential problems with ASPs include limited ability to customize the software to meet institutional needs, data security and ownership issues, and the difficult issue of who is responsible for HIPAA compliance (the provider or the ASP organization) (Monohan 2001).

Spilsbury (2000) describes the use of an ASP to support outcomes measurement at Memorial Care in Fountain Valley, California. ASP software is used to process patient satisfaction questionnaires and functional health status data. "The simplicity, flexibility and delivery of the software allows us to focus on processing the best possible patient information and not on IT issues" (Spilsbury 2000).

Maimonides Medical Center in Brooklyn, New York, has developed a for-profit subsidiary company to develop and offer ASP software. The medical center uses the software itself and targets small and medium-sized institutions as a market for its products (Monohan 2001).

Use of Contractual Services (Outsourcing)

An alternative to in-house development or purchase of packaged systems is the use of contractual services for design and implementation of systems. These services can be purchased from several vendors specializing in systems analysis and programming. Contracts can range from purchase of services on an hourly basis to fixed price contracts for a total turnkey effort, in which the entire process is handled on a contractual basis. The following factors should be considered in evaluating contract services.

1. Carefully review prior experience of the contractor. Talk to several previous clients.
2. Investigate the financial stability of the contractor.

3. Review the credentials (experience and training) of the specific personnel to be assigned to your project. Insist that the contractor identify those individuals to be assigned to your work rather than merely presenting a general portfolio of credentials for all professionals in their firm.
4. Ensure that the contractor employs well-established principles of systems analysis and design in its work plans and procedures.
5. Carefully examine all cost estimates and ensure they are thoroughly prepared, complete, and comprehensive. For major projects, insist on fixed-price and fixed-time contracts.
6. If necessary, use a neutral, disinterested party (independent consultant) to assist in the technical evaluation of proposed services.
7. Design a formal review process to evaluate the work of the contractor and manage the contract closely.

A discussion of negotiations and contracting for major projects is included later in this chapter. Further discussion of outsourcing as an alternative to in-house staffing is covered in Chapter 14.

The Selection Process

Selection of a vendor to provide software, hardware, or other contract computer services is a critical step in the IS development process. Depending on the size and complexity of the system to be installed, an informal or a formal, more structured, process may be followed.

For smaller system acquisitions, an informal process requiring limited documentation is most common. The process often includes development of an RFI that is used to obtain general product information and to prescreen vendors and their capabilities. The RFI includes a general description of the product (hardware and/or software) that the healthcare organization seeks to acquire. Vendors are asked to respond with information about their products and how they would meet the general requirements stated in the RFI. Responses to the RFI are used to screen the vendor list and select a smaller number (two to five) from whom additional information will be obtained. Those selected will be invited to submit proposals for providing the product, including price, delivery, and support services included. These proposals are evaluated through meetings with vendor representatives and checking with other clients. *Request for Information*

The formal vendor-selection process usually involves a selection team of users and analysts, requires more documentation, and includes a formal RFP. An RFI might also be used to prescreen vendors and limit the number to be included in the formal bidding process. *Request for Proposals*

There is some debate about the degree of specification that should be included in an RFP. Some argue for minute specification of every detail for the proposed system to ensure that the healthcare organization knows in advance exactly what it is buying. The counter argument calls for greater flexibility and latitude in the specifications so that vendors are free to propose a variety of approaches in meeting the functional requirements included in the RFP. The answer usually lies somewhere between these two extremes. Specifications should be reasonably focused to ensure that system objectives are met and to provide a common base for evaluating proposals. Some flexibility should be included, however, to permit creative approaches on the part of prospective bidders.

The RFP describes functional requirements and states guidelines for bidders to follow in their proposals. For a major system acquisition, the RFP should include the following elements:

1. An introduction to the organization in which the system will be used, including organization charts, operating statistics, number of personnel, and financial information
2. Statement of functional requirements, categorized as mandatory or desirable, and listed in priority order
3. Specification of content and format to be followed in proposals, including vendor profile, software and hardware descriptions, training plans, documentation to be provided, maintenance coverage, list of other clients who have used similar products or services, cost schedule, and performance guarantees
4. Statement of criteria to be used in evaluating proposals
5. Requirements for on-site demonstrations and system testing
6. Requirements for the vendor's role in system implementation
7. General contractual requirements, including warranties, performance bonds, payment schedule, and penalties for failure to meet time schedules specified in the contract.

In the introduction to the RFP, the vendor should find information on how the system is to be used and who will use it. Statistics on normal and anticipated levels of activity (bed capacity, occupancy rate, admissions/discharges, outpatient service levels, numbers of records on file, number of personnel, and levels of activity by category in departments) are necessary to "size" the system needed. A description of the current computer configuration will help in orienting vendors to the operation and will provide detailed information on interface and conversion problems. The implementation schedule should be outlined.

If collaborative proposals (in which more than one vendor is responsible for the system) will not be accepted, a statement should be included stating that all hardware, software, and maintenance is to be supplied by a single vendor. Whether or not a turnkey system is required should be stated. If facilities management can be bid by either the system vendor or separately, a statement to that effect should be included.

It is prudent to stipulate that the successful vendor will be responsible for any interface problems between the system acquired and any existing installations, such as a data switch or local area network. Where modems and communication lines are involved, each party (installations at both ends and the communication facility, such as a telephone company) has a tendency to assume the problem is in someone else's territory.

To avoid unexpected charges in conjunction with the proposal and bid process, a clear statement should be included disclaiming responsibility for expenses of the vendors for demonstrations or delivery of information. The name, address, and telephone number of the contact for proposals should appear in the introduction.

General requirements for proposals should specify the format for the reply to the RFP. If all the vendors adhere to the reply format, it will be easier for the buyer to compare proposals.

The vendor profile is intended to ensure that the company is stable financially and is capable of providing the kind of long-term support needed for computer products. Examples of pertinent information are the most recent annual report and the company's Dun and Bradstreet rating. The vendor's quality-control program should be adequately described to satisfy the purchaser. Information about the history of availability of the product offered can be useful. If the system proposed has appeared on the market recently, attention will be focused on assurance of reliability of hardware and software.

The vendor should state what types of training will be necessary for the system, what training materials will be needed, and the minimum skill levels of the persons to be trained. It should be clear where training is to be conducted, how long it will last, and what it will cost

The purchaser may wish to have the option of a system demonstration. Any demonstration should be of a system identical to the one proposed for purchase. The purchaser should select the demonstration site from a client list provided by the vendor. The vendor preferably should not be present during the demonstration to allow free exchange of information with personnel from the organization demonstrating the system. The fault tolerance of the system and conditions of transfer to backup systems in emergencies should be determined.

Criteria for evaluating responses to the RFP will vary depending on the nature of the system to be acquired. However, general criteria would include the following:

1. Established record of performance of the software, system, or equipment the vendor is proposing
2. Extent of vendor support to be provided, including expertise, availability, and capacity for support
3. Reliability, maintainability, and quality control
4. Projected economic and noneconomic benefits
5. Adaptability and provisions for expansion

6. Costs of acquisition, implementation, and maintenance
7. Number and scope of any conditions attached to the proposal

Once the RFP has been finalized and evaluation criteria have been developed, the document is submitted to selected vendors. As mentioned previously, initial vendor screening can be accomplished by reviewing the responses to a preliminary RFI. After the RFP has been distributed, the healthcare organization may wish to schedule a bidder's conference to answer questions about the RFP in a public forum with all vendors present and receiving the same information.

All vendors should be required to submit proposals by a common date specified in the RFP. After proposals are received, screening can begin. The screening process may involve vendor demonstrations as stated above. Proposals will be evaluated in reference to stated criteria with a small group of vendor finalists selected as a result of the evaluations. Careful reference checking of each finalist, including site visits to organizations where vendor products are installed, is an essential step in the final selection process. Conducting preliminary contract negotiations with the two top finalists may be desirable to determine if any insurmountable contract problems come up before the final selection of a vendor is made. Once the finalist has been selected, contract negotiations can begin.

A Word of Caution

No universal agreement exists about the value of using formal RFPs for acquiring information systems in healthcare organizations. The process can become so involved that prospective bidders may be discouraged from responding. Healthcare organizations often need to move quickly in developing or modifying information systems in response to competition and changing requirements in the managed care environment. Smaller IS selections may rely more on prototyping and gathering of information for quick decisions

Negotiation and Contracting

The healthcare organization should take the lead in contract negotiations. As stated above, negotiations should proceed concurrently with the vendors of first and second choice for as long as possible. This provides leverage during the negotiations and provides an alternative if negotiations with the primary vendor break down completely.

Vendors may propose using their standard contract. This should be rejected out of hand because the standard contract will contain features favorable to and designed to protect the vendor. The healthcare organization should form a negotiating team and utilize legal counsel from the beginning of the process. Although internal legal counsel may be utilized, consideration should be given to retaining assistance from a law firm that specializes in computer software and hardware negotiations because of the complexities and nuances involved in these types of contracts.

The final contract should be designed to put the vendor at financial risk for failure to meet requirements as specified in the RFP. In general, the healthcare organization should insist on fixed-price and fixed-time conditions in the contract. The RFP should be made part of the contract by reference in the main document.

Important issues that should be addressed in the contract include the following:

1. *Delivery dates.* Financial penalties should be included for failure to deliver and install software and hardware on the dates specified in the contract.
2. *Acceptance testing.* The contract should spell out performance requirements and the nature of an on-site acceptance test(s) to verify that these requirements have been met.
3. *Payment schedule.* As a general rule, no payments should be made until the system has been installed and acceptance tests have been met. Final payments should be scheduled to allow some period of time for the system to function satisfactorily in operational mode, perhaps six months after system conversion. Cancellation provisions, including penalties (if any), should be clearly stated.
4. *Warranties and guarantees.* Hardware warranty periods should be specified, and reliability guarantees on software should be included. The contract should specify the response time for service calls and the maximum allowable time for correcting software errors. Penalties for failure to meet these response-time requirements should be included.
5. *Software ownership (source code).* The contract should specify who owns the software included in the system acquisition. If the vendor retains proprietary rights to the software (as often is the case), then the contract should specify the conditions under which the healthcare organization may modify the software for its own purposes. The contract also should specify rights to transfer source code ownership from vendor to contractor if the vendor goes out of business.
6. *Interface responsibilities.* If the system to be acquired must interface with existing information systems, the contract must clearly state who will be responsible for building the necessary interfaces: new system vendor, existing system vendors, or the healthcare organization's programming staff.
7. *Maintenance and updates.* The contract should specify the responsibilities of both parties for system maintenance. If periodic software updates or upgrades are part of the agreement, the time intervals for them and costs should be clearly stated.
8. *Training.* Vendor responsibilities for training user personnel, if any, should be clearly specified in the contract.
9. *Documentation.* The contract should specify the level and types of system documentation to be provided, including technical manuals for

hardware and software and user manuals specifying operating procedures to be followed.

10. *Expiration date and cancellation provisions.* The contract should state the period of time that it will remain in effect and should include provisions covering a request for cancellation by either party.

Negotiations with vendors should be carried out in a professional manner, and efforts should be made to obtain a final contract that is satisfactory to both parties. Most new IS acquisitions result in a long-term partnership with the vendor, and mutual respect and trust is important to the success of the relationship (Hubbard and Garets 2001).

Role of Consultants

Healthcare organizations frequently use consultants to assist in the evaluation and selection of IS vendors. Consultants can provide the following services:

1. *Facilitate the selection process.* Consultants with special expertise in system evaluation and selection can help design an objective process to followed. However, decisions must ultimately be made by appropriate management and technical personnel from the healthcare organization. The role of the consultant should be limited to that of a facilitator.
2. *Provide technical information.* A large number of vendors provide information services to the healthcare industry. Keeping current on the available technology is difficult for any organization. Consulting firms offer specialized information services to assist in the evaluation process.
3. *Provide an outside perspective.* An independent consultant can help provide objectivity and expertise to the process, unencumbered by organizational politics or other internal factors that may influence the decision process.

In selecting a consultant, avoid firms that may have a conflict of interest. Some consultants have joint-venture agreements with software or hardware vendors that could influence the advice they provide. An independent consultant should have no ties to any particular product.

Always examine the credentials of the individual consultants to be assigned to your project. This is particularly important when working with large firms. Ensure that your agreement with the consulting firm contains a provision that those assigned to the project will not be pulled off and reassigned before the engagement is complete.

Check with other healthcare organizations that have used the consulting firm you are considering before making a final decision.

Baldwin (2001) discusses the potential benefits of using consultants, but he cautions that effective use of their expertise requires strengthening of the healthcare organization's own capabilities.

Life Cycle Step 5: System Implementation

Once a new or replacement information system has been selected, planning for implementation begins. System implementation may include acquisition of new hardware, computer programming, training, database preparation, system testing, and final documentation (see Figure 12.11). As with all phases of system development, implementation does not just happen; it must be carefully planned and managed.

Equipment Acquisition

New equipment will be required for some systems. This task can range from complete installation of a general purpose computer or new computer network to the relatively simple addition of some workstations or terminals to an existing system. Whatever the magnitude of equipment requirements, equipment ordering and installation must be carefully planned. Sufficient lead time must be allowed to ensure delivery when needed. In some cases renovations and site preparation will also be required, and good space planning must accompany all new equipment orders. A more detailed discussion of computer equipment is included in Chapter 3.

Computer Programming

For information systems being implemented by in-house staff, preparation of application programs is part of the implementation process. Most systems in healthcare organizations use application software acquired from vendors. Some in-house programming may still be required for building interfaces to other applications or changing network configurations to accommodate the new software being installed. See Chapter 4 for detailed information on computer programming and software.

Training

An extremely important element of system implementation is training of personnel who will operate and use the new information system. For systems designed and implemented in-house, training plans should be drawn up by the project team, and team members should take responsibility for coordinating and conducting the training sessions. For systems purchased from commercial firms, the company will usually include initial training as part of the contract.

1. Equipment acquisition
2. Programming or software installation
3. Training
4. Database preparation
5. System testing
6. Final documentation

FIGURE 12.11
Information System Implementation

These sessions should include general orientation for top management and more specific training for managers and first-line supervisors. Managers and supervisors, in turn, should take responsibility for training employees in their areas, and at the same time they will become more familiar with the new system.

For information systems procured from software houses, the vendor often will be required to provide some or all of the necessary user and operator training. Some vendors have self-instructional, computer-based training packages available for use by clients in implementing their systems. A training director designated by the healthcare organization should plan and coordinate the training program and ensure that vendor responsibilities for training as specified in the software contract are carried out.

A well-designed and well-managed training program can help overcome employee anxiety and potential resistance to change and make the difference between a successful and unsuccessful system implementation.

Database Preparation

Another task that is sometimes overlooked in implementation planning is database preparation or modification. Some healthcare information systems will require that one or more organizational databases be converted from manual form to electronic storage in the computer. Other systems may require modifications to an existing electronic database prior to operation. For example, an ambulatory care center installing an automated patient appointment and scheduling system must build a database that includes appointment times available for each physician and a list of treatment facilities available for scheduling. The electronic database must be created prior to conversion to the automated system. In some cases, the decision to convert back records may be optional, and the costs and benefits of conversion should be considered. For example, in the implementation of a computer-based patient record system, a decision must be made whether to convert all or some of the existing patient records to computer format, or whether to start with new records only and maintain back records in manual form.

System Testing

No healthcare information system should be put into operation without complete system testing. The test should be carefully planned and cover all aspects of the new system in as realistic an environment as possible. Elements to be tested include system objectives, proper functioning of computer hardware and software, training of personnel who operate and use the system, accuracy of cost estimates, and adequacy of system documentation (see Figure 12.12).

The test should be designed to determine whether specific goals and objectives for the information system have been met. Each objective should be measured against specific test criteria. The ability of the system to generate correct output data in a timely manner should also be tested.

FIGURE 12.12

Elements of a
System Test

1. System objectives
2. Computer and network hardware
3. Computer software
4. Personnel training
5. Accuracy of cost estimates
6. Adequacy of system documentation

A major element of the test is checking that data collection and input procedures are functioning properly. Is computer input generated with a minimum of errors? When errors do occur, does the system detect them and permit timely correction? Error and correction procedures are important elements of any information system. Most systems will handle routine transactions without difficulty, but those few exceptions that inevitably do occur often generate confusion and frustration unless good exception procedures are built into the system design. The adequacy of these procedures must be tested thoroughly.

The system test should also be designed to check the sufficiency of personnel training. Are procedures for gathering and reporting data understood and functional? Procedures manuals should be developed before the system test begins so that they are available to operating departments during the test period.

The test will check the adequacy of computer software and machine processes involved in the system. Software problems are often uncovered when a program is operated under live conditions in conjunction with all the other elements of a system.

The system test should aim at estimating as closely as possible the actual operating costs of the new system. If the costs appear to be much higher than the estimates contained in the system specifications, then management should carefully review the entire system and decide whether or not to proceed with full implementation. Proceeding with implementation in the face of evidence of significant cost overruns constitutes irresponsible management. Changing requirements, renegotiating contracts, and/or looking for other ways to reduce costs may be necessary. In extreme cases, scrapping the system altogether may be necessary.

Finally, the system test should check the completeness of system documentation, including procedure manuals, documentation of computer programs, and machine operating manuals. Documentation is the key to good system maintenance, and it should be in order before the new system goes into production.

Although every test element described above is important, the overriding purpose of a system test is to test the system as a whole. Will the various components function together in an orderly and systematic manner? To answer this question, the test should be as realistic as possible. Actual data from operations should be used if at all feasible. Although not always feasible, a parallel test may be the best way to simulate actual operation of the system. In parallel testing, the new information system operates along with the existing system, and cross-checks for accuracy are conducted on a systematic basis. Parallel testing places considerable strain on day-to-day operations because two systems must be operated by the personnel involved. Temporary staffing often is required during this period, and it is recommended that the temporary staff be assigned to the old system so that permanent employees may gain the experience of using the new system procedures.

More than one system test may be required for complex applications. After the first test is completed, the system is modified, and the modified system is then retested. Conversion to full operation of the new system should not occur until all system tests have been completed satisfactorily and no further modifications are required.

Final Documentation

The final aspect of system implementation is completion of all system documentation. Documentation should be a continuous process carried out during all phases of the system project. Just before production, the project team should do a final check to ensure that system documentation is adequate for effective maintenance of the new system.

Life Cycle Step 6: System Operation and Maintenance

Information systems require both scheduled and unanticipated maintenance after they become operational. No matter how well a system is designed and regardless of how well it has been tested, errors inevitably will be uncovered after the system goes into production. Systems analysts and programmers must be available to find such problems quickly and to initiate immediate corrections.

In addition, alterations in the system will be required from time to time, because healthcare organizations are dynamic and subject to frequent changes in operating policies and procedures. These changes flow from a variety of sources: new programs initiated by the board of trustees, changes in the composition of the community served, expansion of facilities to meet increased demand, and ever-changing regulation by external agencies. Information systems must be sufficiently flexible so that these changes can be accommodated, and trained technical staff must be available to initiate them.

Adequate staffing is required for maintenance of systems developed in-house. If system maintenance is to be provided by outside contractors or software suppliers, contracts must be negotiated that guarantee timely response to requests for emergency maintenance and system updates.

In addition to providing quick-response maintenance, designers of healthcare information systems must develop emergency backup procedures to be followed any time operational systems are down for any reason. These backup procedures should be carefully documented, and personnel must be well trained in their use so that they can be employed with a minimum amount of disruption to regular operations. Effective backup procedures are particularly critical for information systems that support direct patient care.

Life Cycle Step 7: System Evaluation and Improvement

Operational information systems should be evaluated periodically to determine ways in which they can be improved to better serve organizational objectives.

Total quality management (TQM) principles can be used to improve healthcare information systems. The guiding principles behind TQM are that all processes (clinical and administrative) can be improved and that the improvement must be continuous. The continuous improvement cycle includes measurement of current performance, implementation of actions to improve the process, checking to ensure that the actual performance improvements have been realized, putting the new process into operation, and monitoring it continuously over time (Austin and Boxerman 1995, 197–198).

IS evaluations should include a formal review of at least the following elements:

1. *Functionality:* the degree to which the system meets the organizational objectives for which it was designed (patient care, improved management, better decision making).
2. *User sastisfaction:* confirmation of the extent to which the system meets or exceeds expectations of personnel from the major user departments.
3. *Costs and benefits:* analysis of the extent to which the system performs within cost estimates and documentation of benefits achieved.
4. *Errors and exceptions:* analysis of system error rates to determine whether they are within tolerance levels established in the design specifications for the system.

Periodic system reviews should be used as the basis for improvements to be made by system maintenance personnel. Evaluation and TQM are major responsibilities of IS management.

Summary

Application development projects should be carried out by a project team, headed by a senior systems analyst and including representatives of relevant user departments, the medical staff, and management. If an outside contractor is to be employed for systems development work, the same form of project organization should be a requirement of the contract.

The life cycle for development of an information system in healthcare organizations includes seven steps: (1) systems analysis of functional requirements, (2) selection of a design approach, (3) system design, (4) system acquisition or construction, (5) implementation, (6) operation and maintenance, and (7) system evaluation and improvement.

Systems analysis is the process of collecting, organizing, and analyzing data about IS requirements prior to decisions being made about system design and implementation. Systems analysis provides the benefits of self-examination, improvement of operations, and development of standards. Of greater importance, systems analysis provides a strong foundation on which to build automated information systems.

In selecting an approach to system design, the project team can choose among the following alternatives: (1) purchase of predesigned "packaged" software from commercial vendors, (2) use of applications service providers, (3) in-house design and programming, (4) employment of contractors for design and programming, and (5) combination of these approaches. Most healthcare organizations are using commercial software for the majority of their applications because of the wide array of products available and the lower cost of development.

Design of a healthcare information system should flow readily from the statement of functional requirements determined through systems analysis. Detailed design specifications are required for systems being developed in-house. Less detail is required when packaged software is used. However, essential requirements must be specified and matched against the capabilities of software packages being considered.

Most healthcare organizations now use predesigned application software and other vendor services in implementing information systems. Careful attention to software evaluation, system selection, and contract negotiations is essential.

Factors to consider in evaluating application software include (1) congruence with functional requirements; (2) level of satisfaction of other users; (3) compatibility with existing hardware and software; (4) ability to interface with existing applications; (5) support available, including training, documentation, and maintenance; (6) costs of software, system implementation, new releases, and maintenance; and (7) financial stability of the vendor.

In evaluating contract services, healthcare organizations should (1) review the prior experience of the contractor, (2) investigate the company's financial stability, (3) review the credentials of personnel to be assigned to the project, (4) ensure that well-established principles of systems analysis and design are followed, (5) carefully review costs, and (6) use a neutral consultant for technical assistance if necessary.

A request for proposals (RFP) is often used in major system acquisitions. The RFP should specify functional requirements, content and format for proposals, criteria to be used in evaluating proposals, demonstration and system test requirements, and general contractual requirements. In less-complex system acquisitions, a request for information (RFI) sent to selected vendors may substitute for the more formal and costly RFP process.

Legal counsel should be employed in negotiating contracts. Special attention in the contract should be given to delivery dates, acceptance testing, payment schedule, warranties and guarantees, software ownership, interface responsibilities, maintenance and system updates, personnel training, and documentation.

Consultants can assist in the evaluation and selection process by serving as facilitators, providing technical information, and offering an outside perspective. Consultants should be chosen carefully to ensure they have the necessary expertise and have no conflict of interests through ties to a particular IS vendor.

Implementation of an information system includes ordering needed computer and telecommunications equipment, writing computer programs and/or procuring packaged software, orientation and training of management and operating personnel, database preparation, system testing, and final documentation.

System testing should include a complete check of system objectives, output screens and reports, input forms and procedures, error and correction procedures, computer programs and equipment operations, adequacy of system documentation, and accuracy of initial cost estimates. If the tests show that costs are much higher than estimated or that the system is not meeting its objectives, then the organization should not proceed with implementation.

Healthcare information systems require both periodic and unscheduled maintenance after they are operational. Changing requirements in a dynamic healthcare environment will also necessitate system changes from time to time. Maintenance personnel should periodically evaluate the information system and make improvements based on these evaluations.

The case study, "Developing an Electronic Medical Record for an Integrated Physician Office Practice" by Andrea White and Gloria Wakefield, following this chapter illustrates several of the concepts discussed in this chapter.

Discussion Questions

12.1 What is the purpose of systems analysis in healthcare organizations?

12.2 Give examples of the kinds of questions that systems analysis should address.

12.3 What kinds of data are collected in a systems analysis?

12.4 What alternatives are possible in the selection of an approach to system design? Discuss the advantages and disadvantages of each alternative.

12.5 List the major elements that should be included in the design specifications for a computer application to be developed by in-house staff.

12.6 What are some of the sources of information for identifying healthcare software packages?

12.7 Discuss some of the more important elements to consider in evaluating application software packages.

12.8 Discuss the pros and cons of using a request for proposals in a system acquisition?

12.9 What are some of the major elements that should be included in a contract for information systems?

12.10 What role can consultants play in the evaluation and selection of systems?

12.11 What kinds of training should be carried out before implementation of an information system in healthcare organizations? Who should be trained? Who should conduct the training?

12.12 What elements should be included in a system test?

Problems

12.1 Draw up an organization chart and work plan for a systems analysis of the order-entry and results-reporting process for clinical laboratory testing in a hospital.

12.2 Conduct a study of information flow of the patient registration process in an outpatient clinic in your area. Develop a systems flowchart with accompanying narrative notes. Describe improvements that could be made in the present system as a result of your study.

12.3 Select five vendors that provide software for the healthcare industry. Using the Internet, determine as many as possible of the following:
a. Headquarters address and telephone number
b. Names of the manager(s) in charge of marketing
c. Ownership status of the firm
d. Percent of gross sales due to healthcare software
e. Number of employees in the firm
f. Profile of software products offered by the firm

12.4 Select three applications service providers that provide online software for the healthcare industry. Prepare a profile of the products offered and the lease agreement for use of the software.

12.5 Schedule an interview with the CIO of a healthcare organization in your community. Obtain the opinion of the CIO on the use of request for proposals in selecting information systems for the organization.

12.6 Prepare a system test plan for a patient scheduling information system for the outpatient clinics of a university medical center.

References

Austin, C. J., and S. B. Boxerman. 1995. *Quantitative Analysis for Health Services Administration*. Chicago: AUPHA/Health Administration Press.

Baldwin, F. D. 2001. "Expert for Hire." *Healthcare Informatics* 18 (1): 47–50, 52, 54.

Healthcare Information and Management Systems Society. 1995. *Guide to Effective Healthcare Management Engineering.* Chicago: HIMSS.

Hubbard, S., and D. Garets. 2001. "United We Stand." *Healthcare Informatics* 18 (6): 93–95.

Jerva, M. 2001. "BPR (Business Process Redesign) and Systems Analysis and Design: Making the Case for Integration." *Topics in Health Information Management* 21 (4): 30–37.

Lauer, T. W., K. Joshi, and T. Browdy. 2000. "Use of the Equity Model to Review Clinical System Implementation Efforts: A Case Report." *Journal of the American Medical Informatics Association* 7 (1): 91–102.

Lee, F. W. 1996. "Can Computer-Aided Systems Engineering Tools Enhance the Development of Health Care Information Systems? A Critical Analysis." *Topics in Health Information Management* 17 (1): 1–11.

Monohan, T. 2001. "ASPs." *Healthcare Informatics* 18 (2): 54, 56.

O'Neil, J. 2001. "Project Management." *Health Management Technology* 22 (6): 32.

Reynolds, G. W. 1995. *Information Systems for Managers,* 3rd Edition. Minneapolis/St. Paul, MN: West Publishing Company.

Spilsbury, L. 2000. "ASP Brings Added Benefits." *Health Management Technology* 21 (8).

Additional Readings

Austin, C. J., and K. A. Wager. 1998. "Health Information Systems." In *Handbook of Health Care Management,* edited by W. J. Duncan and L. E. Swayne. Malden, MA: Blackwell Publishers.

Austin, C. J., and R. C. Howe. 1994. "Information Systems Management." In *The AUPHA Manual of Health Services Management,* edited by R. J. Taylor and S. B. Taylor. Gaithersburg, MD: Aspen Publishers.

Carroll-Barefield, A., and S. P. Smith. 2001. "Case Study: Incorporating Project Management Skills in the Design of a Clinical Research Patient Management System." *Health Care Management* 20 (1): 70–76.

Marietti, C. 2001. "Workflow: Working Software Can Streamline Many Administrative, Financial and Clinical Tasks." *Healthcare Informatics* 18 (2): 66, 68.

Orens, J. 1996. "Grasp Operational Processes Before Selecting Systems." *Health Management Technology* (July): 26–28.

Rogers, S. V. 2002. "Automating Procedure Workflow to Boost Productivity." *Health Management Technology* 23 (3): 32–34, 36.

Souther, E. 2001. "Implementation of the Electronic Medical Record: The Team Approach." *Computers in Nursing* 19 (2): 47–55.

DEVELOPING AN ELECTRONIC MEDICAL RECORD FOR AN INTEGRATED PHYSICIAN OFFICE PRACTICE

This case study was originally published in 1998.

by Andrea W. White and Gloria R. Wakefield

The Beaches Clinic located in Florida is a prestigious, highly specialized, 180-member integrated physician office practice offering 32 specialty services. Its mission is threefold: patient care, research, and education. Patient care is the primary mission but interdependent with the other two. The clinic has grown impressively since its opening in 1986 and now reports having more than 33,000 patient registrations and more than 160,000 office visits per year. The clinic was built on the premise that serving the whole patient is of paramount importance. When a patient is seen at the clinic, the patient is assigned a primary physician who guides the patient's care and receives prompt assistance, when necessary, from the many specialists who also are employed at the clinic. Most diagnostic and therapeutic services are performed within the clinic. Should the patient require hospitalization, the patient is admitted to neighboring PrimaCare Hospital, with which all Beaches Clinic physicians are affiliated.

During the last three years, the clinic has been involved in an ambitious undertaking: replacing its labor-intensive paper medical record system with a fully electronic patient record. The electronic patient information is now accessible to Beaches physicians from numerous terminals throughout the clinic and from a number of terminals within PrimaCare Hospital as well. The intent of the new electronic system is to reduce administrative inefficiency, improve access to patient information to benefit patient care, and improve access to research data. This case study provides readers with an understanding of the process used by the Beaches Clinic personnel in planning, developing, and implementing its electronic medical record.

The Paper Medical Record System: Benefits and Disadvantages

The original record system utilized paper medical records enclosed in a plastic pouch. The record consisted of multiple forms of heavy paper folded width-wise in thirds, color coded by specialty, placed back-to-back; the forms are arranged according to ease of accessibility for the individual clinicians. The records were handwritten except for the electronic information generated by the Cycare Registration System, the Cerner Laboratory System, and the SD&G Radiology System.

These records were housed in the health information services department when a patient was not undergoing treatment at the clinic. When a patient was undergoing treatment, the record resided in the particular area of the clinic where the patient was being treated. If a patient needed the services of several specialties, the record traveled from one area to another, and if the patient needed to be hospitalized, the record was sent to PrimaCare Hospital. This continual movement of the record created numerous opportunities for the record to be misplaced and created location difficulties for physicians wishing to access the record. The loose material generated by the patient's visits to the various areas of the clinic continually followed the record and required personnel to locate the record and file the material. It was essential that newly generated material be filed within the record before the patient's next visit so that physicians would have access to the most complete information.

As can be imagined, the number of employees required to manage the information in the record was high. About 330 desk attendants worked on the eight floors of the clinic and had the sole responsibility of tracking individual records, filing loose material, gathering x-ray films, and transporting the films and the record to the various locations in the clinic where the patient was being seen.

The health information services department served as the storehouse for the completed record. The department employed 17 clerical people called completion assistants. After a patient's treatment ended, the record returned to the completion assistants for final analysis and completion. The completion assistants made certain that the forms were signed and that all of the necessary reports were included. The completion assistants spent a considerable amount of time out of the department, walking the floors to obtain the necessary signatures and reports. Despite their efforts, it was not unusual for the record to take up to six months to be completed and filed, and therefore a tremendous backlog of records waiting for processing existed. Hundreds of records could be found throughout the clinic waiting for attention. Not surprisingly, physicians often had difficulty obtaining information when they needed it and frequently were frustrated by the system's inefficiency.

In addition to physicians needing information, the physicians' secretaries also needed access to patient information as they frequently called and spoke to patients. Locating the record could be quite a task. It was possible that a single patient's record could have been taken to and found in numerous locations—the completion assistants' area, a number of different clinic areas, a number of different physicians' offices, a number of secretaries' offices, the business office, or the legal department. A computerized chart tracking system (a part of the Cycare System) was used, which helped manage the process a great deal. Occasionally, however, some human error would occur, and the record was then not readily located. When this unfortunate situation occurred, or when needed patient information was not available in the record, a very labor intensive "all-points bulletin" search would be initiated. If a search failed to locate the misplaced record, the physician would be forced to cancel and reschedule the patient's visit, which was irritating and inconvenient for all concerned.

One benefit of the existing system, however, was that when everything worked, and the record was able to be accessed, physicians knew exactly where to locate the information they needed. The system called for all loose material to be filed into the record prior to a patient returning to the clinic. The specific service's desk attendants arranged the record for their physicians according to the physicians' specifications. Thus, all needed information was located in the front of the record and readily accessible to the physician providing the care. Additional information was easily accessible to the physician who knew the system and needed only to sort through a few colored forms to locate information of interest.

Planning for the Electronic Medical Record

In 1992 a group of physicians and administrators began discussing the possibility of developing an electronic medical record (EMR). The chief executive officer of the clinic, the associate administrator of PrimaCare Hospital, the president of the clinic's medical staff, seven clinic physicians, and the director of the clinic's information services department formed a steering committee to look into the possibility of creating an EMR for the Beaches Clinic's patients. This group of people recognized that the present system of record keeping was very inefficient. It required the employment of an exorbitant number of people just to manage a record.

The committee wanted a system that would allow data integration between the clinic, the hospital, the newly developing HMO, and other primary care physician practices, which were increasingly being networked into the Beaches Medical System. They wanted all Beaches physicians to have access to patient information from a number of locations within the medical system. They wanted test results immediately accessible once the tests were completed. They also wanted pertinent patient information from the hospital available to physicians at the clinic. Because physicians were used to having the desk attendants arrange the forms in the paper record specifically for each specialty, with the information that was considered important to the specialty located at the beginning of the record, they wanted the electronic record to also be maintained in a specialty-specific manner. The group wanted diagnostic and procedural billing data to be electronically transmitted to the business office. They wanted data entry to be an easy process that did not require physicians to key in anything. They also wanted the electronic statistical data to be available for research efforts. They expected that an electronic record system would reduce costs in time and labor because there would be no need to shuffle the paper record from area to area in the clinic and there would be no need to send the record to the hospital for an admitted patient. In essence, they wanted an electronic application that replicated the paper medical record they had but that would be readily available in multiple locations to multiple users at the same time.

The EMR steering committee began looking for a vendor that would be able to provide a product to meet their needs. The in-house information services department at this time included only 10 people within the clinic and 17 people within the hospital because there was minimal automation in the medical system. The committee realized they did not have the technical expertise in-house to build the system and sent out an RFP to three vendors. The committee members made site visits to talk to the vendors and to see their systems. The results were disappointing. What they learned was that there was no one vendor that could deliver all of what the committee had required and that if they wanted to continue pursuing the idea of acquiring an EMR, they were going to have to choose the best of a less-than-ideal system.

The committee members were unimpressed with two of the vendors but were intrigued with the third. This vendor was owned by physicians, and therefore personnel "could speak their language." The committee was already somewhat familiar with the vendor because it also had developed the clinic's laboratory system. This vendor explained to the EMR steering committee that they had developed a clinical data repository that allowed the integration of all patient data. This idea interested them, but the committee explained that they wanted the system to serve not just as a data repository but also to actually become its medical record. Although the vendor already had several clients, none of these clients had any intention of using the system as its medical record. The company was interested in partnering with the Beaches Clinic and working toward developing the system so that it could be used as the medical record. It offered to act as a consultant in helping the clinic select other systems that would work well with its clinical data repository and help facilitate its functioning as a medical record. The vendor presented a very convincing proposal to the clinic: their company could customize the system and could meet the needs of the clinic through a developmental partnership for an alpha product that would greatly enhance the support of the practice.

The clinic's EMR steering committee agreed to partner with the vendor, and in 1993 the vendor began planning how it would implement the system. It recommended the use of an optical imaging system and suggested an imaging vendor. The plan called for having all handwritten notes scanned into digital format from the year 1992 forward. The health information services department hired five clerical people who could scan the handwritten reports that would allow physicians to access the scanned information from the terminals. Additional systems were also brought in to support dictation and transcription.

Implementing the Pilot Program

An expanded steering committee—with seven physicians, one clinic administrator, one hospital associate administrator, one information systems director, and the vendor project manager—decided that the best way to implement the creation of the EMR was to initiate a pilot program. The sixth floor of the clinic, which treated internal medicine patients, was designated as the opening site. Two of the five internal medicine physicians on this floor who were selected to treat patients using the EMR were serving on the steering committee and were eager to test the system. While learning to use the EMR, the physicians were also to have access to and routinely use the paper medical record. In January 1994, the pilot program began.

When word spread that the pilot program was being initiated, there was some concern expressed about its feasibility. Not many Beaches physicians expected it would be successful, much less continued. With the exception of the seven physicians serving on the committee, the clinic physicians had only been minimally informed of the concept of changing to an EMR. There had been no formal announcement or communication informing the physicians that a plan was being considered and tested. The rumors of a change to an EMR were somewhat unsettling, but few physicians could anticipate the impact of the change. While the physicians recognized the disadvantages of the paper record system, they were at least familiar and comfortable with it. The Beaches Clinic had used paper records since its origin and still boasted of having its first medical records in hard copy. These physicians did not expect that the clinic would break with tradition.

The clinic information systems (IS) department designated an individual to serve as a trainer for the five physicians testing the system and set up training sessions. The trainer carried a pager and was readily available to offer assistance. The IS department also instituted a help line. The vendor developed training manuals and a quick reference guide that could easily be carried in a pocket. The pilot program was initially planned to last three months. As the weeks progressed, the five physicians appeared pleased with the EMR. They were still able to practice with their paper medical records but also use the EMR. Some of them used the EMR more frequently than others.

In March 1994, the clinic administrator asked the health information services director of PrimaCare Hospital to serve in an advisory capacity on the steering committee and to spend some time each week consulting in the health information services department of the clinic. This individual knew what information was required in the medical record and had expertise in the presentation of data, data integrity, and the legal aspects of confidentiality and security of patient information. She was able to act as a liaison between the IS people and the clinicians using the EMR. Eventually, this individual was appointed director for the health information services department in the clinic as well as in the hospital.

The pilot program continued for six months, and as problems or issues developed, the steering committee addressed them. Although the pilot program had been established as a pilot program, it actually functioned as the vehicle to implement the plan to move from the paper medical record to the EMR rather than as a testing and evaluation mechanism of an EMR idea. At the end of the six months, despite holding no formal evaluation of the system, the steering committee continued with the implementation, confident in its commitment to the project and in its decision that there would be no turning back. The clinic and the vendor were moving forward in their partnership to develop the EMR.

The rollout was done by specialty, with the easier specialty services rolling out first and the more complicated services implemented later. The primary care practice at the hospital was also done. As the rollout progressed, physicians began expressing concern about the time it was requiring to actually use the system. They were unfamiliar with the system and required training, but this training and unfamiliarity were affecting the physicians' productivity. Clinic physicians were employed by the clinic and were expected to meet certain productivity standards. The new system was interfering with their ability to meet these standards. The physicians were not able to see as many of their patients, and the time they spent with each patient was significantly increased as they searched for information on the EMR. Moreover, physicians found it difficult to talk to patients and maintain eye contact as they also scanned computer screens. It was hard to do both activities at the same time when they felt so unfamiliar with the system. For example, the ophthalmologists had been spending about ten minutes with each patient using the paper medical record. With the EMR system they were spending about 25 minutes seeing patients as they clicked through the record trying to locate specific information they needed to evaluate the patient. Administration recognized their concerns and made arrangements for them to have decreased productivity while they learned the system.

The last departments implementing the EMR were surgery and hematology/oncology. These departments were the most productive and the most complicated. They also were quite content with the present paper medical record system and the most resistant to practicing solely with the EMR. However, the clinic IS personnel continued the training. Formal training sessions had been established, and the IS department practiced a "train the trainer" method, training personnel in the clinic's education and development department who then trained the physicians. Eventually the last departments were also comfortable with using the EMR.

Maintaining a Parallel Operation

Although it was always the clinic's intention to develop the EMR to replace the paper medical record, it was recognized that both the electronic and the manual systems would have to be maintained for a period of time. The paper record was the official medical record of the clinic and the only one sanctioned by state law at that time. The paper record was also necessary to serve as the backup to the electronic record during computer downtime. Initially, it was expected that implementing the pilot program of the EMR would have little impact on current medical record operations and that the paper medical record system would continue to be maintained exactly as it had been during the past ten years. However, the pilot program immediately affected the paper record and its operations.

The pilot program began on the sixth floor, which housed three specialties. The first issue to be resolved was how to simultaneously get the new paper information, which was being generated during patient visits, onto both the electronic record and the paper record because it was needed on both records. With the exception of the sixth floor, the paper record was in use exclusively in all other areas of the clinic. Even though patients were seen in the pilot specialty areas, they were also being seen and receiving treatment in other areas of the clinic as well. Therefore, the newly generated information needed to be maintained in both paper and electronic formats. This dual system created a tremendous paper chase to ensure that all results were returned to the pilot floor area where they could be scanned into the EMR. As a result, point-of-service scanners were purchased and implemented on each of the floors and also placed in the health information services department to better capture all loose material.

It was noted by physicians that results of tests that they knew had been performed were not present in both the EMR and the paper medical record. This became a frequent enough occurrence that a quality-control process had to be implemented to check the EMR against the paper record and to be certain that all results and necessary reports were found in both the EMR and the paper record prior to a patient's scheduled appointment. As the EMR was rolled out to other floors, this quality-control process became extremely labor intensive. Approximately 30 temporary staff were hired to perform the process; in addition, ten other temporary staff were hired to maintain the filing of loose reports. The quality-control process continued for two years until it was believed that the majority of scheduled appointment records had been reviewed and that the paper records and the electronic records contained the same information.

The EMR steering committee recognized that the clinic needed to maintain the dual record system for at least two years. The process of rolling out the EMR to all the specialties had been planned to take place over a two-year time frame. Physicians' mixed acceptance of the EMR as well as performance and stability issues of the new system required that the process not be rushed. Also the paper medical record served as the backup during system downtime.

Three years into the conversion, the paper record continues to serve as the legal record and the downtime backup record. A legal record must have reports with authorized physician signatures and must be easily retrievable and easily hard-copied so that it can be sent to designated locations when patients authorize a release of information. The EMR system, at this time, is not able to easily satisfy these requirements. The vendor is continuing to work on enhancements and upgrades, but progress has been slow. A new product version that is under development and is scheduled to be implemented in the fourth year will soon meet all of the legal requirements and will allow the EMR to truly serve as the legal medical record. Until that time, however, both systems must be maintained.

By March 1996, everyone in the clinic was using the EMR system. No longer were paper medical records allowed to be used by physicians along with the electronic record. Physicians were expected to practice using the EMR alone. The paper record was continuing to be maintained, however, for legal reasons. Although no survey had been conducted at the time, it was estimated that the majority of physicians had become familiar enough with the system and appeared pleased with it. User groups have now been established and are able to present their issues about the system to the EMR steering committee. A formal survey of physicians to solicit user input is also being conducted at the time of this writing (1997).

Impact of the Electronic Medical Record

The new EMR system at the clinic has achieved many of the goals for which it was intended. Electronic patient information is almost always available at multiple locations and by multiple users and is used to support practice. There has been minimal computer downtime and when it has occurred, a paper medical record has been available because it is still being produced. State law has only recently been changed to allow for electronic signatures. Therefore, the EMR can now serve as the official medical record once electronic signatures have been incorporated into the system. It is expected that this electronic signature implementation will be initiated sometime in the near future, eliminating the need for the dual systems.

The new system has produced dramatic changes in the number and use of clerical and technical personnel and the associated personnel costs. During the first two years of implementation, costs associated with increased personnel and equipment purchases rose dramatically. During the third year, however, costs decreased substantially and are expected to continue declining. The initial conversion required additional low-cost clerical personnel and high-cost technical staffing. Because physicians continued to dictate their reports and clinic notes rather than key in information, the information still needed to be transcribed into the new electronic system. A significant number of transcriptionists were and are needed to accomplish this task. The director of health information services had originally employed only eight transcriptionists, but she now employs 55 transcriptionists and estimates that she needs at least ten others to transcribe all of the clinic notes, patient referral correspondence, and outpatient operative reports. Some of these transcriptionists are located in the main clinic building, but most work in a separate building several miles away. Three contract services are also being utilized to ensure a 48-hour turnaround time.

Paper test results also had to be scanned into the electronic system. The clinic purchased optical scanners and currently employs 12 people who serve as scanning personnel, optically scanning test results into the system. These scanners are located on each of the clinic floors and do point-of-service scanning as documents are generated on the floor. Two scanners in the health information services department scan information into newly created electronic records as previously seen patients reenter the clinic for evaluation and treatment.

The number of computer terminals used in the clinic has dramatically increased. Computer terminals can now be found at each desk attendants' area, in each patient examining room, and on all nursing units on all floors. The need for in-house technology support substantially grew. Because of the continuation of system enhancements and the planned conversion of the hospital medical record, additional positions were required, increasing the in-house clinic technical staff from the original 10 to 30 and the hospital technical staff from 17 to 35.

The importance of receiving feedback from users has been recently recognized. The health information services department during the past year employed two individuals to talk with physicians in specific specialties to find out what information they particularly need and want to have at their fingertips. These individuals then work with the IS personnel and convey those needs so that the IS department and the vendor can design the EMR screens to be more user-friendly for the specialists. Although more work is needed in this specific customizing, the efforts are beginning to pay off. While the patient record screens are a far cry from the sophisticated, colorful, and attractive Windows® computer screens so commonly in use today, the specialty screens are functional. A Windows-based graphical user interface is being developed for the next upgrade of the system.

Obviously the initial additional personnel and the technological requirements were costly to the clinic during the first two years of implementation. By the first quarter of the third year however, a significant reduction in clerical staff associated with paper record movement was achieved. The number of desk attendants and completion assistants was substantially reduced. Paper record maintenance is currently being accomplished by the use of low-cost temporary staffing. It is expected that the need for the temporary staffing will be eliminated once the paper record functions are eliminated at the end of the fourth year of EMR implementation

Although technical staff were also increased, it is predicted that by the fourth quarter of the fifth year, the technical staff will be reduced by one third and will only be involved in performing system maintenance functions. The current health information services staff, numbering 106 and presently involved in paper and electronic record functions, is expected at that time to be reduced to 25 because it will only be performing EMR maintenance functions.

In the third conversion year, the clinic realized a $6 million increase in revenue. This increase reduced an existing $8 million deficit to $2 million. The trend in revenue enhancement is expected to exceed the five-year revenue enhancement projections.

The benefits of the new electronic system are numerous. In 1994, approximately 50 records were listed as "unable to locate." Optical imaging of paper documents has now eliminated "lost" information. Access to medical information has been greatly improved, thus improving turnaround times for patient appointments and follow-up visits, obtaining billing information, abstracting data in registries, and conducting quality management reviews. Duplication of work in sharing information between physician offices and the hospital has been greatly reduced; no longer is information needed to be copied, faxed, or mailed to different locations. Physicians have immediate online access to patient information. Record retrieval for scheduled patient appointments has been reduced from a 24–48-hour retrieval time to retrieval at time of the appointment. Optical imaging at the point-of-service provides a complete medical record in a more timely manner than the previous practice of filing late reports in the paper record, which in some cases resulted in a record not being completed for several months.

All of these improvements have greatly enhanced the quality of patient care provided to the clinic's patients and have improved the efficiency and reduced the costs of delivery. The system currently in use at the clinic is well on its way to serving as the legal and electronic medical record of the clinic, and the members of the EMR steering committee are feeling confident that they have helped the clinic make dramatic improvements in their information system and in their delivery of patient care.

Benefits of the Electronic Medical Record

- Immediate physician access to patient information from within either the hospital or the clinic
- Improvement in creation of a timely and complete medical record, benefiting patient care
- Elimination of "lost" information in the record
- Improvement in turnaround time for scheduling patient appointments and follow-up visits
- Improvement in timeliness and access to billing information
- Improvement in capability for abstracting research data
- Improvement in access to quality management data
- Elimination of faxing, copying, and mailing of patient information between hospital and clinic
- Reduction of clerical personnel involved in record movement and record retrieval
- Additional cost reductions projected as system performance improves

---

Discussion Questions

1. How did the organizational culture of the clinic affect the planning and decision-making process of this project?
2. What were the benefits and disadvantages of the process used by the Beaches Clinic in planning and implementing the electronic medical record?
3. What might you suggest to improve the planning and decision-making process?
4. Why is communication essential among administrators, clinicians, information systems personnel, and the vendor?
5. Why is it essential that data integrity be ensured in a multisystem integration?

INFORMATION SECURITY

Information system managers in healthcare facilities must develop policies and procedures to protect the security of information contained in automated systems throughout the organization. This chapter discusses the need for protecting information confidentiality and methods for accomplishing this goal. Disaster protection and recovery procedures also are covered.

The Need for Information Security

Healthcare information systems contain sensitive information. Clinical systems process medical information about individual patients. Human resources information systems contain personal information about employees. Financial and decision-support systems include proprietary data used for planning, marketing, and management of the enterprise.

Clinical information systems require comprehensive programs to protect the privacy of patient medical records. Three categories of clinical systems must be considered:

1. *Patient care systems* (order entry and results reporting; electronic medical records; lab, pharmacy, radiology; etc.) store information about a patient's medical history, diagnoses, and treatment plans. Organizations that provide care are required by law and by ethical considerations to ensure that patient-specific information is available only to authorized users.
2. *Public health information systems* support disease prevention and surveillance programs. Protecting public health requires the acquisition and storage of health-related information about individuals. Public health benefits sometimes conflict with threats to individual privacy. Breaches of privacy of sensitive information can potentially lead to discrimination in employment or insurance eligibility. Individuals concerned about privacy who avoid clinical tests and treatments may endanger the health of others in the community. For example, sexually transmitted infections can be spread by failure to test and/or report the presence of the infections in certain patients (Gostin, Hodge, and Valdiserri 2001).
3. *Medical research information systems* use large repositories of individual patient records to study patterns of health and disease in populations. Data-mining techniques are used to search for potential relationships among patient characteristics and other factors. Research data often are accessible to a number of investigators and their staff, and information

security measures are essential to protect patient privacy rights (Lau and Catchpole 2001).

Security issues related to public health and medical research information systems can be addressed in a number of ways such as scrambling or encrypting patient identification numbers. In some research projects, identification numbers can be removed completely when only aggregate information is needed.

Governmental Requirements

Federal, state, and local governments have passed laws designed to protect patient-information privacy.

Gostin, Hodge, and Valdiserri (2001) contend that state privacy laws are inconsistent and fragmented. In response, "The Model State Public Health Privacy Act provides strong privacy safeguards for public health data while preserving the ability of state and local public health departments to act for the common good" (1388).

The individual's right to genetic privacy was addressed in Oregon's Genetic Privacy Act of 1995 that provides legal protection for medical information, tissue samples, and DNA samples. Harris and Keywood (2001) point out that individuals "have a powerful interest in genetic privacy and its associated claim to ignorance . . ."; however, "any claims to be shielded from information about the self must compete on equal terms with claims based in the rights and interests of others" (415). Cummings and Magnusson (2001) state, "As genetic privacy legislation is developed and enacted at state and federal levels, the needs of individuals must be balanced with the needs of institutions and of research in the larger context of societal needs" (1089).

In addition to government agencies, a number of private organizations have developed programs to protect medical-information privacy. The Expert Panel on Privacy and Confidentiality has established a set of expectations for ethical conduct that include consent for use and disclosure of information, individual access to one's own health records, security requirements for storage and transfer of information, and limitations on how identifiable information may be used (Wynia et al. 2001).

The most comprehensive legislation related to information security and privacy is the Health Insurance Portability and Accountability Act of 1996 (HIPAA), described in detail in the section below.

Health Insurance Portability and Accountability Act

HIPAA was passed by the United States Congress in 1996. It is designed to allow individuals who change jobs to retain health insurance coverage by eliminating the use of "pre-existing" conditions—refusal to cover health problems that exist at the time of a job change.

Two components of HIPAA have particular relevance to health information system managers: administrative simplification provisions and privacy protection regulations. The administrative simplification component of HIPAA establishes standards for the electronic transmission of certain health-care information:

> The stated purpose of [the] administrative simplification provisions of the law is to improve the Medicare and Medicaid programs, and the efficiency and effectiveness of the health care system . . . through the establishment of standards and requirements for the electronic transmission of certain health care information. Standards adopted under that section of the law are to apply to health plans, health care clearinghouses, and any health care provider who transmits any health information in electronic form for financial and administrative transactions, including: health claims or equivalent encounter information; enrollment and disenrollment in a health plan; health care premium payments; health claim status; and referral certification and authorization (Joint Healthcare Information Technology Alliance 2000).

The definition of organizations covered by the law is very broad and includes those who provide or pay for the cost of healthcare under many federal programs, including Medicare, Medicaid, military healthcare (including CHAMPUS), veterans healthcare program, the Indian healthcare program, and the federal employees' health benefit program.

Privacy protection components of the law "limit the non-consensual use and release of private health information; give patients new rights to access their medical records and to know who else has accessed them; restrict most disclosure of health information to the minimum needed for the intended purpose; establish new criminal and civil sanctions for improper use and disclosure; and establish new requirements for access to records by researchers and others" (Joint Healthcare Information Technology Alliance 2000).

Work on the development of standards and implementing regulations was still in process in mid-2002. The Working Group for Electronic Data Interchange, a voluntary group of private organizations and public agencies, has been developing recommended standards for implementation of HIPAA. Standards under development include the following:

- National Standards for Transactions and Code Sets
- National Employer Identifier
- National Provider Identifier
- Security and Electronic Signature Standards
- National Health Plan Identifier
- Claims Attachments
- Unique Health Identifier for Individuals

Numerous delays have been encountered in reaching agreement on the final standards. Of particular concern is the standard for identifying individual patients and maintaining privacy protection of their records.

HIPAA originally called for Congress to establish the privacy protection regulations. However, Congress delegated this responsibility to the Administrative Branch. The Clinton administration established an initial set of regulations in summer of 2000, but these were revised by the Bush administration in 2002. Needless to say, HIPAA compliance and modification of information systems to meet HIPAA standards have become major issues for healthcare organizations. In discussing HIPAA readiness, Wilson and McPherson (2002) call for the development of organizational strategies because "these transactions are the key to cost savings and business efficiency . . . and noncompliance with the HIPAA transaction standards could result in a substantial increase in denied payments and/or lost revenue" (14).

Many organizations have established HIPAA task forces. Some have appointed compliance and/or privacy offices to lead the efforts. Others are using existing organizational units including the office of the CIO, medical records, and risk management (Marietti 2002).

Software vendors will play a critical role in HIPAA compliance because most organizations use vendor-supplied software in their information systems. HIPAA patches to existing programs will be needed and some in-house work may be required to interface applications with one another (Wilson and McPherson 2002). In addition to software updates, changes to business processes and procedures will be needed as well. Marietti (2002) notes that "80 percent to 85 percent of HIPAA compliance issues will depend on adjusting human behavior" (55).

Education of employees throughout the enterprise is particularly important. The University of Alabama at Birmingham (UAB) is the major medical center for the state. As one component of its employee education program, the data security officer in the Office of the Vice President for Information Technology published a full-page article about HIPAA in the official staff newspaper. After describing the provisions of HIPAA, the article discusses UAB's implementation activities. "UAB has formed a campuswide steering committee to guide consistent implementation and has several working groups under this umbrella for each of the major areas on campus involved, including students, employees, research, clinics and hospitals" (Piazza 2002).

As mentioned above, HIPAA regulations and requirements are still evolving, and changes are likely even after full implementation is achieved. The best way to stay current on this topic is through the Internet. A list of web sites that provide this information is included in Figure 13.1.

Information Security Policies and Procedures

Healthcare organizations must establish enterprisewide standards to maintain data security and protect the privacy and confidentiality of information, par-

FIGURE 13.1

Information About HIPAA on the Internet

- U.S. Department of Health and Human Services
  http://www.hhs.gov
- Centers for Medicare & Medicaid Services (formerly Health Care Financing Administration)
  http://www.hcfa.gov
- HHS Administrative Simplification
  http://aspe.hhs.gov/admnsimp/Index.htm
- National Committee on Vital and Health Statistics
  http://ncvhs.hhs.gov/index.htm
- HHS Data Council
  http://aspe.os.dhhs.gov/datacncl/index.htm
- National Uniform Claim Committee
  http://www.nucc.org
- Joint Healthcare Information Technology Alliance (JHITA)
  http://www.jhita.org
- Workgroup for Electronic Data Interchange (WEDI)
  http://www.wedi.org
- American National Standards Institute
  http://www.ansi.org
- Data Interchange Standards Association
  http://www.disa.org

ticularly patient records. Data security involves two essential elements: (1) protecting against system failures or external catastrophic events, such as fires, storms, deliberate sabotage, and other acts of God, where critical information could be lost and (2) controlling access to computer files by unauthorized personnel.

Disaster Protection and Recovery Procedures

The information system steering committee (see Chapter 11) must ensure that effective data backup and recovery procedures are implemented at all processing sites throughout the organization. Critical data files should be copied to removable disk packs or tapes and stored in a secure location, away from the processing sites, preferably in a different building. The CIO should develop a data backup plan for approval by the steering committee. The plan should specify which files require duplication and how often backup procedures should be conducted. Recovery procedures to be used if catastrophic events occur should also be included.

The need for disaster planning was underscored by the terrorist attacks in Washington, DC and New York City on September 11, 2001. Disaster plans must be implemented, tested periodically, and refined. Testing of the plan provides training for employees and helps identify shortcomings in technology and/or procedures before they need to be used. A disaster-plan notebook should be developed and stored at the healthcare facility, at an off-site storage location, and at the homes of key employees who will be involved in recovery procedures (Vecchio 2000).

Consultants can be used to assist in disaster planning and recovery. For example, IRM International offers a disaster recovery program that includes four phases: assessment, documentation consolidation, disaster plan development, and testing and refinement. See http://www.irminternational.com/rptcard.html for a disaster recovery report card that rates disaster-planning readiness.

Data can also be lost through computer viruses that are increasingly prevalent and destructive. Each computer program should be inspected by virus-protection software every time the program is run. Acquisition of software should be subject to central review and approval, and particular care must be exercised to ensure that software downloaded from the Internet or obtained over networks has been scanned and proven to be virus free. All incoming e-mail messages should be scanned for viruses, and employees should be trained not to open suspicious files attached to electronic mail.

Protecting Information Privacy and Confidentiality

Protecting data confidentiality is an even more difficult task. A comprehensive information security policy should include three elements: (1) physical security, (2) technical controls over access, and (3) management policies that are well known and enforced in all organizational units (see Figure 13.2).

Physical security includes such elements as using keys or badges to unlock computer terminals and using dial-back procedures to determine that a request to access data has come from a specific terminal and modem.

A number of technical controls to data access can be built into operational information systems. Passwords are the most common. Each user is assigned a password that is known only by that individual and the data security manager. Users should be warned never to share their passwords with anyone else, and passwords should be changed periodically. Passwords should allow access only to those portions of the organization's database appropriate to the individual user and his/her departmental affiliation. For example, personnel in the purchasing department would have access restricted to materials

FIGURE 13.2
Information
Security

Physical Security
- Hardware
- Data files

Technical Safeguards
- Passwords
- Encryption
- Audit logs

Management Policies
- Written security policy
- Employee training
- Disciplinary actions for violations

management data files only, and they could not use their terminals to access patient records.

Encryption is a method of coding or altering information such that it is unintelligible if obtained by unauthorized users. Encryption is used with very sensitive information such as lists of passwords or diagnostic information on mental health or sexually transmitted diseases. It is not a practical method for providing general data protection. The data security manager should be the only one able to decode encrypted information.

The most important technical safeguard may be the maintenance of audit logs that track every transaction associated with use of critical data files. The logs will identify the user and/or terminal; the date and time of access; and the type of transaction carried out (simple access, addition, changes, or deletions to the record). If employees are aware that all transactions are being monitored for violations, they will be deterred from seeking unauthorized use of sensitive information.

Management policies support the physical safeguards and technical controls that protect data confidentiality. Training of all users is essential to ensure they understand the importance of data confidentiality and the procedures in place to protect privacy of records. Every employee should be required to read the organization's privacy protection policy, and sign a statement indicating that he or she will not violate provisions of the policy. Strict disciplinary measures, including termination, should be followed when employee violations occur.

Data security issues are particularly complex for multiple-facility integrated delivery systems. These issues include questions such as who will have ownership of data on computer networks, what criteria will be used to determine who should have access to member and patient data, and who will be legally liable for guarding the confidential patient and financial data that reside on the network (Work, Pawola, and Henley 1996).

The Mayo Clinic has developed a comprehensive set of plans for the security of electronic medical records. A multidisciplinary team formulates policy and provides management oversight of the security program. Leaders of the Mayo Clinic effort suggest that a confidentiality policy should include the following elements (Olson, Peters, and Stewart 1998, 29):

- Access rights—who has access and for what reasons
- Release of information to the patient, other healthcare providers, and third parties
- Special handling, if any, for specific information (e.g., HIV results, psychiatric notes)
- Special handling, if any, for particular patients (e.g., employees or VIPs)
- Availability of medical information, including retention policies
- Integrity of medical information, including authentication, completeness, and handling of revisions or addenda
- Approved methods for communication of medical information

Security administrative procedures are well defined in the Mayo Clinic policies. Data stewards assume responsibility for specific data sets. Data assessment is used to classify information into security categories (internal, restricted, and confidential). Control of access is guided by the premise that users must have access to all the information they need to perform their duties, but not more. Physical and logical access controls are used, and a security awareness and training program helps to provide consistent application of standards and procedures throughout this complex organization (Olson, Peters, and Stewart 1998).

Summary

Healthcare information systems contain sensitive information. Policies and procedures are needed to protect the confidentiality of information about patients, employees, finances, and organizational strategies.

Clinical information is contained in three categories of systems: patient care systems, public health systems, and medical research systems. Benefits of public health and medical research systems sometimes conflict with threats to individual privacy. Particular care must be exercised to protect patients' rights to privacy while still serving the public good.

Laws have been passed at the federal, state, and local levels of government to protect medical information privacy. The most comprehensive of these laws is the Health Insurance Portability and Accountability Act (HIPAA) passed by the U.S. Congress in 1996. Two components of HIPAA have direct impact on healthcare information systems. The administrative simplification provisions of the law are designed to improve efficiency in the healthcare system by establishing uniform, national standards to be used for the electronic transmission of certain financial and administrative transactions. Electronic claims processing will be facilitated when these standards are fully implemented. Standards are being developed for transactions and code sets, employer identification, provider identification, electronic signatures, health plan identification, and identification of individual patients.

Privacy protection components of HIPAA restrict disclosure of health information to the minimum needed for patient care and administrative support. Patients have gained new rights to access their medical records and to know who has accessed them. HIPAA compliance requires that most healthcare organizations and their software vendors make modifications to computer software to meet the data standards and privacy protection provisions of the law. Changes to business processes and procedures are needed as well. Education and training of employees is particularly important.

In response to HIPAA and for ethical reasons as well, healthcare organizations need enterprisewide standards and policies to maintain data security and protect the confidentiality of certain information. A comprehensive information security program requires disaster protection and recovery procedures as well as procedures for limiting access to certain information stored in computer databases.

The disaster plan should include data backup and recovery procedures to be followed in the event of system crashes caused by technology failures, fires, storms, deliberate sabotage, and other acts of God. The plan should be tested periodically to provide employee training and identify shortcomings that need to be fixed. All computer programs should be scanned for viruses before being used. Acquisition or downloading of software should be centrally controlled to protect against infection of systems by viruses.

Protecting data confidentiality and limiting access to sensitive information requires a comprehensive security program with three elements: physical security, technical controls over access, and management policies. Physical security includes lock and badge systems and automatic dial-back procedures to protect computer terminals. Technical controls include use of passwords, data encryption of particularly sensitive information, and audit logs that identify who accessed information at a particular date and time. Management policies should clearly state the organization's procedures for protecting information privacy. These should be distributed to all employees, and disciplinary measures should be employed when violations occur.

Discussion Questions

13.1 Discuss some of the potential conflicts between a patient's right to privacy and information needed for disease surveillance and public health.

13.2 Discuss some of the potential conflicts between a patient's right to privacy and information needed for medical research.

13.3 What is HIPAA? What are the potential benefits to healthcare organizations to be gained by compliance with HIPAA standards? What are the potential drawbacks?

13.4 What are the two major elements of a comprehensive information security program for a healthcare organization?

13.5 What major elements should be included in an information technology disaster protection and recovery plan?

13.6 What components should be included in a plan for protecting information privacy and confidentiality?

13.7 Discuss the potential impact of genetic testing on health information systems security.

Problems

13.1 Review the information technology disaster plan for a healthcare organization in your area. Comment on the strengths and weaknesses of the plan.

13.2 Review the procedures for limiting access to medical information at a healthcare organization in your area. Comment on the strengths and weaknesses of these procedures.

13.3 Review a copy of the Model State Public Health Privacy Act. Comment on the potential benefits of this act to states that implement legislation of this type.

13.4 Meet with a CIO of a healthcare organization in your area. Discuss HIPAA and its impact on information systems for this organization.

References

Cummings, L. A., and R. Magnusson. 2001. "Genetic Privacy and Academic Medicine: The Oregon Experience." *Academic Medicine* 76 (11): 1090–93.

Gostin, L. O., J. G. Hodge, and R. O. Valdiserri. 2001. "Informational Privacy and the Public's Health: The Model State Public Health Privacy Act." *American Journal of Public Health* 91 (9): 1388–92.

Harris, J., and K. Keywood. 2001. "Ignorance, Information and Autonomy." *Theory of Medical Bioethics* 22 (5): 415–36.

Joint Healthcare Information Technology Alliance. 2000. "Issue Summary: HIPAA." [Online information]. www.jhita.org.

Lau, R. K. W., and M. Catchpole. 2001. "Improving Data Collection and Information Retrieval for Monitoring Sexual Health." *International Journal of STD and AIDS* 12: 8–13.

Marietti, C. 2002. "HIPAA: Blueprint for Privacy and Security." *Healthcare Informatics* 19 (1): 55, 56, 58, 60.

Olson, L. A., S. G. Peters, and J. B. Stewart. 1998. "Security and Confidentiality in an Electronic Medical Record." *Healthcare Information Management* 12 (1): 27–37.

Piazza, J. 2002. "Privacy, Security Law Will Have a Sweeping Impact." *UAB Reporter* (March 4): 4.

Vecchio, A. 2000. "Plan for the Worse Before Disaster Strikes." *Health Management Technology* 21 (6): 28–30.

Wilson, K. J., and C. E. McPherson. 2002. "It's 2002: How HIPAA-ready Are You?" *Health Management Technology* 23 (1): 14–15, 20.

Work, M., L. Pawola, and A. Henley. 1996. "CHINs, IHD Systems Remain in Evolutionary State." *Health Management Technology* (March): 54–58.

Wynia, M. K., S. S. Coughlin, S. Alpert, D. S. Cummins, and L. L. Emanuel. 2001. "Shared Expectations for Protection of Identifiable Health Care Information." *Journal of General Internal Medicine* 16 (2): 100–11.

Additional Readings

Alessi, N. 2001. "Information Technology and Child and Adolescent Psychiatry: Ethical Issues." *Drug Benefit Trends* 13 (9): 24–27.

Bourka, A., N. Polemi, and D. Koutsouris. 2001. "An Overview in Healthcare Information Systems Security." *Medinfo* 10 (Part 2): 1242–46.

Curtin, L., and R. N. Simpson. 2001. "Can You Keep a Secret?" *Health Management Technology* 22 (6): 44.

Eisenberg, J. M. 2001. "Can You Keep a Secret? Measuring the Performance of Those Entrusted with Personal Health Information." *Journal of General Internal Medicine* 16 (2): 132–34.

Kendler, K. S. 2001. "Family History Information in Biomedical Research." *Journal of Continuing Education in Health Professions* 21 (4): 215–23.

Lawrence, L. M. 1994. "Safeguarding the Confidentiality of Automated Medical Information." *Journal on Quality Improvement* (November): 639–46.

Reuters Health Information. 2002. "Policy Gaps Leave Genetic Data Vulnerable to Potential Abuse." *Reuters Health* (May 6).

Conclusion and Future Directions

SENIOR MANAGERS' ROLE IN INFORMATION TECHNOLOGY MANAGEMENT

This final chapter discusses the human resources and management expertise required to make effective use of information technology in healthcare organizations. The chapter concludes with a brief examination of future trends and how the senior manager's role in information technology may be affected.

Organizing for Information Management

Determining the locus for management of information technology in the healthcare organization is a key responsibility of the chief executive officer and the governing board. Historically, many healthcare organizations have assigned this responsibility to the chief financial officer, reflecting the high priority assigned to fulfilling the need for accurate and timely financial information.

However, given the increasing importance assigned to clinical information systems and the use of information in strategic planning and decision support, many healthcare organizations have assigned the responsibility for information management and communications to a separate executive-level position, the chief information officer (CIO).

Role of the Chief Information Officer

Reporting directly to the chief executive officer (or chief operating officer in some large organizations), the CIO serves two important functions: (1) assist the senior management team and governing board in using information effectively to support strategic planning and management and (2) provide management oversight and coordination of information processing and telecommunications systems throughout the organization.

In larger organizations, the CIO should be a full-time position. In smaller hospitals and clinics, these responsibilities may be assigned to another administrative officer. The CIO must possess a good understanding of the healthcare environment, be an experienced manager, and have sufficient understanding of information technology to ensure that information systems are properly planned and implemented.

Healthcare CIOs have consistently listed the following as the three most important attributes needed for success in the job:

1. Leadership ability
2. Vision/imagination
3. Business acumen

Although some technical competence is important, most CIOs emphasize their strategic role rather than their technical management role (Morrisey 1996).

Charles Emery, Ph.D. of Horizon Blue Cross Blue Shield of New Jersey was selected as CIO of the year by the College of Healthcare Information Management Executives. Emery sees the role of the CIO as the ability to "translate his or her understanding of a technological or process challenge into a business opportunity and help move the organization forward. . . . There are jobs in senior management that are visionary jobs; our task is to be both a visionary and someone who executes" (Hagland 2001, 19).

Respondents to a 2001 web-based survey of healthcare information technology management personnel (including CIOs) were employed by a variety of organizations, including integrated delivery networks, academic medical centers, single hospitals, physician groups, and managed care organizations. Salaries of the CIOs in the survey ranged from $50,000 to $234,000, with an average of $115,000. Ninety-two percent of the CIOs reported being satisfied, very satisfied, or extremely satisfied with their careers. When asked to identify the most important challenge in their current positions, the top two responses were (1) the culture and structure of the organization and (2) financial constraints (Morris 2001).

In discussing the changing role of healthcare CIOs, Wood (2000) states "In the past, chief information officers were responsible for nothing else but assuring a constant flow of information. Today, they are being asked to do a great deal more. From E-business to E-health strategy, the chief information officer is the focal point of an organization's ability to leverage new technology" (81).

Organizing and Staffing an Information Systems Department

The organizational structure for information systems development should be guided by the institution's strategic objectives and information systems plan (see Chapter 11). The size and complexity of tasks to be carried out by a central information systems department in a healthcare organization are affected by a number of factors including:

- the degree of centralization or distribution of computer systems throughout the organization,
- the extent to which systems are developed in-house or implemented through use of packaged software or contracts with application service providers, and
- the extent to which tasks are outsourced to contractors.

A typical information systems organizational structure for a single hospital or medical center is shown in Figure 14.1. The information systems department manager reports to the CIO along with the director of management engineering and the director of telecommunications.

The information systems department is generally organized into three divisions. Professional staff members in the system development division are responsible for system design and implementation. The division is organized into three sections: programming, systems analysis, and system maintenance. The operations division includes three sections: network maintenance, data preparation and editing, and computer operations. The software evaluation and user support division is responsible for evaluation of software systems in the health applications area. This division also reviews and approves all hardware and software acquisitions proposed by user departments and provides technical support on software utilization. The user support staff often will operate a "help desk" that users can contact for hardware and software assistance.

An experienced technical manager, reporting to the CIO, should head the information systems department. He or she must have up-to-date knowledge of the technical aspects of systems analysis, computer programming, hardware and software, networks, and telecommunications systems. The manager must be willing to spend the time and effort necessary to stay up to date with the latest technical knowledge in a rapidly changing field. In addition, the manager must be an experienced financial manager and must be skilled in interpersonal relations.

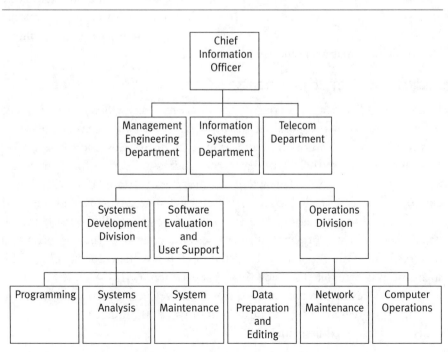

FIGURE 14.1
Information Systems Organization

Three levels of personnel must be recruited for staffing an information systems department: professional, technical, and clerical. Professional staff includes systems analysts and computer programmers. Although finding talented persons who can fill both roles is possible, care must be exercised in not equating the two. Systems analysis requires broad-based skills that computer programmers often do not possess. It is a highly creative process requiring someone with both technical knowledge of analytical and design techniques and a broad organizational focus. Because most systems are complex and involve substantial man-machine interaction, the systems analyst must be able to deal effectively with people and must understand the way in which the organization functions in carrying out its mission. Programmers often have a more narrow orientation and are skilled in the technical tasks of software development and maintenance. Programming requirements are changing. As healthcare organizations move toward the implementation of client/server architecture (see Chapter 5), network programmers are replacing those who write and maintain large programs for mainframe computers.

Technician-level personnel operate the computer and maintain the communications network. Skilled network managers are highly trained and are often in short supply. The operations supervisor must be both a skilled technician and an effective manager. Equipment maintenance is usually handled by contract with vendors who supply periodic preventive maintenance and emergency repairs on call.

Organizing and staffing for an integrated delivery system composed of multiple facilities are more complex. Some systems are highly centralized with all software development carried out by a corporate information technology (IT) staff. In other systems, more responsibility is delegated to operational units. Whatever the approach, the organizational structure must facilitate electronic information exchange across the enterprise.

Budget and Staff Requirements

Budgets for IT in healthcare organizations are increasing. Sixty-seven percent of the organizations responding to the 2002 Leadership Survey conducted by the Healthcare Information and Management Systems Society (HIMSS) indicated that their 2002 IT budget would increase. Reasons for the increase in budgets included overall growth in the number of systems and technologies employed, increases called for in organizational strategic plans, and the need to upgrade IT infrastructure. The amount of funds controlled outside the IT department also was expected to increase. One quarter of the organizations that responded to the survey reported that more than 20 percent of IT spending was controlled outside the IT department (HIMSS 2002).

Forty-seven percent of the HIMSS survey respondents expected IT staffing to increase during the next 12 months. Staffing needs listed in rank order (greatest need first) include:

- Network and architecture support
- PC/Server support
- Internet/intranet support
- User training
- Help desk
- Process/workflow redesign
- Application support and development

Outsourcing

Many healthcare organizations are considering outsourcing of some or all information systems functions as an alternative to in-house staffing. Traditionally, the term *outsourcing* has been associated with a contract for facilities management. More recently, however, the term is used in a broader context to denote contracting with the best-qualified company to meet a specific information system objective. This may involve *multisourcing* to a number of different vendors.

Some of the major potential benefits of outsourcing include the following:

1. Reduction of in-house staffing requirements
2. Smaller investment in capital equipment
3. More flexibility in meeting changing requirements and adopting new technology
4. Reduction in the time required to implement new applications
5. More predictable cost structure, particularly if fixed-price contracting is employed

Outsourcing is not without potential danger and risks; some of these are

1. too much dependence on vendors with the possibility that a critical contractor might go bankrupt or change business direction,
2. high costs associated with vendor fees and profit structure, and
3. employment of contractors who do not understand the operation and culture of healthcare organizations.

Hensley (1997) describes some of the principles to follow in outsourcing in a list of "dos and don'ts." He emphasizes the importance of weighing the cultural fit with the vendor; suggests that outsourcing be part of a long-term strategy (not just a quick fix); and recommends good reference checking, looking for staying power among vendors being considered. He states that healthcare organizations should not contract out the things they do best, should not become obsessed with short-term savings, and should not negotiate such favorable terms in a contract that a business partner is put out of business.

Waymack (2000) offers the following four suggestions for selecting outsourcing firms:

1. Seek long-term commitments because the costs of switching vendors can be substantial.
2. Require relevant experience with the specific service to be outsourced.
3. Develop performance measures for selection based on the services to be outsourced.
4. Do not base evaluation solely on the lowest bid.

Texas Health Resources (THR) in Arlington, Texas, is the largest non-profit healthcare system in the state. THR has an enterprisewide outsourcing strategy. According to Stewart (2001), selective outsourcing is used when

- there is a well-defined function involved,
- outsourcing will provide a financial benefit,
- there is an opportunity to at least maintain and preferably improve service levels, and
- outsourcing adds value to the organization.

Results of the 2002 HIMSS Leadership Survey indicate that 35 percent of the organizations responding to the survey outsource their web sites, 19 percent outsource applications development, 11 percent outsource system installation, 11 percent outsource network operations support, and 10 percent outsource personal computer support (HIMSS 2002).

Senior Management's Role Today

The basic thesis of this book is a simple one: Information systems can be useful to management provided the process for planning, designing, installing, and operating such systems is itself well managed. The CEO and other senior managers of healthcare organizations must assume the responsibility for planning and controlling the development of effective information systems to serve their organizations. These tasks cannot be delegated to technical personnel if information processes are to be truly supportive of high-quality patient care and managerial decision making. Information is essential in today's competitive environment for strategic planning, cost and productivity management, continuous quality improvement, and program evaluation purposes. Important senior management responsibilities that have been presented throughout the book are summarized in Figure 14.2.

To meet these responsibilities, a solid and mutually supportive relationship between the CEO and the CIO is essential. According to Charles Emory, CIO of Horizon Blue Cross Blue Shield of New Jersey, "Two-way communication, especially between CIOs and CEOs is particularly critical now . . . with use of the Internet making the results of senior management efforts visible to everyone, inside and outside the organization" (Hagland 2001, 19).

Austin, Hornberger, and Shmerling (2000) report on the results of management audits conducted by senior management at ten healthcare organizations. The audits evaluated how well the following seven responsibilities for IT management were carried out: (1) strategic information systems planning, (2) employment of a user focus in system development, (3) recruiting of competent personnel, (4) system integration, (5) protection of information security and confidentiality, (6) employment of effective project management in system development, and (7) post-implementation evaluation of systems.

The audit results suggest that most of these responsibilities were being met "to a considerable extent" or "very well." System integration received the lowest scores, with three organizations scoring "to a considerable extent" or "very well," but seven organizations received scores of "to some extent" or "minimally" on this item. As discussed in the section that follows, building effective interfaces for communication across information systems will continue to be an important consideration for IT management in the future.

Senior Management's Role Tomorrow

The management responsibilities described in the preceding section are basic and will continue into the future. However, trends are on the horizon that will likely require increased attention from healthcare managers in the immediate future. This concluding section of the book addresses some of these trends and describes the role of managers in ensuring that healthcare organizations use IT to full advantage.

Priorities for Application Development

Reduction of medical errors and enhancement of patient safety will continue to be "hot issues" among government agencies and private consumer organizations. The Leapfrog Group, a consortium of major purchasers of healthcare, announced in April of 2002 that it was expanding its efforts to reduce preventable medical mistakes to hospitals in 12 more regions of the United States (Reuters Medical News 2002). See Chapter 7 for a description of the Leapfrog Groups' efforts to expand the use of computer-based physician order-entry systems to reduce medication errors in hospitals.

Emphasis on the development of computer-based records will continue, but it will be on a more limited scale than previously predicted. Plans for development of large regional or community health information networks have been abandoned for the most part. Efforts will continue toward the development of enterprisewide repositories of clinical records. However, as Drazen (2001) suggests, these systems will focus on inclusion only of that

FIGURE 14.2

,enior

/lanagement

:esponsibilities

• Management must insist on a careful planning process that precedes all major decisions related to the installation of computer equipment or the design of complex information systems. A master plan for information system development should be created and updated at least once a year. This plan should be linked to the strategic plan of the healthcare organization and should guide all specific implementation decisions.

• Management should employ a user-driven focus throughout the development process. Active involvement of personnel from all segments of the healthcare organization is essential. This participation should begin with a definition of information requirements that should always precede acquisition of hardware and software. It should continue through all phases of analysis, design, system evaluation and selection, and implementation.

• Management must take the responsibility for recruiting competent personnel for the design and operation of information systems. Consideration should be given to recruitment of a chief information officer to serve as a member of the senior management team. When outsourcing is used, careful selection of vendors and contract negotiations with the assistance of legal counsel should precede the award of contracts for software, equipment, or services.

• Intercommunication of data among systems is an absolute necessity in complex healthcare organizations, particularly those involving subsidiary units and central corporate management. Managers at the corporate level must establish policies and procedures to ensure integration of data files or interfacing among individual information systems for tracking patient flows, consolidating cost and financial data, monitoring quality of care, and evaluating individual products and services.

• Management personnel at all levels have legal and ethical obligations to maintain security of information systems and to protect the confidentiality of patients, human resources, and other sensitive information.

• The design of individual computer applications should be carried out by an interdisciplinary project team. Systems analysts and computer programmers will take the lead on technical analysis and design activities. Representatives of user departments should help guide the specification of system requirements and evaluate the technical design plans of the analysts. Management should be involved in all major design projects to ensure congruence with organizational goals and objectives, and it should insist on a user-driven system focus rather than a technology driven focus.

• Once a project team has been organized, careful systems analysis should precede any implementation decisions. Shortcuts in the systems analysis phase will inevitably lead to problems later on.

• The preliminary design specifications for a computer application should be in harmony with the master plan for information systems development.

• Detailed system specifications should be required before any implementation activities take place. These specifications should be reviewed formally and approved by all user departments and by management before proceeding with the next steps in system development.

Continued

FIGURE 14.2
Continued

• Throughout the analysis, design, and implementation phases of a project, management should require careful scheduling of all activities and should receive periodic progress reports as the project proceeds.

• During the implementation phase, thorough training of all personnel involved in the new system should be carried out.

• No computer application should be put into operation without first carrying out a comprehensive system test. The testing should cover all phases of system operation, including computer programs and procedures, personnel training, user satisfaction, ability of the system to meet original objectives, and accuracy of the initial cost estimates.

• Provision should always be made for adequate maintenance after an application is operational. Maintenance procedures are essential to correct operational errors, to make system improvement, and to facilitate changes necessitated by changes in organizational needs.

• Management must ensure that information systems are periodically audited and that all systems are formally evaluated once they are installed and operating normally.

information that is needed to improve the process of care. Emphasis will likely be placed on records systems that can support evidence-based medicine and disease-management programs.

Communications between patients and providers, facilitated by the Internet, will expand in the next ten years. Armed with information obtained online, patients will participate more fully in decisions about their care. Home-based monitoring systems will become more common and will help to reduce the need for repeated outpatient visits and to delay or defer the need for institutional care.

Reemphasis on the use of IT for strategic decision support is likely in the next few years. This topic received considerable attention in the early 1990s. However, attention shifted to other more immediate and pressing issues such as Y2K (Year 2000) readiness and more recently HIPAA. The 2002 HIMSS Leadership Survey indicates the need for increased attention to strategic decision support. Fifty-one percent of the respondents to the survey listed cost pressures as the top business issue facing healthcare in the next two years, and another 41 percent listed improved operational efficiency. Development of enterprise resource planning systems was listed as the second most important application needed during the next two years (HIMSS 2002).

System Communications and Interfaces

Developing efficient communications among and between computer applications on an enterprisewide basis continues to be problematic for many healthcare organizations. As reported earlier in this chapter, management audits conducted by senior managers in ten major healthcare organizations revealed that "most organizations reported concern about this issue [system integration] and stated that they were working toward a solution" (Austin, Hornberger, and Shmerling 2000, 235).

Some organizations continue to have problems in obtaining meaningful data from transaction processing systems to use in decision-support and management studies. More emphasis on process reengineering during systems analysis and selection could help to improve this situation.

A number of experts are predicting that expanded use of Internet technology (transmission standards and protocols) may be the best way to achieve the compatibility needed to link multiple applications through "Webgration" (Oas 2001).

Technology

Technology will continue to improve and will offer new opportunities for healthcare organizations during the next ten years. Two technologies that are likely to affect healthcare organizations are wireless communications and smart cards.

A clear trend will be the expanded use of wireless communications. The delivery of healthcare is increasingly mobile, with services being provided at decentralized locations and patient homes. Improvements in wireless communication systems and devices will facilitate expanded use of this technology in the future. As indicated in Chapter 1, wireless technology led the list of new technologies being considered by organizations responding to the 2002 HIMSS Leadership Survey (HIMSS 2002).

Surprisingly, the U.S. healthcare industry has been slow to adopt the use of "smart card" technology. Smart cards, used extensively in other industries such as banking and retail sales, seem to offer an inexpensive yet powerful approach to information storage and communication in the delivery of healthcare. Tabar (2001) states that smart cards have been discounted in the past, but she predicts that they will receive a second look by many organizations. Smart cards could be used "to get into the building, to log into the network, do a digital signature, gain remote access or store your health records" (Tabar 2001, 13).

Industry Standards

Slow adoption of industrywide standards for data definition and information transmission has been one of the major barriers to achieving effective system integration in healthcare organizations. Pressures to become more cost effective coupled with outside pressure will bring about an increased rate of standardization in the future.

Despite delays and problems in the development of final standards, HIPAA is here to stay and will begin to have an impact in the next few years. Cooperation among providers, insurers, and government agencies will, in time, result in more efficient systems for processing health claims and supporting improved administration in the industry.

Summary

Organizational placement of the information systems department in a health-care organization is influenced by the priority assigned to various applications; the knowledge, attitudes, and style of the chief executive officer; and the overall organizational structure of the institution. Many organizations have established the position of chief information officer to assist the executive team in using information for strategic management and for coordinating all information management and communication activities.

Competent technical personnel must be recruited to participate in the analysis, design, and implementation of information systems. A comprehensive information systems department will include professional analysts and programmers as well as technicians for operation and maintenance of equipment.

An increasing number of healthcare organizations are turning to outsourcing of some or all information system functions as an alternative to in-house staffing. In some cases, organizations are multisourcing different functions to a number of contractors. Potential benefits of outsourcing include reduced staffing requirements and smaller capital investments in hardware and software. Risks of outsourcing include too much dependence on contractors and potential high costs associated with the vendor fees and profit structure.

The chief executive officer and other senior managers must assume the responsibility for planning and controlling the development of effective information systems to serve their organizations. This cannot be delegated completely to technical personnel. Management must also ensure that careful planning precedes all decisions on acquisition of software and hardware and that well-established principles and procedures are followed in the analysis, design, and implementation of systems.

The role of the senior manager in overseeing information technology management will not change substantially in the future. However, information managers will need to consider certain trends.

Priorities for computer applications development will include clinical systems to help reduce medical errors and enhance patient safety. Computer-based medication order-entry systems are examples. Emphasis on computer-based patient records will continue, but on a more limited scale with automation of those components of the medical record that will improve the process of care and support disease-management initiatives. Use of the Internet by patients and providers will result in more involvement of patients in medical decisions. Home-based monitoring systems will become more common. Interest in strategic decision-support systems will pick up after lagging for the last few years.

Priority will be given to improving communications among computer applications throughout the enterprise. Internet transmission standards and protocols will be used more to improve inter-application communications (Webgration). Technological advances will include expanded use of wirleless communication systems and adoption of smart card technology by many organizations.

Adoption of industrywide standards for hardware and software will move forward. After many delays, HIPAA will be fully implemented resulting in more efficient processing of insurance claims and improved administration of services.

Discussion Questions

14.1 What factors should determine where an information systems department is located in the overall organizational structure?

14.2 What kinds of skills should a chief information officer possess?

14.3 Discuss some of the potential benefits and dangers of outsourcing information system activities.

14.4 Discuss some of the factors that will influence staffing requirements for a healthcare information systems department.

14.5 What are the differences in skills required by systems analysts and computer programmers?

14.6 In your opinion, what are the three most important responsibilities of senior healthcare managers for management of information technology?

14.7 What are some likely future priorities for computer applications development in healthcare organizations?

14.8 What new technologies will be important in future applications development?

Problems

14.1 Assume you are the chief executive officer of a health services corporation consisting of a 500-bed tertiary care hospital; three smaller hospitals located in rural areas within 100 miles of the main facility; a long-term care facility; home health agency; outpatient surgery center; and several smaller units, some of which are operated as joint ventures with others. You are about to develop an organizational plan for development and management of information systems for the corporation. Prepare an outline of a presentation to your corporate board discussing the proposed organizational study and some of the major issues to be addressed.

14.2 Interview the chief information officer of a healthcare facility in your area to determine which information systems functions are outsourced and which are handled in-house and the rationale for each. Write a report summarizing the interview.

14.3 Review and comment on the organization chart for the information systems department of a healthcare facility in your area.

References

Austin, C. J., K. D. Hornberger, and J. E. Shmerling. 2000. "Managing Information Resources: A Study of Ten Healthcare Organizations." *Journal of Healthcare Management* 45 (4): 229–39.

Drazen, E. 2001. "Is This the Year of the Computer-based Patient Record?" *Healthcare Informatics* 18 (2): 95, 96, 98.

Hagland, M. 2001. "CIO of the Year." *Healthcare Informatics* 18 (4): 18–19.

Healthcare Information and Management Systems Society. 2002. *Thirteenth Annual Leadership Survey.* Chicago: HIMSS.

Hensley, S. 1997. "Outsourcing Moves Into New Territory." *Modern Healthcare* (January 13): 39–43.

Morris, J. 2001. "CIOs: Their Challenges and Satisfactions." *Health Management Technology* 22 (12): 24–28.

Morrissey, J. 1996. "CIO Pay Averages $110,000 a Year." *Modern Healthcare* (March 4): 122–24.

Oas, B. 2001. "Integration: Organizations Streamline the Business of Healthcare by Joining Disparate Systems." *Healthcare Informatics* 18 (2): 58, 60.

Reuters Medical News. 2002. "Leapfrog Expands Patient Safety Initiative." *Reuters Medical News* (April 26).

Stewart, S. 2001. "The Good, the Bad and the Outsourced." *Health Management Technology* 22 (5): 22–24.

Tabar, P. 2001. "Security and Smart Cards: Power Chips in Hand." *Healthcare Informatics* 18 (5): 13–14.

Waymack, P. 2000. "Four Tips for Selecting Outsourcing Firms." *Health Management Technology* 22 (8): 19.

Wood, G. M. 2000. "The Changing Role of the Health Care Chief Information Officer." *Managed Care Interface* 13 (9): 81–83.

Additional Readings

Austin, C. J., and R. C. Howe. 1994. "Information Systems Management." In *The AUPHA Manual of Health Services Management,* edited by R. J. Taylor and S. B. Taylor. Gaithersburg, MD: Aspen Publishers.

Brandt, M. D. 1994. "Making the Transition to CIO: Building your Skills." *Journal of the American Health Information Management Association* 65 (4): 59–61.

Drazen, E., W. Reed, and J. Metzger. 1995. "The CIO of the Integrated Care Delivery System." *Healthcare Informatics* 11 (6): 18.

Smith, B. 2000. "Outsourcing on a Grand Scale." *Health Management Technology* 22 (8): 18–20.

Stammer, L. 2001. "Wireless: As Technology Improves, New Applications Take Off." *Healthcare Informatics* 18 (2): 50, 52.

Waymack, P. 2000. "Outsourcing Opportunities." *Health Management Technology* 22 (8): 44–45.

GLOSSARY OF TECHNICAL TERMS

Address. The identifier for a storage location in the computer or for an input-output unit.

Addressable sectors. Sectors of a disk, organized on the basis of concentric tracks, with addresses consisting of track and sector identifiers.

Administrative information system. An information system that is designed to assist in the performance of administrative support activities in a healthcare organization, such as payroll accounting, accounts receivable, accounts payable, facility management, intranets, and human resources management.

Algorithm. A step-by-step procedure for performing a task. Computer algorithms consist of logical and mathematical operations.

Analog signal. The representation of data by varying the amplitude, frequency, and/or phase of a waveform. *See also* Digital signal.

Applications program. A program that performs specific tasks for the computer user, such as payroll, order entry, or inventory control.

Artificial Intelligence (AI). A discipline that attempts to simulate human problem-solving techniques in a computer environment. *See also* Expert system.

ASP (Application Service Provider). An organization that contracts with a healthcare facility to provide access to applications that are available online.

Asynchronous transfer mode (ATM). A networking technology that segments data into small fixed-length cells, directs the cells to the appropriate destination, and reassembles the data.

Backbone. The Internet or other wide area network paths that provide long-distance links of local or regional networks.

Bandwidth. A measure of the data-carrying capacity of a transmission medium. The higher the bandwidth, the larger the volume of data that can be moved across networks.

Barcode label. A printed form or plastic card containing a sequence of vertical bars and spaces that represent numbers and other symbols. The contents can be read automatically by specially designed computer input devices.

Barcode reader. An input device that allows a computer user to scan a barcode label and transfer its contents to a computer.

Baud. Early measure for data transmission speed, which has now been replaced by the term **bps** or bits per second.

Bedside terminal. A microcomputer-based terminal that allows nurses and other clinical staff to input and receive patient data at the bedside.

Bit. A binary digit (0 or 1) that is part of a data byte. In most computer systems, eight bits make up one byte.

Bridge. An interface that connects two or more networks that use similar protocols.

Browser. A software application that enables users to view and interact with information on the World Wide Web.

Bus. The term can be used in two contexts. (1) It is the physical network topology in which all workstations are connected to a line directly. (2) Within a computer it is the signal path that links the CPU with primary memory and with input/output devices.

Byte. The smallest addressable piece of information in a computer's memory, typically consisting of eight bits, used to signify a letter, number, or symbol.

Cathode-ray tube (CRT). A specialized vacuum tube with a screen on which characters and graphic patterns are displayed by controlling a beam of electrons.

CD–R (Compact Disk–Recordable). An optical disk used for mass storage of computer data onto which it is possible to write additional data in multiple sessions, as long as subsequent "writes" are made to different areas of the disk.

CD–ROM (Compact Disk–Read-Only Memory). An optical disk used for mass storage of computer data on a read-only basis.

CD–RW (Compact Disk–Rewritable). An optical disk used for mass storage of computer data for which it is possible to record over old redundant data or to remove selected files from the disk.

Cellular Digital Packet Data (CDPD). A network, similar to that used by cellular telephones, in which the user is transmitting or receiving data rather than voice messages.

Central processing unit (CPU). The component in a computer that performs calculations, makes logical decisions, and supervises and coordinates the various functional units of the system.

Client/server architecture. A computing configuration in which users interact with their machines (called the clients) and one or more machines (called servers), store data, and do much of the computing.

Clinical data repository. A database that consists of information from various sources of care and from various departments and/or facilities. The database may represent a longitudinal description of an individual's care.

Clinical (or medical) information system. An information system that provides for the organized storage, processing, and retrieval of information to support patient care activities.

Closed system. A completely self-contained system that is not influenced by external events. *See also* Cybernetic system; Open system; System.

Coaxial cable. A type of copper cable capable of transmitting high-speed digital signals and wide-bandwidth analog signals. It is fast, cost effective, and easy to install, but is subject to rust and corrosion.

Compiler. A computer program that translates instructions and subroutines written in a high-level programming language into language understood by the computer (machine language).

Computer programming. The process of coding a set of instructions or steps in a given data-processing language that directs the computer and coordinates the operation of all hardware components.

Computer virus. A computer program that intentionally tries to alter application programs, operating systems, and/or data files on a computer hard drive or floppy disk. Viruses may be intentionally or unintentionally transmitted from one computer to another by floppy disks, communication links, or downloading from the Internet.

CPU. *See* Central processing unit.

Critical path network. A tool used to define the interrelationships on a time scale for all events and activities that must be accomplished to complete a predetermined objective.

CRT. *See* Cathode-ray tube.

Cybernetic system. A self-regulating system that contains the following automatic control components: sensor, monitor, standards, and control unit. *See also* Closed system; Open system; System.

Cyberspace. A term used to describe the whole range of information resources available through computer networks. It is also used to describe a world in which computers and people coexist.

Data. Facts secured from empirical observations or research. Data in and of themselves often have little value and take on meaning only after sorting, tabulation, and processing into a more usable format (information).

Database. A series of records, containing data fields, stored together in such a way that the contents are easily accessed, managed, and updated.

Database-management system (DBMS). Software that enables the creation and accessing of data stored in a database.

Data definition language (DDL). Software that creates a link between the "logical" names of the items in a database (the user view) and the actual bytes located at a specific location on the disk (the physical view) of the database.

Data dictionary. A file that contains the name, definition, and structure of all the data fields and elements in a database.

Data field. One piece of information stored in a data record as part of a database.

Data manipulation language (DML). A language used to access, edit, and extract information from the data contained in a database.

Data record. A group of individual fields, corresponding to a real-world entity, that are stored together in a database.

Data redundancy. A situation in which the same data item appears in several files of a healthcare organization's computer system.

Data warehouse. A data warehouse enables the collection and organization of disparate data sources into an integrated subject-oriented view of the data to facilitate decision making.

Debugging. The process by which computer programs are tested and programming errors are identified and corrected.

Decision-support system (DSS). A system designed to support the decision-making process of an individual or organization through the use of data retrieval, modeling, and reporting.

Deterministic system. A system in which the component parts function according to completely predictable or definable relationships with no randomness present.

Digital signal. The representation of data as a series of on-off pulses (1s and 0s). *See also* Analog signal.

Digital Versatile Disk (DVD). A secondary storage medium, similar in appearance to a compact disk (CD), available in a read-only, recordable, and rewritable format. A DVD can store data on both of its sides and is available in capacities ranging from 4.7GB to 17GB.

Direct-access computer storage. Data files stored so that any data item can be accessed without the need for sequential searching. Also called *random access storage.*

Disk directory. A disk file used to list all program files or data files stored currently on the disk.

Disk drive. A secondary data-storage device that uses a magnetically coated disk as the storage medium. The disk drive consists of a mechanism to provide rotation of the disk (spindle), a read/write head to establish and detect magnetic patterns on each disk surface being accessed, and a mechanism to position the head appropriately for access.

Distributed processing. A computer network topology in which the workload is spread out through a network of computers that can be located in different organizational units.

Documentation. Written information that provides a description and overview of a computer program or system and detailed instructions on their use.

DOS. Disk operating system for IBM-compatible microcomputers. *See also* Operating system.

Dot matrix printer. A slow, low-quality, inexpensive printer that uses an impact process for printing.

DSS. *See* Decision-support system.

Dumb terminal. A device that can provide input to, and display output from, a central computer but cannot perform any independent processing.

DVD. *See* Digital Versatile Disks.

E-health applications. Healthcare software applications that are delivered through the Internet and related technologies.

Electronic data interchange (EDI). The transfer of structured information between two computers.

Electronic mail (e-mail). The electronic communication of messages between two or more people over computer networks.

Encryption. The scrambling of electronic transmission using mathematical formulas or algorithms to protect the confidentiality and security of communications.

Ethernet. The trade name for a logical network topology that is used to control how devices on the network send and receive messages. The goal is to avoid "collisions" resulting from two devices attempting to send messages simultaneously.

Executive information system (EIS). A generalized data storage and retrieval system that is designed to provide management information to the top executives of an organization.

Expert system. A decision-support system that can reproduce the reasoning process that a human decision maker would go through in reaching a decision, diagnosing a problem, or suggesting a course of action. Components of expert systems include knowledge base, database, inference engine, a user interface, and workspace.

Fiber distributed data interchange (FDDI). A network consisting of two identical fiber optic rings connected to local area networks and other computers.

Fiber-optic medium. Communication transmission medium that uses light pulses sent through a glass cable at high transmission rates with no electromagnetic interference.

File Transfer Protocol (FTP). A communication standard for moving files from one computer to another. Prior to web browser technology, FTP was the only protocol available to receive/download or send/upload files from one Internet resource to another.

Firewall. Hardware and/or software that restricts traffic to and from a private network from the general public Internet network.

Floppy disk. A thin, circular piece of coated plastic used as one type of random access secondary storage. The original floppy disks were flexible. Today's disks are enclosed in hard shell cartridges.

Flowchart. A graphical representation of the steps and sequence that comprise a project, process, or computer program. The graphical representation consists of symbolic shapes, legends, and connecting flow lines,

Front-end processor. The processor with which application users interact directly. In a client/server network the front-end processor would correspond to the client.

Gateways. Gateways represent the interface between two networks that use dissimilar protocols to communicate.

Gigabyte. Technically, storage medium capacity of 2^{30} or 1,073,741,824 bytes. Informally, 1 billion (10^9) bytes.

Hard disk. One of several rigid platters, coated with a thin magnetic film, contained within an enclosure known as a hard-disk drive. These platters serve as random access secondary storage devices.

Hardware. The physical components of a computer system.

Health Level-7 (HL7). A standard for data formatting which helps to facilitate the exchange of data among disparate systems within and across software vendors.

Hierarchical database. A database in which data is stored as nodes in a tree structure with the root node as the top node. Each node has one "parent" node and may have multiple "child" nodes.

High-level language. A computer programming language that is independent of the limitations of a specific computer and uses statements that resemble the problem being solved. *See also* Compiler; Interpreter.

HIPAA (Health Insurance Portability and Accountability Act). Federal legislation passed in 1996 to make health insurance more portable. The administrative simplification provisions of HIPAA establish standards for electronic transmission of administrative information related to health insurance claims. The privacy protection regulations are designed to limit the nonconsensual use and release of private health information.

Home page. *See* Web page.

Host. A computer to which other, smaller computers in a network are connected and can communicate.

HTML (HyperText Markup Language). The set of symbols or codes that define the format (fonts, graphics, hypertext links and other details) to be used by the web browser in displaying a page on the World Wide Web.

HTTP (HyperText Transfer Protocol). The protocols used to deliver documents to a web browser (Netscape or Microsoft Explorer) from a web server.

Hub. A hardware device with multiple user ports to which computers and input/output devices can be attached.

Hypermedia database. A database that can store a variety of media such as text, graphics, motion pictures, audio, or programming code.

HyperText. A method of presenting information on a web site in which there are links to other documents. The HyperText "link" is the Universal Resource Locator (URL) for another web page or other resources.

Indexed file. A file containing records accessible in sorted order according to one or more index fields. A separate sorted file or index contains records consisting only of the index field value(s) from the indexed file and one or more pointers to the location(s) of record(s) containing the value(s) in the indexed file.

Information. A meaningful aggregation of data or facts that can be evaluated for a specific use or set of uses.

Inkjet printer. A medium-speed, medium-quality computer printer that creates characters by "spraying" ink onto the page.

Input. Data fed into a computer system, either manually (such as through a keyboard or barcode device) or automatically (such as in a bedside patient monitoring system).

Integrated system. A set of information systems or networks that can share common data files and can communicate with one another.

Intelligent terminal. A terminal that has the capability to process data independently of the main system.

Interactive system. A system that can provide responses to the user in "real time." *See* Real time.

Internet. An open network of computer networks that permit people and computers to communicate and share applications through standard open protocols.

Internet Protocol (IP). An addressing scheme that identifies each machine on the Internet and is made up of four sets of numbers separated by "dots."

Interpreter. An interactive high-level language that analyzes source codes on a statement-by-statement basis.

Intranet. A private computer network contained within an organization that uses Internet software and transmission standards (TCP/IP).

ISDN (integrated services digital network). A network that uses a local telephone company branch exchange (PBX) to allow separate microcomputer workstations, terminals, and other network nodes to communicate with a central computer and with each other.

Java. An object-oriented software language, developed by Sun Microsystems, for writing web applications. An individual application is call an "applet" and can be embedded within an HTML document.

Key. One or more fields of a record used in identification of that record.

Kilobyte (K or KB). Technically, storage medium capacity of 2^{10} or 1,024 bytes. Informally, 1,000 bytes.

Knowledge engineering. An analysis and design process by which the information components and decision-making processes of an individual are specified and modeled.

LAN. *See* Local area network.

Laptop computer. Powerful microcomputer that is characterized by its small size, lightweight, portability, and range of capabilities.

Laser printer. A high-speed, high-quality printer that can function with several graphic formats and type-font options.

LCD screen. An output device, originally associated with laptop computers, that is thin, lightweight, and makes use of liquid crystal technology to form the output.

Life cycle. The sequence of specification, design, implementation, and maintenance of computer programs. For models of computer hardware, the life cycle is the sequence in market status of development, announcement, availability, and obsolescence.

Light pen. An electronic, pen-like device with which the user of a video computer terminal points to data displayed on a CRT and retrieves that information or executes a command.

Local area network (LAN). A computer network providing communication among computers and peripherals within an organization or group of organizations over a limited area. The network consists of the computers, peripherals, communication links, and interfacing hardware.

Magnetic disk storage. Online or offline data storage in which each data character is stored as a 0 or 1 in magnetic form. Magnetic storage includes hard and floppy disks, multiple disk packs, and reel-to-reel and cassette tapes.

Mainframe. A term used to describe relatively large computer systems, which normally have very large main memories, specialized support for high-speed processing, many ports for online terminals and communication links, and extensive auxiliary memory storage.

Master patient index (MPI). A relational database containing all of the identification numbers that have been assigned to a patient anywhere within a healthcare system. The MPI assigns a global identification number as an umbrella for all patient numbers, thus permitting queries that can find all appropriate data for a particular patient regardless of where that person is within the system.

Megabyte (M or MB). Technically, storage medium capacity of 2^{20} or 1,048,576 bytes. Informally, 1 million bytes.

Menu. A list of options, displayed on a CRT screen, to allow the user to select the function to be performed or another, more specific menu. Programs operated through the use of menus are called *menu driven*.

Microcomputer. A relatively small computer system, with the microprocessor, main memory, disk drives, CD-ROM, and interface cards and connectors installed in a small case or box. *See* Microprocessor.

Microprocessor. A CPU contained on a single semiconductor chip.

Minicomputer. A computer with capabilities somewhere between those of a microcomputer and a mainframe computer. *See also* Microcomputer; Mainframe.

MIPs. Millions of internal computer operations per second.

Modem. A term (short for MOdulator/DEModulator) that is used to describe a data communication device that modulates signals from output devices for transmission on a data link and demodulates signals destined for input devices coming from the transmission link.

Multiplexing. The process of combining two or more signals into a single signal, transmitting it, and then sorting out the original signals. The devices that combine or sort out signals are called *multiplexers*.

Multipurpose Internet Mail Extension (MIME). Used in conjunction with Simple Mail Transfer Protocol to allow users to attach different file types to their e-mail messages (e.g., graphics, audio, and video). *See also* Simple Mail Transfer Protocol.

Network. A collection of computer and peripheral devices interconnected by communication paths. *See also* Local area network; Wide area network.

Network Computer (NC). A low-cost personal computer having minimal equipment and designed to be managed and maintained by a central computing function.

Network controller. A mini or microcomputer that "directs" the communication traffic between the host and the terminals and peripheral devices.

Network interface card (NIC). A plug-in board used in microcomputers and workstations to allow them to communicate with a host computer and other nodes in a local area network.

Object code. The sequence of steps, in language understandable by the CPU, that results when source code is processed by a compiler. *See also* Compiler; Source code.

Object-oriented database. An information retrieval system that manages complex objects containing data and procedures for manipulating these data. Object-oriented databases are effective at storing complex objects such as documents and World Wide Web pages.

OCR. *See* Optical character recognition.

Open system. A system whose components are exposed to everyone and can thus be modified or improved.

Operating system. A set of integrated subroutines and programs that control the operation of a computer and manage its resources.

Optical character recognition (OCR). The capability of a computer to scan text characters and to process the scanned data into character codes that can be understood and processed.

Optical disk. A disk in which data are written and read by a laser. Optical disk types include a number of variations of CDs and DVDs. *See also* CD–R, CD–ROM, CD–RW, DVD, and WORM.

Optical scanner. A hardware device that converts written text or graphics into an array of pixels ("tiny dots") that can then be processed further by a computer.

Output. Any data or information that a computer sends to a peripheral device or other network.

Packaged systems. Generalized computer systems, marketed by a number of commercial firms, that are designed to fulfill the information needs of any healthcare provider or organization.

Parallel processing. The use of multiple CPUs linked together generally for the purpose of more efficiently completing complex tasks.

PACS (picture archiving and communications system). A device that provides online storage and retrieval of medical images for transmission to user work stations.

PC. *See* Personal computer.

Peer network. A network, with no server, in which all computers on the network can be used as workstations.

Peripherals. A general term used to refer to input, output, and secondary storage devices on a computer.

Personal computer (PC). Name commonly used to refer to a microcomputer.

Point-to-Point Protocol (PPP). A TCP/IP protocol used with serial lines for communication between two computers. PPP is generally preferred over SLIP, an earlier protocol. *See also* Serial Line Internet Protocol.

Program. An ordered set of instructions that a computer executes to obtain a desired result.

Programming language. A software system having a specific format or *syntax* used for writing computer programs.

Protocols. Rules and conventions for communication between computers.

Query language. A computer language that allows users to easily retrieve specific information from one or more database files.

RAM. *See* Random access memory.

Random access memory (RAM). Storage that permits direct access to the data stored at a particular address.

Read-only memory (ROM). Storage that contains permanent instructions or data that cannot be altered by ordinary programming.

Real time. Describes a computer or process that captures data, performs an operation, or delivers results in a time frame that humans perceive as instantaneous.

Relational database model. A type of database model that stores data in individual files or tables, with data items arranged in rows and columns. Two or more tables can be *linked* for the purposes of *ad hoc* queries if at least one data item (the *key*) is common in each of the tables.

ROM. *See* Read-only memory.

Router. A device located at a gateway that manages the data flow between networks. *See also* Gateway.

Search engine. Internet software application that helps users locate specific resources on the Internet.

Serial Line Internet Protocol (SLIP). A TCP/IP protocol used with serial lines for communication between two computers. *See also* Point-to-Point Protocol.

Simple Mail Transfer Protocol (SMTP). A TCP/IP protocol that defines how e-mail is exchanged between computers.

Software. The programs that control the operation of a computer, including application programs, operating systems, programming languages, development tools, and language translators.

Source code. The programming statements written in a high-level language that will be compiled to obtain the object code that can be used for the actual running of the program. *See also* Compiler; Object code.

SQL. *See* Structured query language.

Structured query language (SQL). A standard, widely used language for querying a relational database. It was designed to permit users to specify queries with an English-like command structure involving a minimum of attention to the way in which the database was to be manipulated internally. *See also* Relational database model.

System. A network of components or elements joined together to accomplish a specific purpose or objective. Every system must include input, a conversion process, and output. *See also* Closed system; Cybernetic system; Open system.

Systematized Nomenclature of Medical Reference Technology (SNOMED). A standard vocabulary of medical terms. Data from the various entities in a healthcare system can be more easily aggregated into a centralized clinical repository if the data items adhere to the SNOMED standard.

Systems analysis. The process of collecting, organizing, and evaluating facts about information system requirements, processes, and the environment in which the system will operate.

Tape drive. A tape recorder specially designed to work in a computer system for the recording, storage, and retrieval of data. Data stored on tape are accessible in sequential (not direct) fashion.

Telecommunications. Transmission of information over distances through wired, optical, or radio media.

Telnet. A TCP/IP protocol that enables a user to log on to a remote computer and use its applications as if the user were directly connected to it.

Terabytes. Technically, storage medium capacity of 2^{40} or 1,099,511,627,776 bytes. Informally, 1 trillion bytes. *See also* byte.

Terminal. A device consisting of a CRT and keyboard that allows a computer user to perform processing on a host computer directly. *See also* Dumb terminal; Intelligent terminal.

Terminal-host system. A computer network configuration in which dumb terminals are connected to a large central host computer, typically a mainframe, and all of the computing is taking place on the host. *See also* Terminal; Host; Mainframe.

Throughput time. The total time span from collection of the first data element to the preparation of the final report in a given system.

Transaction Processing Systems (TPS). Application programs that form the bulk of the day-to-day activities of an organization, such as financial, clinical, admissions, and business office systems.

Transmission Control Protocol/Internet Protocol (TCP/IP). A collection of data communication protocols used to connect a computer to the Internet. TCP/IP is the standard for all Internet communication.

Turnkey system. A computer system in which all the hardware and software are supplied by the same vendor and are ready to be used for specific application(s) without much in-house alteration.

UNIX. A multiuser operating system used on many midsize computers and workstations. It is an open operating system, which means anyone is able to improve or enhance the system. *See also* Operating system.

Unshielded twisted pair (UTP). Similar to telephone cable, but with higher standards for protection against electromagnetic interference.

URL (Uniform Resources Locator). The address of a resource on the Internet. For example: http://hap.wustl.edu/

VDT. *See* Video display terminal.

Video display terminal (VDT). Often known as a "monitor," the VDT displays the output text and/or graphics created by a computer.

Virtual memory. A storage technique that permits the operating system to address more storage locations than are available in main memory. Disk storage is used to provide the additional memory and thus serves as an extension of main memory.

Voice recognition system. A system capable of receiving and interpreting spoken words. In addition to applications in transcription, this technology can be used for data-entry and for security purposes.

Web browser. Software that enables a user to view and interact with information stored on the web.

Web page. A file that contains text, graphics, or other multimedia information along with HTML annotations that indicate how the information is to be formatted when the page is displayed. A "home page" is the first web page of a particular site.

Wide area network (WAN). A network in which long-distance lines allow computers and local area networks to communicate.

Windows 2000 and Windows XP. Operating systems that allow data from two or more programs to be displayed on a video display terminal at the same time. The use of graphical user interfaces supports a user-friendly environment and allows for multitasking of software applications.

Workstation. (a) A microcomputer connected to a larger host computer in which some independent processing is performed. (b) This can also refer to a high-end microcomputer with a large amount of primary storage, a fast processor, a high-quality sound card, high-resolution graphics, a CD–RW drive, and in many cases a DVD drive.

World Wide Web (WWW). The collection of text, graphics, and multimedia stored in databases all over the world that can be accessed via the Internet.

WORM (Write-Once, Read Many). An optical disk in which data may be written once but read as many times as needed. *See also* Optical disk.

Index

ABOUT THE AUTHORS

Charles J. Austin, Ph.D., is a retired university professor and administrator. He has served in numerous academic leadership positions, including president of East Texas State University (now Texas A&M University, Commerce); vice president for academic affairs at Georgia Southern University; and dean of graduate studies at Trinity University in San Antonio, Texas.

Dr. Austin has served on the health administration faculties of the University of Colorado, Xavier University, Trinity University, the University of Alabama at Birmingham, and the Medical University of South Carolina. His nonuniversity experience includes service as chief of the information systems division of the National Library of Medicine and systems analyst for Procter and Gamble.

During his distinguished career, Dr. Austin served as chairman of the board of the Association of University Programs in Health Administration, chairman of the Accrediting Commission on Education for Health Services Administration, chairman of the editorial board of the *Journal of Health Administration Education*, and chairman of the higher education committee of the American College of Healthcare Executives. He is the author or coauthor of five books and numerous articles published in professional and scholarly journals.

Dr. Austin holds a B.S. degree (summa cum laude) from Xavier University, an M.S. in health administration from the University of Colorado, and a Ph.D. from the University of Cincinnati.

Stuart B. Boxerman, D.Sc., CHE, is associate professor and director of the Health Administration Program at Washington University School of Medicine in St. Louis, Missouri. He teaches courses in quantitative methods and health information systems. His current research activities include improvement of patient care delivery processes, benefits of decision-support systems, applications of simulation modeling, and the quantification of the value of information.

Prior to his current position, Dr. Boxerman has gained industrial experience in computing and information system technology with a defense contractor, an electric utility, and an architectural firm. This experience has included analyses to determine system needs, systems design, programming, and presentation of in-house seminars on computer fundamentals and specific programming languages. In addition, he has held an academic appointment in computer science at a graduate engineering center of a state university.

Dr. Boxerman has been active in the Association of University Programs in Health Administration, including membership on the Quantitative Methods Task Force, the Information Management Faculty Forum, and the Curriculum Development Task Force for Information Management. He served as the editor of the *Journal of Health Administration Education* for six years and has been the author of numerous articles published in professional and scholarly journals. He is a Diplomate of the American College of Healthcare Executives and a member of the Healthcare Information and Management Systems Society, the Institute for Operations Research and the Management Sciences, and the AcademyHealth.

Dr. Boxerman holds B.S. and M.S. degrees in electrical engineering and a D.Sc. in applied mathematics and computer science, all from Washington University in St. Louis, Missouri.